HUMAN NEURAL AND BEHAVIORAL DEVELOPMENT

A Relational Inquiry, with Implications
for Personality

HUMAN NEURAL AND BEHAVIORAL DEVELOPMENT

A Relational Inquiry, with Implications for Personality

By

ESTHER MILNER, Ph.D.
*Associate Professor, Brooklyn College
of the City University of New York
New York, New York*

With Prefatory Notes by
R. W. Gerard, M.D., Ph.D.

CHARLES C THOMAS · PUBLISHER
Springfield · Illinois · U.S.A.

Published and Distributed Throughout the World by

CHARLES C THOMAS • PUBLISHER

BANNERSTONE HOUSE

301-327 East Lawrence Avenue, Springfield, Illinois, U.S.A.

NATCHEZ PLANTATION HOUSE

735 North Atlantic Boulevard, Fort Lauderdale, Florida, U.S.A.

© *1967, by* CHARLES C THOMAS • PUBLISHER

Library of Congress Catalog Card Number: 66-24636

With THOMAS BOOKS *careful attention is given to all details of manufacturing and design. It is the Publisher's desire to present books that are satisfactory as to their physical qualities and artistic possibilities and appropriate for their particular use.* THOMAS BOOKS *will be true to those laws of quality that assure a good name and good will.*

Printed in the United States of America

N-10

To

Hughlings Jackson, Judson Herrick and
Myrtle McGraw on the one hand, and
George Herbert Mead and Martin Buber on
the other, pioneers all, whose ideas have had
a major influence — both conscious and unconscious — on my thinking.

PREFATORY NOTES

Doctor Esther Milner, whom I look forward to meeting one day, is obviously a woman of energy, determination, and courage as well as of intelligence and vision. Facing, as a clinically oriented developmental psychologist, some of the most complex and tortured problems of human behavior and convinced (implicitly more than explicitly) that, indeed, the son is father to the man and that only the material nervous system can carry the residues of past experience (racial and individual) on which current behavior rests, she mounted a ten-year safari into the continent of neurophysiology and neuroanatomy. For trophies, she seeks insights into the development and attributes of behavior, as based upon the development and properties of the nervous system. And the excursion has been fruitful.

From a neurobiological point of view, Doctor Milner reveals certain naïvetés which invite a patronizing attitude toward this stranger in our land, naïvetés I shall enlarge upon later. Failure to look beyond these superficial blemishes would, however, be a grave error. When Schroedinger's *What is Life?* appeared, many biologists, myself included, felt he had belatedly discovered the existence of genetics; this may have been true, but was not the whole truth. Hebb's *Organization of Behavior,* similarly, seemed to neurophysiologists to be "merely" serving their standard dishes to psychologists who hadn't yet sampled them. Yet, partly because he was bringing fare new to his readers, partly because of skillful selection of items from an overwhelming plethora, and partly because of his own creative interpretations of these widely-known facts, this book led to major advances and helped focus psychobiology.

Whether Doctor Milner's contribution will succeed in leading social psychologists into a deeper interest in the biological roots of their subject matter, only time will tell; but this is her goal, she has made a great and good effort towards it, and I am happy to be at the side line cheering her on. The author has gathered and organized a tremendous amount of disparate material. She has strung on the thread of time facts about the anatomy (mainly cells and circuits) and physiology (with much reliance on EEG) and, to some extent, the chemistry and pharmacology and broader biology of the developing human nervous system; she has paralleled these with equally ordered facts about the development of human behavior; and invites—nay, compels—the reader to consider these as a connected whole, as a coherent maturational trajectory of the infant to the adult.

An author who has done a really manful job of gathering and considering the facts in some field of knowledge has the right to make public his interpretations of them. I will go further and assert that this is more than a right, it is a duty. Fruitless speculation without a factual basis led to the excesses of scholasticism or the philosophic era of psychology; but the reaction of hard science has gone so far in the direction of empiricism that workers (perhaps especially in psychology) are actively discouraged by mentors, editors, and colleagues from putting in print the creative thoughts that flow from their findings.

Nevertheless it is important in an introduction such as this one to point out weaknesses where they exist. Doctor Milner has, inevitably, been overimpressed by some of the great neurobiological landmarks and failed to find subtler ones (perhaps even some major ones) that more truly characterize a terrain; she has had to rely heavily on the condensed maps of books, sometimes vintage volumes and not always the ones most relevant or closest to current thinking. And she has reacted with the "ah ha" excitement of the discoverer to features of the terrain that are already so familiar to inhabitants, her enthusiasms occasionally seem like overreactions. To one who has, like myself, lived intimately with the contributions of Hughlings Jackson all his professional life, who was an active participant in the developments spearheaded by Sherrington and Herrick and Lashley but then moved beyond them, and who has seen discarded contributors still given attention by Doctor Milner, the author's enthusiasm, contrasting with her hard-headed appraisal of Freud, would appear not without naiveté. Some of her formulations, based on her voyage of discovery, are, in fact, old hat.

Be that as it may, Doctor Milner has done a manful job with the facts (perhaps in deference to her strong awareness of her sex, I should say "womanful") and she *has* gone on and given us a rich and imaginative interpretation of them. I do not say a correct interpretation, for here, again, only time will tell; and new observations and experiments have a way of shattering beautiful formulations. Yet I find much of the author's thinking plausible and exciting. Few have had the urge and temerity to think across disciplines; Doctor Milner has thought not only across disciplines, but also across levels. She has related the brain to behavior and has drawn on the developmental stages of neurone organizations and capacities, and the influence of individual experience (especially the diadic relation with the mother) on these, to illuminate the healthy or neurotic behaviors of adult humans and to recommend social procedures and institutions to improve the outcomes. So the author develops her story, from attention to the elements of the infant brain to recommendations that bear on the Headstart program for underprivileged children and the future education of psychologists and pediatricians. An exciting story that deserves a wide audience.

R. W. GERARD, M.D., Ph.D.

PREFACE

Wнат BEGAN SEVERAL YEARS AGO as a challenging self-education project has culminated in this attempt to communicate to others what I have learned. This project was initiated by a question of my own formulation, a question for which not only I as a social-psychologically oriented student of human development and personality did not have an answer but, as I soon came to realize, psychology as a field of study did not have an answer:

What role does level of nervous system development play in the ontogenetic sequence and timing of particular personality structures?

This question, once formulated (126), nagged at me sufficiently that I began to look for data on early nervous system development in psychological sources — but most of what was derived from these initial efforts were a number of further questions, among them:

The cerebral neocortex is apparently that part of the brain which makes all uniquely human behaviors possible, yet it is non-functional at birth. What happens developmentally after birth? May there be a relationship between the answer to this question and my original query?

So it was that I embarked on a lengthy journey of intellectual discovery, a journey that proved to be far more difficult and conceptually hazardous than I was then in the position to appreciate. Some of the conceptual milestones along the way are detailed in Chapter II, Developing the Hypothesis, First Phase.

The approach and the organization of this monograph have been dictated by my unwillingness to abandon the search for answers to the questions above (and others) when I discovered, early on, that the literature did not — and apparently still does not — contain enough specific post-natal human neurogenic data to permit deductions from such data alone. I reasoned that if ontogeny really does recapitulate phylogeny, then an inquiry into neural phylogeny should yield some useful clues. Also, because ontogeny has heretofore apparently meant only embryology to neurophysiology, I was obliged to take full advantage of the "law of anticipatory development": the extensive prenatal data available might well yield additional useful clues. Accordingly, Part B, after long gestation, came into existence.

The need for a yardstick by which to judge the structural and functional status of the human nervous system at birth became evident — and data related to the matured human nervous system *were* apparently available in the neurophysiological literature. Also, if I had some conception of the status of the matured nervous system, then I should be able to arrive at an idea of the nature and, hopefully, the details, of the width of *the gap between* the status of the nervous system at birth and its status at neurological maturity, a datum which would surely lend more meaning to the relatively scanty data on the developmental events in between. On both these scores, neurophysiological conceptions of the matured human nervous system became necessary; all the more so since the related psychological literature then available was entirely on the mammalian, not specifically the human, forebrain. In addition to the most rewarding discovery of the ideas of John Hughlings Jackson, this enterprise proved to be more useful than it seemed at first to be: experimental neurophysiologists had anticipated by a number of years physiological psychologists' recent research interest in the functional sub-systems of the *in situ* nervous system. It became evident at the same time however, that neurophysiology still bore the stamp of its historical role as a specialized sub-field of medicine: the needs and concerns of the neurosurgeon, for example, are not at all the same as the needs and concerns of an inquiring developmental cum personality psychologist!

The "new wave" of neuropsychological research began just about the same time as did my self-education project, and symposia after symposia began to roll off the presses. The wealth of detailed information about the functioning of the *in situ* nervous system which so became available further complicated my attempts to formulate a coherent and unified, yet evidence-inclusive, picture of the matured human nervous system. The necessity of curiosity compelled me to persist, however — and eventually to do what I shall probably, as a non-research-neuropsychologist be taken to task for doing: Part C, especially Chapter VI, comprises territory in which wise men still prefer not to tread.

The heart of this inquiry is of course Part D, the systematic relating of neural and behavioral developmental data. Unearthing of relevant studies wherever they might be located was the relatively uncomplicated (albeit time-consuming) first step; organizing them appropriately became the major task. Masses of behavioral and hard-found neural data had to be distilled to their essence and expressed in forms that would lend themselves to relating and conceptualizing purposes. Then, lest I — and the reader — be left with little more than a pot-pourri of age-associated relationships, the need for a culminating, summary cum re-thinking chapter became evident. It was the writing of Part D's closing chapter, XII, Developing the Hypothesis, Second Phase, that yielded my most self-meaningful insights.

I am still not sure whether section E should have been included in this monograph. It has a certain premature quality; is it because parts it actually constitute the first conceptual stage of — is *that* it! — my *next* book?

The theoretical argument presented in Chapter I is the unanticipated "extra" of the whole enterprise, since, as is apparently not unusual for first chapters, this chapter was written *after* most of the first draft of the manuscript had been completed. I believe it to be at least as important an outcome of this inquiry as the inquiry itself.

The hallmark of this investigation is its wide interdisciplinary scope — a characteristic which is at once its core strength *and* its core weakness. Weakness, in that specialists in each of the several fields utilized may consider the material related to their particular discipline overly familiar and/or elementary, not up to latest-research-report date, and even more troublesome perhaps, not interpreted in ways usual for their field. Strength, in that it is the very *bringing together* of disparate, highly specialized and "ethnocentric" perspectives on the human individual which is both the raison d'être of this monograph and the basis for whatever contribution it may make. It is its transcending of traditional data and theorizing boundaries which is responsible for the generation of whatever new insights and research problems it provides.

Two trenchant statements about the nature and the essential methodology of science have been separately made by Ludwig von Bertalanffy and Karl Lashley, here repeated in that author-order:

> Science is not a mere accumulation of facts; facts become knowledge only when incorporated into a conceptual system. ... It may well be that in many biological fields we know not too few but too many facts and that the very accumulation of an enormous amount of data hampers the discovery of the necessary theoretical schemes (19, p. 70).

> It is unfortunately characteristic of scientific method that the facts observed are in large part a function of the questions which are asked (105, p. 545).

To the extent that this inquiry contributes to clearer formulation of the necessary theoretical schemes and raises questions that will foster the discovery of more pertinent facts, to that extent will it have fulfilled its author's purpose.

This Preface cannot be complete without explicit acknowledgment of the many major and minor services that have been rendered me during the course of this lengthy enterprise by many persons and organizations. The assistance of efficient, helpful and unremittingly patient librarians is crucial for a study based on existing literature; Mrs. Camp of the Kings County Medical Society Library (recently merged with the Downstate Medical Center Library) and Miss Antoinette Ciolli, Brooklyn College's Science Librarian, in my experience epitomize these qualities. For the location and/or collation of much basic data, I am indebted to two assistants, Lorette Woolsey Toews and Donald Schiff, then students at, respectively, the University of Alberta and Brooklyn College. For providing me with both a financial and a psychological "boost," I am most grateful to the Canada Council, which awarded me two short-term grants (Summer, 1958 and Winter, 1958-'59) towards the furtherance of this study. In an organizational setting, the understanding and steady support of one's immediately superior officer is an invaluable aid, and I am privileged to thank E. J. Gergely, Deputy Chairman of Education (SGS) during most of the period of this endeavor, for providing me with this boon. I am also appreciative of a semester's abatement of my teaching-load by Walter Mais, Brooklyn College's Dean of Faculty.

As my self-education proceeded, my lack of first-hand experience in at least two quite-disparate areas, the severely emotionally disturbed child and the electroencephalographic technique *per se* technique, seemed to constitute a sufficient deterrent to my knowledgeable prosecution of my project to seek practical remedies. For permitting me to observe regularly one of the more disturbed groups of children served by Brooklyn's League School, I am indebted to this unique institution's director, Carl Fenichel. My conviction that the developmental-research role of the EEG has scarcely been tapped made me especially eager to learn whatever a rank amateur might be permitted (and able) to learn about this complex technique. I have three people to thank in this connection: Grey Walter, for permitting me to observe and to participate briefly in one of his many ingenious research projects at Bristol's Burden Neurological Institute, as well as for providing me with much developmental data and useful literature "leads"; Charles Henry, then director of Hartford's Institute of Living's EEG Laboratory, for free access to his extensive personal library of EEG-research reprints, and Mrs. Helen Maher, the EEG Lab's Senior Technician, for her valiant attempts to cope with an exemplification of a datum well known to those in the field of individual differences: technical aptitude and the kinds of abstract mental abilities that can earn one the Ph.D. do not necessarily coincide!

For countless small and large favors promptly and graciously done, I am much indebted to members of my college department's office staff: Gene Galtman, Mrs. Ida Wiener, and Mrs. Pauline Gershuny.

I also want to acknowledge three special "debts." First to Ralph W. Gerard, for taking the time to react critically to an early-draft manuscript and for encouraging someone not personally known to him to go ahead and finish her project. Second, to

the Committee on Human Development of the University of
Chicago, for having provided me with the kind of program of
instruction and orientation that has permitted me to conceive
of and to seek out answers to a problem as inter-disciplinary, challenging and complex as this one has been. And lastly, to the
project itself, which has been a demanding companion for so
many summers now, it has acquired a life and character of its
own. Even while being thoroughly relieved over its long-delayed
"departure," I shall miss very much its mental-health-giving
challenge!

Ancram, New York   ESTHER MILNER

COPYRIGHT ACKNOWLEDGMENTS

THE FOLLOWING LIST of individuals and publishers have granted copyright permission for the direct quotations and the reproductions of sketches or diagrams included in this monograph: my thanks to each and all of them. Complete citations are given in the text and/or bibliography.

Addison-Wesley Publishing Co., Reading, Mass., for the table from W. F. Caveness, *Atlas of Electroencephalography in the Developing Monkey,* 1962.

American Academy of Arts and Sciences, Boston, for the quotations from Bruno Bettelheim's paper in *The Challenge of Youth,* 1965, which originally appeared in *Daedalus.*

American Physiological Society, Washington, D.C., for the several quotations from articles in Volumes I, II, III of the *Handbook of Physiology.*

Annual Reviews, Inc., Palo Alto, Calif., for the quotation from Pribram's 1960 review article.

Association for Research in Nervous and Mental Disease, Inc., New York, Wilder Penfield, and Jerzy E. Rose for quotations from their respective papers in the 1952 *Proceedings* of the Association.

Atherton Press, New York, for the passage reprinted from Bernice L. Neugarten and Associates, *Personality in Middle and Late Life,* 1964.

Basic Books, New York, for quotations from S. Arieti, *Interpretation of Schizophrenia,* 1955, and from B. Bettelheim's paper in *The Challenge of Youth,* 1965.

The Clarendon Press, Oxford, for quotations from N. Tinbergen, *The Study of Instinct,* 1951.

Loren Eiseley, for the quotations from his paper in the 1955 *Yearbook of Anthropology.*

Elsevier Publishing Co., Amsterdam, and D. B. Lindsley for the concluding table in Orientation Supplement 6.

Harvard University Press for the quotation from J. L. Conel, *The Cortex of the Fifteen-month Infant,* 1955.

W. Heffer and Sons, Cambridge, England, and Williams & Wilkins, Baltimore, for the reproduction of Figures 288, 289, 290, 291, 293 in W. J. Hamilton, *et al., Human Embryology,* 2nd ed. 1952, as Figure II.

Macdonald and Co., Ltd., London, and Macmillan Co., New York, for the passage by Grey Walter taken from J. D. N. Hill and C. Parr, eds., *Electroencephalography,* 2nd ed., 1963.

McGraw-Hill Book Co., New York, for the table from B. M. Patten, *Human Embryology,* 2nd ed., 1953.

The Nation, New York, for quotations from Theodore Roszak's article, "The Historian as Psychiatrist," which appeared in the November 24, 1962, issue.

The Philosophical Review, Cornell University, for the passages from Roy Wood Sellars' 1938 article.

Prentice-Hall, Englewood Cliffs, N. J., for the passage from Solomon E. Asch, *Social Psychology,* 1952.

Publishers Newspaper Syndicate, New York Herald Tribune Division, *and* Johnny Hart for the reproduction of one of Mr. Hart's "B.C." cartoon sequences.

W. B. Saunders Co., Philadelphia, for material from: D. O. Hebb, *A Textbook of Psychology,* 1958; L. B. Arey, *Developmental Anatomy,* 6th ed. 1954; J. F. Fulton, ed., *A Textbook of Physiology,* 1955; and T. C. Ruch and J. F. Fulton, eds., *Medical Physiology and Biophysics,* 1960.

Ernest Gardner and W. B. Saunders Co. for the reproduction of the figure from E. Gardner, *Fundamentals of Neurology,* 3rd and 4th editions.

Science — and the AAAS — for the quotation from Novikoff's 1945 paper.

Springer Publishing Co., Inc., New York, for the passages by and from M. Greenblatt and H. C. Solomon, eds., *Frontal Lobes and Schizophrenia,* 1953.

University of Minnesota Press, Minneapolis, for the few lines from T. C. Schneirla's article in D. B. Harris, ed., *The Concept of Development,* 1957.

University of Texas Press, Austin, for the many quotations as well as the sketch from C. J. Herrick, *The Evolution of Human Nature,* 1956.

University of Wisconsin Press, Madison, for the quotation from D. O. Hebb's article in Harlow and Woolsey, eds., *The Biological and Biochemical Bases of Behavior,* 1958.

John Wiley and Sons, Inc., New York, for the quotations from von Bertalanffy's *Problems of Life,* 1952.

Williams and Wilkins, Baltimore, for the material from H. E. Himwich, *Brain Metabolism and Cerebral Disorder,* 1951.

Yale University Press, New Haven, for quotations from A. S. Romer's article in Roe and Simpson's *Behavior and Evolution,* 1958.

E. M.

CONTENTS

        Page

Prefatory Notes vii

Preface xi

Copyright Acknowledgments xvii

PART A

NEEDED: A SPECIES-APPLICABLE PICTURE OF MECHANISM

Chapter

I. THE HUMAN NERVOUS SYSTEM'S POTENTIAL RAPPROCHE-
MENT AND THEORETICAL ROLES 5

    The Human Nervous System's Potential Rapprochement
Role 6

    The Human Nervous System's Potential Contribution
to Personality Theory 20

II. DEVELOPING THE HYPOTHESIS, FIRST PHASE 24

PART B

THE SEARCH FOR DEVELOPMENTAL PATTERNS I: MAN'S DEVELOPMENTAL BEGINNINGS

III. MAN'S NEURAL AND BEHAVIORAL INHERITANCE 41

IV. THE HUMAN NERVOUS SYSTEM'S FIRST TEN MONTHS 63

    Patterns of Prenatal Neural Development 63

    The Behavioral Repertoire of the Human Neonate 83

    A Re-examination of the Coghill-Windle Controversy .. 89

PART C

THE POINT OF DEPARTURE: THE MATURED HUMAN NERVOUS SYSTEM

V. THE HIERARCHICAL-REDUPLICATIVE FUNCTIONAL ORGANIZA-
TION PATTERN 95

Chapter   *Page*

Preamble to Part C 95
The Hierarchical-Reduplicative Phylogenetic-Legacy
    Pattern 98
The Cerebral Cortex 108

VI. THE FUNCTIONAL SUBCIRCUITS PATTERN 125
Some Complex Subcircuits 126
Some Behavioral Implications 139

VII. THE TRIPLE-SYSTEM PHYLOGENETIC-LEGACY PATTERN 152
The Phylogenetic Legacy 152
The Intraorganismic Subsystem 157
The Transactional Subsystem 158
The Integrative System 158
The T-O-P Association Area and the Perceptual Process 160

PART D

THE SEARCH FOR DEVELOPMENTAL
PATTERNS II:
RELATING OF POSTNATAL NEURAL AND
BEHAVIORAL DEVELOPMENT

VIII. APPROACH, AND NEURAL OVERVIEW 167
Preamble to Part D 167
Approach 168
Overview of Neurogenic Data and Trends 171

IX. FROM BIRTH TO TWO YEARS 178
From Birth to One Month 178
At One Month 180
From One Month to Three Months 182
From Three to Six Months 188
From Six to Twelve Months 194
From One to Two Years 204

X. FROM TWO TO SIX YEARS 215
Behavioral and Neural Events 215
Initial Stages in the Development of the Self 226

XI. FROM SIX YEARS TO NEURAL MATURITY 240
From Six to Eleven Years 240
From Twelve Years to the Third Decade 253

Chapter   *Page*
XII. DEVELOPING THE HYPOTHESIS, SECOND PHASE: A TENTATIVE
ANSWER TO "WHAT HAPPENS DURING THE DEVELOPMENTAL
GAP BETWEEN BIRTH AND NEURAL MATURITY?" 261
  Overview of Neural-Behavioral Developmental Relation-
    ships 261
  Developmental Stages 264
  Principles of Human Development 277

PART E

**A TREE-TRUNK, A WALL, A SNAKE—
OR THE WHOLE ELEPHANT?**

XIII. SOME IMPLICATIONS 293
  For Individual Differences 293
  For Sex Differences 295
  For the Role of "Mothering" in Human Development .. 307
  For Freudian Constructs 309
  For Personality Theories—And Theory 314
  For Additional Research 320
  For Psychiatry's Present "Pre-Pasteur" Period 322
XIV. SOME APPLICATIONS 326
  The Possibility of a "Cultural Rating-Scale" 326
  "Unabling" Variations in Our Own Society 332
  Preventive Measures 344
  Postscript: A Word to Students in the Behavioral
    Sciences 356

Appendix A—Sources for Behavioral Development Data of
  Part D 359
References 363
Index 381

ORIENTATION SUPPLEMENTS

Number   *Title*   *Page*
  1. The Mammalian Nervous System: Basic Concepts 32
  2. The Primate Neuraxis: Neural Tube Derivatives 34

3. Functional Contributions of Subcortical Human Neuraxial
   Centers 36
4. The Human Subcortical Forebrain 96
5. Excerpts From the Writings of J. Hughlings Jackson 100
6. Electrical Activity, Index of Neurophysiological
   Functioning 120

FIGURES & TABLES

Figure		Page
1.	"So *show* us already!"	8
2.	Reconstructions Illustrating the Development and Developmental Role of the Four Neural-Tube Flexures.	72
3.	Embryological neurogenesis: CNS developmental sequence.	75
4.	Major functional divisions of the human neocortex	112
5.	Cytoarchitectural map of monkey brain	114
6.	Feedback loops to and from motor cortex	133
7.	Hypothesized sensory aspect of the intraorganismic and transactional subsystems	154

Table		
I.	Nervous System Phylogenesis	43
	A. Neural Phylogenetic Trends Up To the Vertebrates ...	43
	B. Phylogenesis of the Vertebrate Brain Above the Medulla	52
	C. Structural Phylogenesis of the Mammalian Neocortex ..	56
II.	Human Prenatal Ontogeny	64
	A. From Two and One-Half to Seven Fetal Weeks	64
	B. From Seven and One-Half to Fifteen Fetal Weeks	66
	C. From Sixteen Fetal Weeks to Birth	68
III.	Myelination Development Pattern of Myelinated Nerve Tracts	81
IV.	The Human Neonate	84
	A. Behavioral Status	84
	B. Neural Status	86
V.	Relative Growth Rates of Neocortical Lobes	174
VI.	Postnatal Developmental Trends in the EEG	176
VII.	Neural Developmental Indices: One to Three Months	184
VIII.	Neural Developmental Indices: Three to Twelve Months ..	190
IX.	Neural Developmental Indices: One to Two Years	209
X.	Neural Developmental Indices: Two to Six Years	222
XI.	Neural Developmental Indices: Six Years to the Thirties ..	245
XII.	Successive Neural Organizations Underlying the Postulated Nine Stages of Human Development	266

HUMAN NEURAL AND BEHAVIORAL DEVELOPMENT
A Relational Inquiry, with Implications for Personality

PART A

NEEDED: A SPECIES-APPLICABLE PICTURE OF MECHANISM

Chapter I

THE HUMAN NERVOUS SYSTEM'S POTENTIAL RAPPROCHEMENT AND THEORETICAL ROLES

 T HE FINDINGS OF neurophysiologists and psychologists of only the last decade or so are creating a quiet revolution within the comparative-experimental branch of psychology, traditionally the field with the greatest influence on psychological theorizing. As yet fragmentary from a psychological standpoint and highly technical to the "outsider" as the data of this resurgent research area are, it is important for those whose work utilizes psychological knowledge but who are not in immediate contact with this highly specialized field to know about these findings — and their implications — for a reason which goes well beyond the intrinsic meaningfulness of the data themselves. That reason is their great potential relevance for the resolution of two long-standing debates within psychology:

(1) The schism between those who insist on the primacy for the discipline of a rigorously controlled and quantified methodology, and those who hold that methodology must be secondary to the proper data and problems of psychology, which are considered to involve primarily those behaviors which are unique to man.

(2) The limited usefulness for those who work with and theorize about *human* behavior and personality of a picture of "mechanism" derived from experimentation utilizing lower animals, unidimensional observational perspectives, and narrow conceptual frameworks.

Why — and under what conditions — these new findings have major potential for overcoming this schism and for at last providing a picture of mechanism that can be accepted and *used* by those who work with and theorize about human beings deserves examination.

THE HUMAN NERVOUS SYSTEM'S POTENTIAL
RAPPROCHEMENT ROLE

The first controversy involves a long-simmering intra-discipline dissatisfaction with what perceptive Europeans term the "American cult of method," which emphasizes the *how* of scientific study at the expense of its *what* and its *why* (83). This dissatisfaction persists in spite of a thorough respect for the motivations of those who emphasize purity of method.

The old-line comparative-experimentalists' rationale for their "primacy of method" value-system may be stated as follows:

(1) The common biological characteristics of mammals means that inter-species differences are ones only of degree, not of kind; from this postulation, it follows that all behavioral characteristics of higher mammalian forms are present in some simplified version in lower mammalian forms, so that data we derive from the study of subhuman forms are, with certain qualifications, extrapolatable to the human being.

(2) Since both investigative ethics and the difficulty of strictly controlling human subjects proscribe their use for many kinds of experimentation, we have in any case no recourse but to use lower forms for our research.

(3) Unless psychologists apply the methodological dicta of the older, established — and therefore higher in status — sciences, psychology would continue to be considered a parascientific study; and if we did not do so in this era of the supremacy of science and the scientific method, we would have no standing whatsoever as a scientific discipline.

The new-generation counterparts of the earlier experimentalists, the conceptual and the actual behavioral model-builders, might not subscribe unreservedly to the first two points above, but assuredly would the third, and would add:

(4) If it is necessary to postulate as yet nonspecifically identified — and therefore unquantifiable — variables as intervening between a (quantifiable) stimulus-input and a (quantifiable) response-output (which we are reluctant to do, but which the results of our own investigations oblige us to do), then we must

be able to demonstrate that the invisible something which inter-
venes between a specific input and a specific output *can* exist,
objectively, unequivocally and non-metaphysically. If we are able
to construct a conceptual model or an actual machine-model
which can do what man's "intervening variables" seem to be
doing, then we have demonstrated, even to the most skeptical
nonvitalistic nonpsychologist, that the human nervous system may
also function as a mechanism in this complex manner.[1]

One of Johnny Hart's cartoon-sequences has presented this
dilemma of psychology as an experimental science so admirably,
it is here reproduced, with permission, as Figure 1.

Psychologists who are dissatisfied with the comparative-experimental tradition's dominant role within psychology may be identified as representing either one or both of these two positions:

(1) Those in applied fields who have come to recognize there
is very little of relevance in the theoretical fruits of that tradition
for their day-to-day work with human beings, even while paying
lip-service to it as solid members of the psychological establishment.

(2) Those who believe, on both philosophical *and* scientific
grounds, that the ways in which psychology as an investigative
science has heretofore applied science's methodological dicta of
analysis of a phenomenon into its simplest component parts as
preliminary to their respective intensive study, strict experimental
control, exact quantification of data, have not taken the special
and unique nature of man adequately into account in their
research-designs — and that, as but one disastrous result, psychology has made a major contribution to a distorted picture of man.

There are several grounds for the second position. The first,
and probably most fundamental, is that most psychological investigators whose research designs have utilized lower animals and
whose subsequent theorizing has reflected the direct extrapolation
of such research findings to human behavior have virtually ignored

---

[1]Chein's apparent misunderstanding of the methodological rationale behind the
current theoretical fashion of mechanical-model building has vitiated somewhat
his otherwise very-well-taken criticism of the comparative-experimental tradition
(35).

Figure 1. "So *show* us already!"

the experimental and theoretical implications of the biological concept of integrative levels. Alex Novikoff, in a discussion of this concept (141), makes a point of major methodological implications — a point which lies at the heart of the second group's objections:

> In the continual evolution of matter, new levels of complexity are superimposed on the individual units by the organization and integration of these units into a single system. *What were wholes on one level become parts of a higher one.* Each level of organization possesses unique properties of structure and behavior which, though dependent on the properties of the constituent elements, appear only when these elements are combined in the new system. Knowledge of the laws of the lower level is necessary for a full understanding of the higher level; yet *the unique properties of phenomena at the higher level can not be predicted, a priori, from the laws of the lower level. The laws describing the unique properties of each level are qualitatively distinct, and their discovery requires methods of research and analysis appropriate to the particular level.* These laws express the new organizing relationship, i.e., the reciprocal relationships of elementary units to each other and to the unit system as a whole (p. 209). (Italics EM's.)

Novikoff's point has been taken one step further by Roy Wood Sellars (165):

> Evolution signifies the local rise of new systems with new properties. Such [novel] properties must not be considered to be 'stuck on' externally and miraculously, but to be *functions of the [new] organization* (p. 462). (Italics EM's.)

The investigative implications of this reminder have been reiterated by Tinbergen. In his *Study of Instinct* (179), he mentions von Uexküll's comment that each species has its own perceptual world (p. 16), having stated earlier in the same book:

> In view of the differences between any one species and another, the only thing that can be said for certain is that one should not use identical experimental techniques to compare

two species, because they would almost certainly not be the same for *them* (p. 12).

Doctors Novikoff and Tinbergen had the related disciplines of biology and of ethology, respectively, in mind as they wrote the foregoing passages. Solomon Asch, in another context (10), has pointed explicitly to the effect on the data of psychology of our experimental tradition's oversight of the concept of integrative levels:

> In the hands of later psychologists, the main consequences of the doctrine of evolution was not to *enrich* the realm of biological phenomena to include the unusual properties of man — his particular capacities for social life, his potentialities for science and art[2] — but to *reduce* the latter to the model of action observed in the lower organisms. The strange consequence of Darwin's thought was that although it placed man in nature, it also stripped him of the qualities most distinctive of humanity. The properties distinctive of man — his social relations, speech, and art were assigned the role of complex means to the gratification of needs that he shared with other, lower, organisms. . . . In terms of method, this mode of thinking represented an attempt to proceed directly from [lower-mammalian] biology to a social psychology and a theory of society" (p. 11).

Professor Asch's criticism merits further elaboration. From a phylogenetic standpoint, it is possible to group all behavior expressed by human beings into three generalized categories:

(1) Unlearned behaviors which man shares with other, lower, mammals. The inborn processes of growth and maturation ordinarily see to it that such basic physiological and psychological functions as: breathing, sucking, chewing, swallowing, digesting, coughing, feeling hungry and thirsty, urinating and defecating, basic temperamental tendencies, sexual tension, anger, feeling primary fear; ability to smell, taste, hear, touch, distinguish grada-

---

[2] I would also add: penchant for formulating philosophical and religious and scientific conceptual systems.

tions of light, orient self in space; showing primary curiosity; development of voluntary motor control, will appear before, at, or not long after birth, so long as food and responsive physical care are provided.

(2) Learned behaviors which we share with other higher mammals; for example: the manner in which we see the physical world around us and the basic recognition-meanings of what we see, hear, smell, touch, taste, and so on.

(3) Learned behaviors which we share with no other form of life; for example: language spoken and written, self-awareness and self-judgment, abstract thought, values and ethics.

Physiology and psychology have shared the study of the first phylogenetic category of behavior, comparative-experimental psychology has also concentrated on the second — and the surface of the third has scarcely been scratched by any scientific discipline. Nor, in supplementation of this last comment, has the comparative-experimental tradition shown sufficient appreciation in the past for the circumstance that "learning and many other higher processes are *secondary modifications of innate mechanisms*," and that therefore a study of man's learning processes must be preceded by a study of the innate foundations of behavior in *man* (adapted from Tinbergen, p. 6).

One of the major reasons scientific psychology has been reluctant to focus directly and explicitly on man as its primary datum of study, if not the major reason, has been that tenacious conceptual booby-trap known as the "mind-body problem." Apparently unprovable constructs such as "consciousness" and "the self" do not arise when the behavior of lower animals is studied — so why not leave well enough alone? Behavioral theorists seem not yet to have realized that this once-powerful trap has become so heavily rusted with its own lack of contact with modern biology as no longer to pose a serious threat to the wary. The most potent of the arguments which have made the "mind-body problem" biologically — *and* psychologically — obsolete rests upon the implications of (again) changing phylogenetic levels of integration. Roy Wood Sellars, after explicitly rejecting both "epi-phenomenon" and "by-product" as explanatory of consciousness and of mind (165) , goes on to say:

> Consciousness is not a physical system but a qualitative dimension of the existential content of a highly evolved physical system (p. 476) .
>
> In the human organism at least . . . we are allowed to speak of consciousness as *a unique co-emergent with nervous organization* (p. 484) . (Italics EM's.)

The investigative implications of this point are both major and fundamental. They are presented here in two sets of excerpts, the first series from the article by Sellars just referred to, and the second series from the book by Herrick (78) that has played so dominant a role in my own neurological hypothesizing. Especially significant passages are italicized.

> A. Do we have a double knowledge of ourselves — behavioral, physical, external knowledge in which mind is disclosed in what mind does, disclosure to an external observer; *and* a self-knowledge in which the knower is internal to himself and for which consciousness in its full range is not merely epistemic but also inseparable from the self, the object known (p. 467)?
>
> This self-knowledge should enlarge and supplement the concept of mind gained by external study. There would be essentially the philosophical problem [the investigative problem also — EM] of coalescing the results of *two ways of knowing the same reality* (p. 468) .
>
> It is the naturalist's belief than an adequate empiricism will recognize the validity of such categories [as choice, preference, reasoning] for human behavior and will seek to give them a physiological expression. . . . There must be a basic categorial parallelism between external knowledge of the organism and self-knowledge (p. 473) .
>
> In consciousness, we are on the inside of the functioning brain (p. 476) .
>
> Just as we ordinarily think of physical systems only in terms of formal knowledge-about, so we ordinarily think of such

acts and states as thinking, believing, willing, feeling and striving in terms of direct experiencing and concepts founded on, and interpretive of, that direct experiencing. What I ask is that these two approaches be seen to *supplement* each other, that *both* be seen to be valid (p. 480).

B. When I say that I am a thinking body, this implies that my body is different from every other body and that one of its distinctive properties is my private awareness. *I know about my own body and I know about my own thinking just as I know about other things,* and every object in our physical universe has its own distinctive properties that distinguish it from all other objects. My personal knowledge about these things is necessarily private, and I know enough about them to believe that they have substantial existence independently of my knowledge about them. *My capacity for knowing implies a mechanism that does the knowing* (p. 278).

The process of nervous conduction [is] a metabolic process which includes chemical changes in the nerve fiber *and* changes in its electrical potential. The one process is manifested in two ways which must be investigated by quite different methods. It will not do to ignore either of them and say the conduction is exclusively chemical *or* exclusively electrical. Similarly, the psychobiological processes of the brain have qualities that are observable perceptually as metabolic functions, and other qualities that are observable only introspectively, and *the difference between these manifestations of the one process can never be explained by ignoring it* (p. 292).

Personality theorists' adoption of "theoretical constructs" to bridge the gap between the rich subjective data related to the human personality and the far leaner data obtained by observation of overtly manifested behavior is an intermediate means of dealing with the problem of "coalescing the results of two ways of knowing the same reality" to which Sellars has pointed. Fortunately, attempts at a more direct solution to the problem are also beginning to be made. In citing Craik's observation that "neural models (e.g., cell assemblies), once established, have the property of making imagery possible in the absence of stimulation," Bruner recently initiated the construction of a solidly neurological — i.e., mechanistic — foundation for the "second way" of knowing the same reality (29). Psychologists' long years of "explaining" the difference between the physiological and the subjective-psychological manifestations of brain functioning by ignoring it appear to be drawing to a close.

Grey Walter has highlighted still another psychologically relevant aspect of the experimental imperative to take changing integrative levels explicitly into account (187) :

> There exists a class of systems which is *inherently* complex, in a special sense. Such systems are characterized not so much by their size or by the number of elements which they contain, but rather by the way in which their elements may be interconnected. A human brain is not a very large object, but we know that it contains something like ten thousand million nerve elements, any or all of which as far as we can tell may be connected functionally with any or all of the others. . . . It can easily be shown that *the number of patterns of interconnections in a human brain is as large as the number of elementary particles in the Universe.*
>
> An important corollary to the proposition about complex systems of this class is that such systems tend to elude investigation by conventional means; *the classical scientific method which depends on simplification by isolation of a single variable, when applied to a complex system, must destroy or at least grossly disturb the very functions which it attempts to analyse* (p. 21). (Italics EM's.)

One of psychology's most creative experimentalists can also be counted on the side of the angels — and in no uncertain terms. Hebb has written (73) :

> We are past the era in which the kind of oversimplification made by Thorndike, Pavlov and Watson is scientifically fertile. Such theories, all of the s-r type and providing no autonomy whatsoever in cerebral processes, were useful and necessary clarifications at one stage in the development of knowledge. . . .

The critical level of complexity has gone up if theory is to continue to be a guide to research instead of mere verbal flux (p. 455).

And again, in the same article:

> Our current sophistication with respect to the design of experiments, statistically speaking, is a brilliant development of method without which we would be much better off (p. 463).

Tinbergen has put his finger on what is probably the essential reason for the persistence of the "oversimplified" approaches which Hebb criticizes (179):

> Every experimental worker has a certain inclination to stick to a method that has served him well and has given him results. . . . The scientist who limits himself in this way becomes more and more inclined to let his work be determined by a certain preoccupation with the question: 'What can I do with this method?'. This, however, is not the natural way of expanding a science. . . . In the long run, it is more useful to ask, 'What method shall I apply to solve this problem?' rather than, 'What can I do with this method?' " (p. 12).

It is also legitimate to point out to the new experimentalist generation of mechanical-model builders, heuristic as the contributions of information theory appear to have been, that a C-A-T (computer average transience) can be-become just as limiting, conceptually and experimentally, to psychology-as-a-science as RATs have so often been. The circumstance that a gifted mathematician-engineer (Norbert Wiener) discovered the mechanical principle of "feedback," applied it to construct far more complex machines than had before existed — and subsequently discovered that feedback is also a basic functional principle in complex *living* systems (193), does *not* mean that psychologists can use this homology to reason that the behaving human individual is no more than such a machine, really — just a bit more complicated one, that's all. With all their semantic sophistication, these psychologists' ad reductam logic takes theoretical psychology right back to the very argument that they themselves have questioned — that is, to "Since man is, after all, no more than a mammal, we are studying man whenever we study any mammal."

Another of the grounds upon which the second-position group base their criticism of the comparative-experimental psychological tradition is related to the fundamental differences between "closed" and "open" systems. In wishing to establish a thorough-going mechanistic basis for human behavior, representatives of that tradition have been overinfluenced by the older physical sciences, which usually deal with "closed" systems. They have not taken adequately into account the circumstance that the functional laws governing closed systems are different from those governing living organisms, which are all "open" systems. Von Bertalanffy has pointed to three crucial differences between closed and open systems (19) :

(1) Embryonic development from the scantily differentiated ovum to a highly organized multicellular structure connotes an increase of order due to factors lying within the system itself. From the point of view of physics, such behavior seems at first paradoxical. A physical system cannot increase in order by itself; on the contrary, the second law of thermodynamics demands that in every closed system a decrease of order is the natural course of events. This is exactly what happens in a decomposing corpse, but the process in the developing embryo is just the reverse. The behavior of the latter presupposes first, that there are specific organizational forces working towards higher levels of order, and secondly, that the embryo is not a closed system (p. 64) .

(2) [In contrast to inanimate systems, the living organism expresses] the phylogenetic accumulation of dispositions that unfold progressively in ontogenesis (p. 64) .

(3) In contrast to the general trend in closed systems, a *decrease* of entropy can take place in open systems, and with it, a transition to states of higher heterogeneity and complexity" [A re-statement of the concept of changing integrative levels. — EM] (p. 113) .

A third basis for criticism of the primacy-of-method tradition within psychology involves the narrowness of the observational perspectives which that tradition has typically utilized. Sellars' reference to two ways of knowing the same reality emphasizes psychological experimenters' devotion, with overly rare exceptions,[3] to the exclusively external vantage-point. In an earlier publication I have pointed to unrealized differences in observational perspective as having created unnecessary barriers to communication among behavioral scientists (128); twenty-two different perspectives that have been used in research by behavioral scientists were referred to, most of them grouped into related dichotomies. Five of these differing perspectives are especially relevant in this context and are here repeated:

(1) There are many examples of the influence on research findings of lack of recognition that differing orders of functional complexity are frequently imposed or provided for by the research design used. Tinbergen, in his provocative and illuminating analysis of the nature of the instincts (179), refers to several of the classic — and in his eyes, unnecessary — controversies among biologists in this area. He shows why they were unnecessary by pointing to the differences in the results obtained by one investigator who had unknowingly abstracted for study one limited aspect of behavior from a complex behavioral sequence, as over against findings obtained by another investigator who had unknowingly abstracted for study *another* limited aspect of behavior from the *same* complex behavioral sequence. One such controversy has been between those investigators who have maintained that instinctive behavior is the result of 'spontaneity' or innate reflexes, and those who have maintained that it is a reaction to external stimuli — and both groups were able to back up their contentions with seemingly impeccable research findings. When the problem was formulated more adequately and research approaches more suited to the problem were used, it was found that *both* intrinsic and extrinsic factors obtained — and in predictable fashion. . . .

[3]I am aware that multidimensional approaches have become almost the rule in studies of personality.

Closer to home, the many years of controversy between the classical S-R group and the cognitive experimenters, still not quite resolved, has also stemmed, I believe, from a lack of appreciation that behavior of different orders of complexity were provided for in the respective research designs adopted by each group. The S-R learning experimentalists provided for, and focused on, the evoking of lower-order, reflexive behaviors mediated by the lower neuraxial centers, while the experimental designs of the cognitivists not only used phylogenetically higher-order forms, but also provided for and looked at the more complex behaviors which are mediated by the higher brain centers (pp. 252-3).

(2) and (3) Perspective-dichotomy 2: "surface" (i.e., overt motor and verbal) behavior versus "depth" (i.e., inner ideational-emotional-motivational) behavior. . . . The researcher who obtains data on the experiential history and the inner perceptual and self-reactive world of the individual almost surely subscribes to a multidimensional picture of human behavior, while the investigator who has borrowed his observational methods directly from animal work obtains gross motor and physiological data and tends to conceptualize human behavior in simple-mechanistic and unidimensional terms (p. 254).

(4) and (5) Perspective-dichotomy 4: behavior observed at a moment-in-time versus behavior observed over time or developmentally. This "time dimension" is not identical with the cross-sectional and longitudinal design dichotomy, although these two methods of studying one or another aspect of child development may be seen as subtypes under this dimension. Rather, it highlights the difference between studies where the time factor is seen as incidental — as over against those studies in which developmental change is a major variable. Again, each investigator will tend to conceptualize human behavior quite differently (pp. 254-5).

Indeed, in continuation of the over-time perspective, the conviction that neurophysiology's investigative inclusion of the developmental dimension is crucial for understanding both the functional organization of the matured human nervous system *and* personality development, is a central motivation for this monograph.

It must be stated as explicitly as possible that the quarrel of the second group with the comparative-experimental tradition has never been on the overall aim of psychology as a science: they are just as dedicated to the discovery of non-metaphysical explanations for even the most complex and uniquely human behaviors as are those when they are criticizing. Rather, it has been the *route* that this dominating tradition has chosen to follow towards that goal with which they take issue.

It is as one who on the one hand counts herself a member of both groups of "dissatisfieds" and on the other hand shares the experimentalists' faith that nonmetaphysical explanations exist for the most complex of human behaviors, that the present writer applauds the readmission of human neurophysiology to psychology after decades of disassociation — primarily because this new-old research area has been showing much more recognition, as we shall see, of the implications of changing integrative levels than the old-line comparative-experimentalists have done. Whether or not this new era of collaboration eventually fulfills its present promise for effecting a rapprochement between the traditional position and those who wish to see *human* behavior as psychology's central subject-matter is dependent upon the broadening implementation of the following research conditions, all governed by the implications of the biological principle of changing levels of integration:

Devoting more and more attention directly to the *human* nervous system and continuing to develop new techniques and refine old ones which permit study of the intact, *in situ* human nervous system;

Further developing research designs which provide for the study of nervous system functioning from both the objective and the subjective vantage-points *simultaneously*;

Utilizing animals only to check out theoretical constructs derived from observation of human behavior, which is a direct reversal of the former comparative psychology orientation; Harlow's skin-comfort and Hebb's sensory deprivation and Thompson's early deprivation studies are exemplars of this reversal in approach (70, 74, 177) ;

Adding the developmental dimension to the present dominant interest in the matured nervous system;

Addressing serious attention to scientific psychology's development of a research-applications value system much better suited to its subject-matter — human behavior — than its present apparently unquestioning subscription to the scientific goal of "control" in its old, simple, natural-sciences sense.

THE HUMAN NERVOUS SYSTEM'S POTENTIAL CONTRIBUTION TO PERSONALITY THEORY

The second controversy mentioned in the opening paragraph is an offshoot from the first and relates to the keen awareness of students of personality development and dynamics both that the primary datum of psychology must come to encompass a more complex-yet-unitary gestalt than has yet been generally accepted, and that the complexities of the human personality must be explainable in solidly mechanistic terms before their theorizing will be acceptable to the more rigorous methodologists and theoreticians within our discipline.

The latter necessity is maintained in the face of the bad odor that biologically oriented approaches have acquired for students of personality because of past misconceptions and excesses. Classical behaviorism could have arisen only during biology's naively mechanistic period of reaction against vitalism. Freudian theory, joining forces with the evolutionists in their reaction against Victorian-era religion's overglorification of man, was excessively insistent on the dominant, even the exclusive, role of common-mammalian influences in human personality formation. And during the beginning phases of applied psychology, the primacy of hereditary factors in such complex human behaviors as "intelligence" was asserted without qualification — a proposition still typical of introductory psychology textbooks, in apparent oversight of the thickly accumulating body of data on the role of very early sensory and perceptual experience in human cognitive development; thanks to Hunt's recent review and examination of the implications of these data (86), a situation we may hope to see remedied shortly.

Subsequent to the early overemphasis on innate-biological factors in human behavior, the burgeoning field studies of cultural anthropology came to psychological attention — and there was a pendulum-swing in the opposite direction: emphasis upon cultural and familial, i.e., environmental, influences in personality formation became the order of the theoretical day. In turn, Lewin's topological and vector psychology drew attention to the theoretical holes left not only by both the biologically and the culturally oriented theories of personality, but also by theories of learning derived solely from external-perspective animal experimentation. This awareness of "something missing" has contributed to the revival to investigative respectability of the perceptual-cognitive-experiencing processes, as well as to the overdue realization that the influences on human behavior are far more complex than rodents dream on.

The data of modern neurophysiology and the work of such lonely neuropsychological pioneers as Boring, Lashley and Stevens, which had been accumulating in parallel manner during this same period, converged not much more than a decade ago, largely as a result of overlapping findings and use of potent new investigative techniques. This recent era of active collaboration between physiologists and psychologists may well contribute to yet another personality theory pendulum-swing. Not back merely to a reasserted emphasis on physiological factors in behavior, tempting as the new, phyletically unique picture of the human nervous system and a fuller appreciation of the fundamental and pervasive role in behavior of the nervous system may make such a re-emphasis, but to a period when students of personality, reluctant to accept any one clearly influencing factor at the expense of other such factors, recognize the aptness for personality theory of Tinbergen's analysis of the long controversy among biologists concerning the "true" nature of instinct already referred to (p. 17). Similarly for personality theorists, there is recognition that it is necessary to postulate as the essential point of departure for most psychological research not the importance of social factors as over against organismic factors or the reverse, but a complex-yet-unitary gestalt in which the social and organismic and experiential factors are all accounted for.

But in spite of the urgent theoretical need for it, a solidly mechanistic foundation for the complexities of the human personality still eludes us. This state of affairs is not due to want of conceptual effort on the part of individual neurophysiologists and neuropsychologists, who have been trying for years to bridge the conceptual gap between the physiological and behavioral levels of analysis — a gap at least partly imposed by the traditional differences in observational perspective of the data-gatherers of each discipline. The only recent removal of three handicapping limitations — an inadequate concept of mechanism or system, already referred to, experimental data derived almost entirely from mammals lower than man, and certain fundamental defects in neural experimental methodology (such as the functionally contaminating use of anesthesia) — have put fresh life into such bridging efforts. Much research *and* conceptual progress has been made as a result, as Part C of this inquiry attempts to document.

Paradoxically enough, students of *behavioral* development, who are concerned with "understanding what changing integrations of development underlie successive functional stages characteristic of the species" (163), have not been recently engaged in attempts to identify what changing patterns of *neural* development and functioning may underlie the changing integrations of development to which Schneirla refers. Perhaps previous disappointments with the inadequacies of past attempts at "neurologizing," such as Thorndike's connectionism and the apparently conflicting findings on early patterns of neural development, represented by the Coghill-Windle controversy, have temporarily obscured the inescapable relevance for their concerns of Tinbergen's already cited reminder that "learning and other higher processes are *secondary modifications of innate mechanisms.*"

Whatever the reasons behind this investigative hiatus, it is the present writer's conviction that the neurogenic dimension constitutes an essential conceptual *and* research perspective, and that neurophysiological knowledge in depth and detail of this dimension can and will make a basic contribution to the yet-to-be-enunciated gestalt concerning human personality formation — a complex gestalt that must become the primary focus of psychological study. This inquiry is dedicated to the furtherance of this eventuality.

Chapter II

DEVELOPING THE HYPOTHESIS,
FIRST PHASE

IT IS NOT MERELY FORTUITOUS that the present writer's special interest has been — and continues to be — a social-psychological approach to personality development, and that a psychologist with such an orientation is here speaking to the necessity explicitly to incorporate into any theoretical analysis of personality formation a richly conceived picture of the individual human organism — not merely to imply, nor to give lip-service to, the fundamental relevance of "physical factors." The circumstance that the "solidly mechanistic" base earlier referred to has not yet been established does not provide an excuse for its being relegated to indefinite theoretical limbo, but must instead lead to redoubled efforts, both investigative and conceptual, *to* establish it.

What was originally a guess — that detailed information on the neurogenic dimension is crucially relevant to this enterprise — has, with additional knowledge, become certainty. Even the most hasty comparison of the functional and behavioral status of the human nervous system at birth with its status at neural maturity reveals the gap to be that between the neural resources and behavioral repertoire of almost any mammal at birth and a being with so complex a neural organization, such behaviors as a personal value-system, a strong sense of guilt when he does not live up to his own expectations, the habit of carrying on the most complex and sustained mental processes involving the manipulation of symbols — i.e., human adult behaviors — are possible.

The thinking which led to the preparation of this monograph has a ten-year developmental history of its own, a history which it is pertinent to recount here. It began with the relatively uncomplicated hunch that the pattern of cortical development after birth has much to do with the postnatal pattern of behavioral development, and has arrived at an inquiry which includes as background prerequisite to the examination of data bearing on this hypothe-

sis, a relatively detailed analysis of neural phylogenesis, of prenatal human ontogeny, of theories and findings bearing on the
functioning and functional organization of the matured human
nervous system.

The request in the Fall of 1953 of Frances Robinson, that year's
editor of the *Journal of the National Association of Deans of
Women,* that I prepare a theoretically oriented article stressing
an interdisciplinary approach to personality formation happened
to come at a germinal time in my thinking. Doctoral studies with
the Committee on Human Development at Chicago had provided
the across-discipline basis for such an approach, but it was the
subsequent college-teaching obligation to communicate such an
orientation in an organized and comprehensible way that led to
the formulation, circa 1949-52, of the hypothesis that

> the growing individual human organism, surrounded by its
> social environments, through continuing interaction with them,
> develops an individually unique personality.

This "organizing hypothesis" was the requested article's conceptual point of departure (126).

This formal attempt to present the contributions of each of
the various factors influencing personality formation resulted in
several conceptual clarifications for its author. Not the least of
these was a much greater appreciation of the role of the nervous
system in behavior than I had had when I undertook to write
New Frontiers in Personality Theory. Two passages from it, following, indicate both this appreciation *and* the germinal beginnings of the hypothesis that is basic to this inquiry.

> The complexity of the implications of the relationship be-
> tween environmental factors and nervous system development
> and functioning is evident when we realize that nervous system
> structure-functioning enters into every phase of human experi-
> encing and behavior: from smelling, to moving, to feeling
> afraid, to creative thinking. A major implication is that since
> the nervous system's primary function from the individual's
> point of view is *to experience,* then each individual must have
> a unique experiencing matrix. Since we do not know the limits

of the range of individual experience, we can assume that each individual experiences in a *unique* fashion, irrespective of the nature of his external stimulus-world. This is the sort of uniqueness which is cumulative, since later experiencing-under-standing has been found to be influenced by what is retained by the individual from his earlier experiencing-understanding. Here is probably the biological basis for the psychological concept of the individually unique "ego" (p. 108).

It is fairly safe to say that *at least* until the cerebral cortex has achieved its full adult size, specific cortical developments undoubtedly underlie almost all individual behavior. Not only is level of cortical development involved in the individual's basic capacity to experience, it is also involved in his capacity to understand and to profit from experience, whether such experience is externally or internally induced. The important point is that the direction of development of cortical function is accepted as being from little or no cortical involvement in the newborn, to the cortex's role as coordinator and controller of almost all human functioning and behavior in the mature organism.

It seems to me that the major implication of this direction in the development in structure-function of the nervous system is for the inner experience of the individual: it points to the emergent nature of subjective experience-understanding, not only during the first several years of life, but probably for as long as the individual remains mentally curious and active. This emergent character of inner experience may well explain why conceptual development, which depends far more on experience and learning than on innately unfolding patterns, proceeds from the immediate and specific to the distant and general (pp. 108-9).

Perhaps because of the subsequent realization that the article had not actually dealt with it, the second question raised in the introduction to "New Frontiers in Personality Theory" continued to echo after the paper's completion and publication: What role does level of nervous system development play in *which* personality "structurings" develop *when*? Attempts to answer this question at that period prompted such musing as the following:

As the part of the human nervous system which makes possible those behaviors peculiarly distinctive of our species, the cerebral cortex's structure and functional characteristics must constitute a fundamental lead to the solution of many of the mysteries of personality development and dynamics. What I recall of the data on early development reinforces this hunch by its indication that in human beings the highest part of the brain, the neocortex, is not functioning at birth. Well then, *what happens after birth?* Surely there must be *some* significant relationship between the post-natal development of the part of the nervous system which apparently provides for the expression of uniquely human behaviors *and* the development of those behaviors!

A trusting search for data on the postnatal development of the human cerebral cortex was begun in physiological-psychology sources through 1952 — from which a disconcerting discovery emerged:

(1) Fragmentary material on the *mammalian* neocortex was available, but none on the *human* neocortex appeared to exist in such sources; apparently all neuropsychological data had been derived from subhuman animal experimentation.

Even mammalian neurophysiology was inaccurately dealt with in standard psychological sources, later augmented knowledge made clear. Witness a major error which persists even into an introductory textbook dated 1962 (79, p. 46) : the nervous system is described as being divided into two sections, the central nervous system, a *structural* concept, and the autonomic nervous system, a *functional* concept (and one, moreover, comprising both central and peripheral structural components!) . This ubiquitous error was unknowingly incorporated into the "new frontiers" article.

Somewhat later, a small but most relevant body of data in developmental psychology sources was found, right under my nose, so to speak: Carmichael's reports on his and others' prenatal studies of evoked and spontaneous behavior (30, 31), Pratt's detailed neonatal report (152), and McGraw's pioneering *Neuromuscular Maturation of the Human Infant* (119), which has recently been accorded the tribute of being reprinted. All three investigators attempted to relate their behavioral findings to the developmental status of the human nervous system.

Still naively certain that such important data as postnatal cortical ontogenesis must exist *somewhere* in the available literature, I began to foray directly into the neurophysiological literature. This second exploratory phase (from 1954 to 1957) yielded additional "disconcerting discoveries":

(2) The postnatal development of the entire nervous system was also, obviously, a research frontier for neurophysiology as well. The chapter on "development of the nervous system" in even the most reputable textbooks consisted primarily of a telescoped review of the embryology of the nervous system, sometimes preceded by a brief discussion of neural phylogenesis. Only Conel's then four-volume meticulous histological studies (38) were drawn to my attention by instructional personnel at the University of Chicago Medical School; such resources as Lindsley's early electroencephalographic studies (108) and Langworthy's myelination analyses (102) were located later.

(3) At first, brain-map after brain-map of the human neocortex seemed to be all the information that could be found about the neocortex in neurophysiological textbook sources — each one with a different precise cortical-area designation-system. Then, as the current literature was dipped into, I realized that I had happened to begin my data-hunt at the very time that freshly burgeoning new-techniques research was in active process of radically changing neurophysiology's picture of the functioning and functional organization of the nervous system. Not only was the former approach of attempting to arrive at more and more exact cortical-localization maps now obsolete; the neocortex was no longer to be conceived of as a discrete functional entity but as one major, highly complex component of a still more complex entity, the human nervous system — the functional characteristics of which are likely to constitute an active investigative frontier for some time to come.

I also found later that neurophysiologists and comparative neuropsychologists were beginning to talk directly to each other during this same period about some of the very questions I was trying to find answers to — and that research of a collaborative, across-discipline nature was beginning to fill in basic data-gaps. Aspects of the new picture of the human nervous system that is resulting are given in Part C.

Fortunately, not all the discoveries of this period were disconcerting. Others were also most germinal:

(4) My discovery of the developmentally relevant, far in advance of his time postulations of the neuropsychiatrist John Hughlings Jackson, was especially felicitous (89). The heuristic ideas of this English contemporary of Freud will be referred to in subsequent chapters.

(5) My original hunch concerning the necessity to know more about the early developmental pattern of the neocortex was revised early on; for "neocortex" has been substituted: the entire nervous system as a complexly organized entity, with the neocortex as one major component of that entity.

(6) A number of insights derived from this early phase of my exploration of the literature were incorporated into a paper, "A Species Theory of Anxiety," presented before the Fifteenth International Congress of Psychology in Brussels in 1957. Although inaccurate in some of its neural details, this paper anticipated some very recent shifts in basic approaches to the nature of human cognitive motivation and functioning (*viz.*, 154 and 155).

(7) Available developmental data made two things clear at the same time: there is a marked developmental gap between the neonatal and the matured nervous system; and there is a marked scarcity of neurophysiological information to fill in the details of this gap. It further became evident that even if more such data *were* available, their relevance to my enterprise would be limited in their "raw" form as a mere catalogue of findings. Not only was some conception of the prior developmental history of the nervous system essential to an understanding of the meaning of these findings; knowledge of the functional characteristics of the matured human nervous system and of authoritative theorizing about its functional organization was also necessary for the same reason. Clearly, my curiosities had led me into a far more complex undertaking than I had been in a position to realize at the outset!

(8) Fortunately, the literature has also yielded enough related data — phylogenetic, embryological, pre- and post- natal neural,

behavioral, as well as sufficiently heuristic speculations by such pioneering thinkers as Hughlings Jackson and Judson Herrick, to permit this attempt to relate the rich behavioral data to the less rich neural data.

The decision to organize these materials and to relate them systematically to each other within the format of a speculative monograph led first, to more thorough forays into the rapidly growing neurological and neuropsychological literature and second, to deeper contacts with such cognitively oriented theorists as Piaget, Werner, and most recently, Hunt. These theorists, specifically or by implication, accord an important role in cognitive development to developmental changes in underlying neural structures. As a result, their postulations have raised this question:

Does available neural data contribute information about such underlying developments *beyond* Hebb's cell-assembly thesis, as summarized in this modified excerpt?

> To form a [cortical] cell-assembly [takes] a considerable time, requiring many sensory stimulations during the period of early infancy. Perception and thought [thus depend] on exposure to a normally varied sensory environment during infancy (75, p. 263).

Hunt's recent reemphasis on the role of very early experience, especially in the development and expression of intelligence, seems to have brought the postulated role of learning in development almost full circle. First, Behaviorism posited practically all human behavior which emerges subsequent to birth to be a direct outcome of conditioning — i.e., as entirely or primarily dependent upon external stimulation; subsequently, Dennis' cross-cultural and McGraw's co-twin control studies (40, 118), among others, documented that innately predetermined maturation of neural structures is prerequisite to the unfolding sequence of locomotor and manipulative behavior — that is, to the development of voluntary motor control; and that acquisition of complex "cultural" skills is dependent upon the prior functioning of related neural tissue. Now Hunt is postulating that experience plays a major role in the course of neural maturation, at least so far as cognitive and intellectual development are concerned. Is psychology here repeating, perhaps, biology's innate reflexes vs. external stimulation controversy over the "true basis" of instincts earlier referred to?

The discussion to follow does not attempt to undertake a definitive review and critical analysis of related literature: the territory of inquiry is so broad and so complex, such a goal is manifestly unrealistic — at least for only one unsubsidized explorer. Rather, its purpose is to develop, on the basis of pertinent literature derived from both primary and reputable-secondary sources, provisional, hopefully research-promoting answers to these questions:

(1) What can already existing data tell us about the basic patterns of human neural ontogeny?

(2) When neural and behavioral developmental data are related to one another in an organized manner, do any systematic relationships between the two orders of data become evident?

(3), (4), (5) If such relationships are found, what light do they throw on

   (a) How behavioral development is related to neural maturation and functioning?
   (b) The patterns of cognitive development?
   (c) Which aspects of the human personality are structured when?

(6) For personality theorizing purposes especially, what gaps in present knowledge of human neural development most need to be filled in?

Since the audience for this monograph may be comprised of persons of widely varying degrees of neurological sophistication, a formidable communication challenge presents itself. The explicit attempt to solve this problem will consist of provision, through the supplementary insertion of basic orientation materials at key points throughout the text, for attainment of fairly knowledgeable levels on the part of readers with minimal neural background. Orientation Supplement 1 (following) is the first of these insertions, and presents basic concepts and information concerning the mammalian nervous system. Orientation Supplement 2 adopts an embryological perspective and gives a more detailed structural picture of the primate neuraxis than is provided in section C of Orientation Supplement 1. Orientation Supplement 3 (A and B), which provides an overview of the respective human neuraxial centers' functional contributions with the exception of those of the cortex, is also presented at this early stage, even though much of its data anticipate text discussion yet to come. Structural and functional data on the cerebral cortex are included in Chapter V. Also, elaborative material of a specialized-technical nature is included in smaller print in the text when appropriate.

ORIENTATION SUPPLEMENT 1

THE MAMMALIAN NERVOUS SYSTEM: BASIC CONCEPTS

A. CENTRAL VERSUS PERIPHERAL DIVISIONS

The two basic-anatomical divisions of the nervous system, the *central* nervous system or *neuraxis*, and the *peripheral* nervous system, stem from this conception of overall bodily structure:

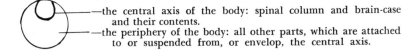

—the central axis of the body: spinal column and brain-case and their contents.
—the periphery of the body: all other parts, which are attached to or suspended from, or envelop, the central axis.

(1) The central nervous system (CNS) or neuraxis is made up of:

(1. Nerve-centers of spinal cord and brain.
(2. Sensory-afferent and motor-efferent nerve-tracts
(or pathways which interconnect the several
(nerve-centers of spinal cord and brain.

(2) The peripheral nervous system (PerNS) is made up of:

(1. Receptor-sensory cells and associated afferent
((*into* the CNS) nerve- fibers and tracts.
(2. Efferent (*out of* the CNS) fibers leading to
(motor cells in skeletal muscles (= the somatic
(n.s.) and to viscera and glands (= the visceral
(n.s.) .[1]

B. NERVE CELLS, NERVE CENTERS, NEURAL TRACTS OR PATHWAYS, NERVE IMPULSE

(1) The nerve cell or *neuron* (of which there are several different types) is the *primary structural unit* of the nervous system. Neurons are located in both *nerve-centers* (in the CNS only) and in nerve-fiber tracts or pathways (in both the CNS and the PerNS) .

(2) A particular nerve-centers-interconnecting nerve-tract is usually named according to the nerve-center in which it originates (first half of its name) and the one in which it terminates (second half of its name) . This style of nomenclature automatically indicates whether the tract is sensory (from a lower to a higher center) or motor (from a higher to a lower center) .

---

[1] It is this *peripheral component* of the Autonomic Nervous System which some psychology textbooks still call *the* ANS!

(3) A nerve-center or *nucleus* is a complex cluster of neurons; all such nuclei are located in the CNS. It comprises a neural locus or a complexly organized set of such loci where the nerve impulses to that point are modified in some way.

(4) The *nerve-impulse* consists of the passage of electro-chemical excitations along the membrane of a nerve-cell and from one neuron to the next via a synapse; it is the nervous system's *primary functional unit.* As such, it becomes significant for behavior when it is related to larger, organized functional units.

C. MAJOR NERVE-CENTERS OF THE MAMMALIAN NEURAXIS

The diagrammatic organization below approximates both the actual-anatomical and the hierarchical-functional relationships. All nerve-centers are profusely inter- and intra- connected by nerve-tracts.

(Top: last to differentiate, phylogenetically)

```
Fore-  ( – the cerebral  hemispheres  ( – cerebral cortex.
brain  (     (two):                   ( – cerebral  medulla,  in  which  the
       (                              (    basal ganglia (corpus striatum be-
       (                              (    low primates) are embedded.

B      ( – the  diencephalic  centers:  ( – thalamus.
R      (                                ( – hypothalamus.
A
I  Brain- ( – mid-brain centers.
N  stem   ( – lower-brain centers:     ( – pons  and  two-lobed  cerebellum.
          (                            ( – medulla oblongata or "bulb" (still-
          (                            (    segmented  upper  extension  of  the
          (                            (    spinal cord).
```

S   (1) It is divided externally into segments (thirty-one in higher mammals),
P   each of which has a set of sensory-in-function ganglia associated with
I   it.
N   (2) Nerve-cell wise, it is made up of *inner-gray matter,* its *active* com-
A C   ponent (these nerve cells generate and dispatch either sensory or
L O   motor impulses); and *outer-white* matter, its interconnecting com-
   R   ponent (these nerve cells form nerve-tracts which *transmit* impulses
   D   to and from the active gray matter).

(Bottom: first to develop, phylogenetically)

ORIENTATION SUPPLEMENT 2
THE PRIMATE NEURAXIS: NEURAL TUBE DERIVATIVES

The neural-tube forms through the invagination of the ectodermal embryonic layer by the end of the third postconception week.

(Top: *last* to differentiate embryologically)

← cum ontogenetic direction of development

B R A I N

Higher brain centers or forebrain (prosencephalon) (III)

Cerebral Hemispheres (telencephalon) (5)

Cerebral Cortex:
- Neocortex: multilayered, four-lobed, cerebral cover.
- Meso- or paleo- cortex or limbic lobe: also multi-layered.
- Archicortex or Hippocampus: three-layered.

Cerebral Medulla:
- Nerve-tracts (white matter): inter- and intra-cortical, and ascending and descending.
- Basal Ganglia or striatum: nuclei embedded in the white matter.

Fourth (telencephalic) flexure appears here..............

Diencephalon (4)
- Thalamus, plus sub-thalamus and epithalamus: cluster of many nuclei.
- Hypothalamus: cluster of a few nuclei.
- (Also pituitary gland, optic tracts and retinae, olfactory bulb and tracts.)

R

Second (mesencephalic) flexure appears here..............

A

Mid-brain (mesencephalon) (II) (3)

Lower part of the reticular formation. Corpora quadrigemina (nerve tracts): inferior (auditory) and superior (visual) colliculi. Ruber (red) nucleus. Substantia Nigra. Cerebral peduncles: nerve-tracts connecting the cerebrum with lower centers.

B R A I N

I

Lower-brain (rhombencephalon) (I)

(Metencephalon) (2)
- Cerebellum: neocerebellum and archicerebellum.
- Pons: chiefly nerve-tracts, both intercerebellar, and ascending and descending.

Third (pontine) flexure appears here..............

N

(Myelencephalon) (1)

Medulla (Oblongata) or Bulb: Various spinal-reflex coordinating centers; also ascending and descending tracts.

S T E M

First (cervical) flexure appears here.................

Sub-pattern of   development ⟹

(The spinal cord's definitive internal structure and connections are attained by the end of the tenth fetal week.)

Segments:

S
P
I
N
A
L

C
O
R
D

8 cervical
12 thoracic
5 lumbar
5 sacral
(1 coccygeal)

and associated nerves.

Sensory Aspects

Receives the interoceptive and proprioceptive sensory systems from the PerNS and transmits them via *dorsal-root* fibers up the neuraxis. Each sensory system first synapses in specific spinal-segment-associated pre-cordal ganglia *before* entering the spinal cord: hence there are pre-ganglionic and post-ganglionic sensory fibers. The sensory systems which first enter the CNS at the cordal level are:

— sensation from viscera in thorax and abdomen (interoceptive);
— deep sensibility, in muscles, joints, tendons, ligaments, skin (proprioceptive);
— pain, temperature, light touch (exteroceptive).

Motor Aspects

A spinal reflex-arc may involve one segment of the cord (intra-segmental) or several segments (inter-segmental); most are the latter. All motor-efferent-descending tracts traverse the cord via *ventral-root* fibers before leaving the CNS.

(Bottom: *first* to differentiate embryologically)

(1) Refer to Figure 2 in Chapter IV. As soon as the neural-tube is formed, it begins to develop four curves or flexures: the first and second emerge at the same time, then the third, then the fourth.

(2) Each of the first differentiation-stage (I, II, III above) and five second-stage (1-2-3-4-5 above) sections of the brain so marked off is called a "vesicle." Each such vesicle (and the section of the tube which becomes the cord) acts as a relatively discrete focus of growth-differentiation during embryology.

ORIENTATION SUPPLEMENT 3

FUNCTIONAL CONTRIBUTIONS OF SUBCORTICAL HUMAN NEURAXIAL CENTERS[1]

A. Of Sub-forebrain Centers

Spinal Cord

Sensory:
(1) Facilitates and inhibits proprioceptive impulses.
(2) Receives and conducts to higher centers both somatic (from skin and muscles) and visceral-vegetative sensations. Body-segmental localization — *dermatomes* — of these sensations:
— cervical sections innervate the upper extremities;
— lumbar sections innervate the lower extremities;
— thoracic sections innervate the upper viscera;
— sacral sections innervate the lower viscera.

Motor:
The spinal cord is ordinarily under the control of higher centers in all its motor functions. There is body-segmental localization — *myotomes* — of the spinal motor centers.
(1) Plays a role in postural and fine-manipulative adjustments, both automatic and voluntary.
(2) Contributes to protective reflexes.
(3) As the lowest central level of the ANS, mediates basic muscular, glandular, visceral-vegetative reflexes related to digestion, excretion, circulation, respiration, sexual activity.

Lower-Brain Centers

Medulla Oblongata:
Acts as a relay-station for both the motor and the sensory division of the auditory nerve. Provides for the continuity of major nerve-tracts which maintain efficient relations between body receptors and effectors. Mediates phonation and articulation. Has fundamental autonomic functions, mediating the more coordinated (than spinal cord) vegetative functions and reflexes: its respiratory center generates periodic bursts of impulses; it regulates cardiac action, chewing-tasting-swallowing, coughing-sneezing-salivation, vomiting, and sucking in the newborn.

Pons:
Chiefly composed of major nerve-tracts connecting the cerebellum and the cortex in both directions. Also mediates some protective and orientation reflexes.

Cerebellum:
Sensory. Receives tactile, visual, auditory, impulses which apparently contribute to execution of its motor functions. Like the somesthetic neocortex, has a double tactile representation of the body surface on its two lobes.
Motor. Through the medium of a reverberatory circuit between it and the higher motor centers, plays a major role in the maintenance of muscular tonus and posture and equilibrium, and in the regulation of voluntary movements. Is somatotopically organized. The motor cortex controls the purpose and initiates the execution of voluntary movements, while the cerebellum regulates the overall pattern of these acts through inhibitory and facilitatory activity.
Its two parts develop at different phylogenetic and ontogenetic stages: the neocerebellum develops along with the motor neocortex, later than the archicerebellum.

---

[1]Abstracted from 56 and 160 except where otherwise indicated.

Midbrain Centers

Reticular Formation: *Sensory.* Is the lowest component of the ARAS (ascending reticular activating system, described in Chapter VI). Ascending sensory tracts conveying visceral, somatic, auditory, visual, impulses give off branches to the RF. Contains a wakefulness/alertness center: affects neocortex via hypothalamus and thalamus.

Motor. Facilitates spinally mediated reflexes. Exerts a modifying influence upon, and transmits higher-centers feedback to, the primary-receptors.

Superior Colliculi: Help to mediate the least complex visual reflexes: those related to light and visual accommodation, and to control of eyeball movement.

(Also the Inferior Colliculi, which have auditory functions.)

Red or Ruber Nucleus and Substantia Nigra: Are important parts of the extrapyramidal (unmyelinated-motor) tract; are sometimes grouped with the basal ganglia.

In general, the mid-brain centers provide for the continuity of ascending and descending nerve-tracts. A pain center is located in the RF, a "pleasure" center in the septal nuclei (upper section) (142).

B. Of Subcortical Forebrain Centers

Diencephalic Centers

The thalamus and hypothalamus work in close collaboration with one another and with the cortex.

Thalamus: *Sensory.*

(1) All sensory tracts except the olfactory synapse in its lateral portion (which is phylogenetically newer than its anterior portion). Representation of bodily sensation is localized by dermatomal segments within the thalamic nuclei; richness of sensory endings in the skin determines the size of the thalamic area allocated, not the size of the body part (also true of the somesthetic neocortex, to which the thalamus projects).

(2) The anterior portion acts as a relay station, allowing for cortical integration of visceral functions. It also provides for the affective aspect of sensation (as opposed to the discriminative aspect, which is cortically mediated).

(3) Passes on wakefulness impulses from the reticular formation and hypothalamus to the cortex, through the medium of a reverberatory circuit.

(4) Allows for such crude awareness as the recognition of contact, temperature, and pain.

Motor.

(1) Its many connections with the basal ganglia, cerebellum, motor neocortex, indicate it plays an important role in motor functions.

(2) Its connections with the vagus nerve and with the hypothalamus indicate participation in visceral and autonomic functioning (90).

Hypothalamus: *Sensory.* Sends on impulses from the reticular formation which keep the cortex awake, via the thalamus; has a direct effect on the brain-wave activity of the neocortex.

Motor.

(1) The reflex dilatation of the pupil is dependent on it.

(2) Is the principal integrative center for the entire autonomic nervous system. In man, performs this function in concert with the "old cortex." Has the richest blood supply of the entire brain and *its blood vessels are reciprocally connected with the pituitary, the "master gland."* Plays a major role in homeostasis: coordinated interaction between its forepart (parasympathetic) and back-part (sympathetic) results in such complex physiological functions as *regulation* of: body temperature, water metabolism and excretion, and food intake. It is essential for the overall sexual behavior pattern; a "pleasure" center has been located in the same sex-related nuclei. Also regulates certain of the pituitary's hormone secretions.

(3) Is the major subcortical component of the "limbic system," a functional sub-system which is discussed in Chapter VI.

Cerebral Medulla

Basal Ganglia:
(1) Help to coordinate and smooth complex voluntary movements and posture, acting in concert with the neocortex and cerebellum.

(2) The amygdaloid nucleus helps regulate visceral activity and emotional behavior; functionally, it is also part of the "limbic system."

Nerve Tracts:
They allow for coordinated functioning of: the neocortex with subcortical centers, the two neocortices, the areas within each half of the cortex.

PART B
THE SEARCH FOR DEVELOPMENTAL PATTERNS I:
MAN'S DEVELOPMENTAL BEGINNINGS

Chapter III

MAN'S NEURAL AND BEHAVIORAL INHERITANCE

T HE FIRST ASPECT OF THE SEARCH for human neural-developmental patterns consists of the examination of two background sources: pertinent phylogenetic material, and the embryological phase of human neural ontogeny.

After having expressed so negative a reaction to theoretical psychology's overreliance upon data derived from the study of lower animals, it would seem to constitute a self-contradiction to assert that psychological attempts to study the structural and behavioral legacy of lower forms have been minimal and that especially developmental psychology has much to gain from such a study. But when it is added that we need to know a great deal more about the structural and functional legacy of previous evolutionary stages *as this legacy is expressed in the form and functioning and development of the human nervous system,* the contradiction should become only apparent.

In this connection, it is lamentable that developmental psychology has heretofore virtually overlooked the contributions of John Hughlings Jackson, the benign shade of modern neurophysiology, who based his entire psychiatric rationale on a consistently developed postulation of that legacy. Neurophysiological investigators have checked out a number of this late-nineteenth century English neuropsychiatrist's more strictly neurological and neuropsychiatric postulations, and have rejected some and accepted others in somewhat modified form. But apparently no one, neurophysiologist, psychiatrist *or* psychologist, has put under the investigative glass the underlying developmental rationale from which his neurological postulations depart.

Jackson's contributions would probably be disqualified from serious theoretical use by psychology's experimental tradition, however, on two counts. Like his Austrian contemporary, Sigmund Freud, he developed his conceptions on the basis of his clinical practice and direct observation. Also, his theorizing is contaminated (as was Freud's also) by the inadequate picture of the human nervous system of the late 1800s. But, yet again like Freud, one has only to stick one's thumb anywhere into the juicy pie of his prolific writings to come up with plum after tasty plum of a provocative hypothesis begging for controlled investigation.

Hughlings Jackson's key postulation is that the matured human central nervous system is organized in a series of functional-dominance levels, a series which: reflects the phylogenetic pattern of neural development; follows a phylogenetic order in its ontogenetic development; obeys, as each higher level with its corresponding function emerges ontogenetically, the functional and behavioral principle of the "continuous reduction of succession to coexistences" (this most perspicacious principle will be referred to at subsequent points in this inquiry); manifests its phylogenetic basis most clearly in cases of injury and disease of the higher centers, when the sequence of functional and behavioral changes which occur expresses a direct reversal of the evolutionary-cum-ontogenetic pattern — that is, shows a pattern of "dissolution" (89). Jackson would seem to have been attempting to make applied-psychiatric use of the Darwin-inspired dictum of late-nineteenth century biology: ontogeny recapitulates phylogeny.

In order to discover to what extent neural ontogeny does indeed recapitulate neural phylogeny, it is necessary to examine data on *both* categories of development.

Available data on neural phylogenesis may in addition throw light on these also-pertinent concerns:

(1) Do phylogenetic trends provide any clues as to how previous evolutionary stages express themselves in the form and functioning of the human nervous system?

(2) To what extent is the traditional experimental assumption of comparative psychology warrantable: *are* the differences between lower mammals and man essentially ones only of degree, not of kind? Or is the nervous system of human beings sufficiently *unlike* that of rats and cats and even chimpanzees to justify the assertion that psychology needs to give more experimental attention to behaviors *unique to man?*

This last question — and its corollaries — is not merely contentious, nor its answer an academic exercise; rather, it constitutes — or should constitute — a fundamental issue of contemporary psychology.

This chapter comprises relevantly organized data-summaries of neural and behavioral phylogenesis drawn from a variety of reputable sources, along with borrowed and original assessments of these data's implications for the concerns of this monograph. Table I, Nervous System Phylogenesis, is made up of three subtables: IA summarizes neural phylogenetic trends *up* to the vertebrates, IB summarizes the phylogenesis of the vertebrate brain above the medulla oblongata, and IC presents material on the phylogenesis of the mammalian neocortex. Twenty phylogenetically based principles in some way relevant to our species have been derived from these and related data: principles one through four embody *phylogenetic carryovers;* five through sixteen express *phylogenetic trends;* and seventeen through twenty postulate *departures* from our species' phylogenetic inheritance.

TABLE I
NERVOUS SYSTEM PHYLOGENESIS
A. Neural Phylogenetic Trends Up To the Vertebrates[1]

Pre-neural Stage:

The lowest living form, the one-celled ameba, shows *no* functional specialization — that is, it has no nervous system. Electrically, only passive depolarization — reduction of membrane difference of potential without resultant change in permeability — is possible at this phyletic stage.

First Stage:

Appearance of the *nerve-net,* observable in Coelenterates (medusa, hydra, jellyfish). Some cells specialize as receptors of external stimuli and these stimuli are transmitted directly to the muscles via a diffuse, equipotential conduction network. Electrically, active depolarization, allowing for a *graded increase* in permeability, appears as the essential first step of excitation.

Second Stage:

Development of a specialized nerve cell, the *neuron,* and of these cells' *axial arrangement.* The latter shows up clearly in the flatworm. The structurally discrete neuron functions as an independent unit and so for the first time, localized and specialized responses are possible. The neuron's emergence coincides with the gathering of neural fibers into one part of the body, usually in the form of a chain of two parallel nerve-strands running throughout the length of the body from head to tail in an axial arrangement, and terminating in two paired ganglia at the head-end. *All-or-none conduction* appears for the first time, in elongated conductor-cells in the jellyfish, combined with regulation of the intensity of contraction by the summation of impulses at fiber-terminals activating a graded-response muscle. Selective membrane permeability to sodium ions, which underlies all-or-none conduction, must also have

TABLE I NERVOUS SYSTEM PHYLOGENESIS (Continued)
A.   Neural Phylogenetic Trends Up To the Vertebrates

emerged at this very early evolutionary stage. The diffuse nerve-net of the first stage continues to exist along with these more specialized cells; these two conduction-modes, the former manifesting graded-response functioning and the latter all-or-none conduction, are thereafter retained phylogenetically. The functional significance for the organism of this duality emerges more clearly in vertebrates (78).

Third Stage:

Development of a *segmental pattern* and of the *reflex-arc.* Both are evident in the earthworm (an Annelid). The two long nerve-strands of stage 2 become a chain of paired ganglia, each pair subserving a delimited segment of the body. Each ganglion in each set is connected to the skin of its segment with a motor neuron; linking the two neurons within each ganglion is a connector or "association" nerve-fiber, allowing for the basic sensory-connector-motor components of the reflex-arc. This segmental allocation of one set of paired ganglia and associated interconnected sensory and motor neurons allows for localized control of the movement of each body-segment and, through a system of inter-segmental connections, for mediation and integration of the movements of the primitive organism as a whole by the large headganglia. *Here is the prototype of the structure and functional organization of the lowest part of man's CNS, the spinal cord.* (Since the essential components of higher types of nervous systems are now present, stage 4 is basically an extension of stage 3.)

Fourth Stage:

Development of the first *complete neuraxis;* evident in Chordates such as insects. The paired ganglia of stage 3 partially fuse down the central axis of the body and several ganglia in the head-region fuse into one large cephalic ganglion, the first *brain.* This first brain is closely analogous in its structure and its functional relationships with the spinal cord, to the medulla oblongata or "bulb" of higher forms.

Romer describes Chordate neural structure as being fundamentally *dual* in character. In his own words,

"The basic pattern of chordate structure is that of a dual animal:
(1) A component, for which the term *visceral* is appropriate, consists of the essential structures of the ancestral sessile [free-floating filter-feeder] adult — the elaborate food-collecting apparatus, and the gut and gonads, together with such simple nervous and endocrine structures as are associated with these organs.
(2) The new addition, first seen in the larval tunicate, is the active locomotor animal, for which the term *somatic* may be used. Here we find for the first time definite sensory structures strongly receptive to *external* stimuli, and a relatively elaborate nervous system of 'brain,' spinal cord, and somatic nerves, controlling a locomotor apparatus of striated musculature supported by a notochord" (156, pp. 60-1).

With the emergence of the Vertebrates comes the structurally non-segmented, but functionally still segmented, continuous tube, the spinal cord, along with the *phylogenetic arrest in development of all but* the fourth-stage neuraxis' anterior, brain, section.

[1]Except where otherwise indicated, the sources for Table IA are (197, Chapter 3) and Bishop's article on the phylogenesis of electrical characteristics (22).

What are the implications of these prevertebrate data for man? There would seem to be at least the following four carryovers or implications:

Phylogenetic Principle 1. Man shares with prevertebrates the basic structural pattern of his spinal cord and medulla, the two most primitive parts of his central nervous system, as well as the nature and intimate unity of their functional inter-relationship: the medulla has the functionally dominant role of coordinating spinally mediated reflexes. Although in man, spinal cord cum medulla both transmit to, and are subject to the controlling influences of, higher neuraxial centers, together they form a *discrete subsystem* within the human neuraxis — a subsystem closely similar in structure, in functional relationships, and in ontogenetic growth-patterns, to the entire prevertebrate fourth-stage nervous system described in Table IA.

Phylogenetic Principle 2. Bishop's material on the electrical properties of the nerve-impulse would seem to indicate that all the basic conduction characteristics of the neuron have manifested themselves in the prevertebrate evolutionary stages. As already implied by the data in Table IA and as Bishop explicitly states (22, p. 395), various patterns of subsequent phyletic change in neural functioning are dependent upon *changing organizations of nerve cells,* rather than on any fundamental changes in the conduction characteristics of the individual cell; the various types of neurons present in man — and their conduction characteristics — represent one or another of the types first found in prevertebrate and lower-vertebrate forms.

Phylogenetic Principle 3. The phylogenetic retention of both the nerve-net *and* the specialized neuron prompts the question: Are these structural differences correlated with unique functions? Herrick's answer is *yes,* and he discusses at length the functional significance for the organism of the two conduction-modes represented by the nerve-net (slow rate of conduction and a diffuse, graded, fields-of-force style of electrical functioning), and the specialized nerve-fiber (fast rate of conduction and a specific, all-or-none style of electrical functioning) (78, Chapter VIII). The specialized, rapidly conducting nerve-cells exist within fixed, localized (i.e., partial-pattern) pathways and centers which subserve the organism's interactions with its environment — sensory, correlational and motor functions which Herrick terms "analytic." The diffuse, slow-conducting nerve-net is not as firmly bound to definitely localized pathways and centers, parallels and/or surrounds the specialized cells, is more labile and whole-pattern in its functioning. This conduction apparatus is concerned with maintaining the identity of the body and with coordinating the various subparts of the analytic system — functions which Herrick terms "synthetic" or, better, "integrative." These two neural apparati are structurally intertwined and their functions, integrative and analytic, are obviously complementary; in Herrick's words:

> Both kinds of vital processes are primordial and essential components of the action systems of all animals, from the lowest to the highest (78, p. 101).

Evolutionary changes in these two neural functional orders are herewith summarized; these data are drawn chiefly from Chapters 8 and 19 of Herrick (78).

Analytic Conduction Apparatus

Structural and Functional Characteristics.   *At lowest vertebrate levels.* Poorly defined and poorly localized in the central nervous system. In the salamander, the medulla oblongata is the central receptive-station for all sensory fibers except those of smell and vision (true also for man) ; functional localization stops where the peripheral nerve fibers make contact with the neuropil (integrative functions) of the medulla. The sensory end-organs and associated nerves are well developed and separately localized, but converge to only two neural pools which extend the length of the medulla: visceral-sensory and somatic-sensory, with the following basic characteristics:

Visceral-Sensory Pool	*Somatic-Sensory Pool*
Receives all fibers of gustatory and general visceral sensibility associated with the fasciculus solitarius and discharges into the visceral motor mechanisms. These visceral movements are chiefly of the	Receives fibers of all cutaneous and deep sensibility that are concerned with adjustment to the external environment and discharges into the somatic motor apparatus that controls the movement of skeletal muscles. There is *much* evolutionary change in

total-pattern type — in man as well as in salamanders; i.e., there is little more specialization of function in man's fasciculus solitarius neuropil than in that of the salamander. this system: from the salamander's mass-movement of the total-pattern type, to the precise diversification and localization of man's highly specialized sensorimotor system. "In man, this specificity of the analytic apparatus is carried forward as far as the thalamus and the sensory-projections areas of the cerebral cortex" (p. 87).

At highest levels (man). Well defined and clearly localized at every CNS level, right up to the neocortex. The CNS performs these analytic functions in addition to the more general integration of bodily activities.

Behavioral Correlates.

At lowest levels. Basic adaptive functions of an animate, reflexive nature; involves adjustment of a body fixed in time and space to external things and events.

At highest levels. Culminates in human perception ("the things of which the self is conscious"), which is "directly concerned with spatial and temporal relations of things" (p. 97).

Integrative Conduction Apparatus

Structural Characteristics.

At lowest vertebrate levels. Composed of a felt-work or "neuropil" which "permeates the entire brain and acts as a nonspecific conduction system which puts every part of the brain into physiological connection with every other part. . . . It is germinative tissue with potentialities for further differentiation in a variety of ways" (p. 249).

At highest vertebrate levels (man). Still exists as a nonspecific conduction system (recently discovered), but is also clustered into centers or nuclei at successively higher neuraxial levels; the largest of these are the cerebellum, the basal ganglia and the cerebral cortex. The cortical association areas have heavy concentrations of neuropil.

Func-tional Char-acter-istics. *At lowest levels.* Relatively, though not entirely, equi-potential in function (actually, it is under constant activation from the periphery and there are gradations in activity from region to region and from moment to moment).

At highest levels:

Levels of Integration of Adjustments to the Environment	Levels of Integration of Internal Functions
1. The sensory and motor organs of the Per-NS.	1. Non-nervous tonicity and automaticity char-acteristic of all living substance and especial-ly of human muscles and viscera.
2. Primary sensory and motor centers in the spinal cord and brain-stem and their inter-connections with one another and with the peripheral end-organs.	2. Endocrines in the body fluids which control visceral functions.
3. The diffuse neuropil and its specialized de-rivatives of thalamus and basal ganglia.	3. Local regulation of the viscera by intrinsic autonomous sympathe-tic plexuses.
4. Simple cerebral cortex of the reptilian type; present in the human brain at the margins of the cortical field.	4. Central regulation of these plexuses through sympathetic circuits in cranial and spinal nerves.
5. Mammalian type of cortex, concerned with learning and the organization of learned behavior. Founded up-on, and supplements, reflexive and instinc-tive behaviors.	5. Superimposed upon these circuits are vis-ceral centers in the brain-stem; those in the hypothalamus are the most important.
6. Human type of associ-ational cortex, which provides for use of	6. All of these lower levels are under some measure of cortical con-trol.

symbols,   reasoning,
and devising and using
tools.

Be-   *At lowest levels.* Basic functional integrity of the organ-
havi-   ism.
oral   *At highest levels.* Culminates in human rational think-
Cor-   ing, conception, sentiment and volition. Provides for
re-   "consciousness of self" (as distinct from "the things of
lates.   which the self is conscious" — i.e., human perception
         — which is a function of the analytic apparatus). "The
         space-time relations of these central integrative processes
         are . . . relatively independent of those of the external
         environment" (p. 97) .

Herrick concludes his analysis of the successive levels of
functioning of the integrative apparatus with this cautionary
reminder: "It is important to recognize that all levels of integration interpenetrate, and one never operates independently
of the others. Each higher level is derived from the lower and
can work only with the instrumentation provided by the lower
levels (p. 253) .

Phylogenetic Principle 4. Another order of duality, the visceral-somatic duality of neural structure to which Romer points
(and Herrick too — he treats them as subdivisions of the analytic
conduction system) also appears to have been retained in man's
nervous system. It seems to constitute one of the basic functional-
organization patterns of the human nervous system and is being
further examined in Chapter VII on the basis of this premise.

Herrick's lively analysis of the origin and evolution of the
cerebral cortex (78, Chapter 29) is the source for the following
summary of vertebrate trends in cortical development.

The earliest amphibians were descended from a type of
fish *unlike* the modern active fishes, the overt behavior of which
is dominated by the sense of sight, and the primary visual
center in the roof of the mid-brain is large. Rather, the an-
cestors of land-living animals were a type of fish like present
ganoids and lung fishes: a mudfish of sluggish habit, the behavior of which was evidently dominated by the sense of smell,

since the olfactory areas at the front end of the brain were huge. When these fishes emerged onto land, subsequent evolutionary specialization occurred in this part of the forebrain. "The olfactory field of the cerebral hemisphere is a complex center of correlation, where olfactory stimuli are related with diverse other kinds of sensory influences brought into it by fibers which ascend from sensory centers at lower levels of the brain. . . . Here rudimentary cortex had its beginnings" (p. 376).

Amphibians have *two* cortical fields; the medial field has olfacto-visceral functions and the lateral field has olfacto-somatic functions. The medial field is heavily connected with the hypothalamus by fibers passing in both directions; these connections provide for correlation of the olfactory sense with the gustatory and visceral senses and for discharge from the hypothalamus of appropriate excitations to the viscera. (This medial field is evidently the same as Romer's "visceral system.") The lateral field is connected by ascending and descending fibers with the thalamus and mid-brain, where the olfactory sense is related to the exteroceptive and proprioceptive senses. Descending fibers from the thalamus and mid-brain activate all skeletal muscles; ascending and descending connections between the thalamus and the hemispheres are added on to the more primitive, lower-level reflex circuits and regulate these lower functions at a higher level of integration. Unlike the plentiful connections between the hypothalamus and the hemispheres, there are very few connections between the thalamus and the hemispheres in the amphibian brain. (The lateral field is evidently the same as Romer's "somatic system.") There is no further functional specialization in these primitive brains: the several senses are not separately localized either in the hemispheres or in the medulla oblongata; but visceral and somatic centers are well separated in both these centers.

Reptiles have *three* cortical fields: medial, lateral, dorsal. The medial field continues to have olfacto-visceral functions and later gives rise to the mammalian hippocampus. The lateral field continues to have olfacto-somatic functions and later gives rise to the mammalian piriform cortex (uncus or limbic lobe, in man). The dorsal area has large thalamocortical (sensory projection) connections, and a motor cortex in which a small pyramidal tract originates; as the mammalian scale is ascended, this area is progressively emancipated from olfactory influences. There is minimal sensorimotor localization and association tissue in the reptilian brain.

Mammals also have three basic cortical fields, but with these added developments:

(1) Each field shows a marked increase in functional localization, a trend which is directly related to the concomitant marked increase in the multiplicity of reciprocal connections with the mid-brain and diencephalic centers. These multiple connections and increased functional localization serve to refine the analysis of sensory and motor experience — that is, they subserve the cortex's *analytic* functions.

(2) There is also a marked increase in the proportion of associational neocortex, achieved by an increase in surface-area (through the layering pattern and fissuration) ; these areas subserve the cortex's *integrative* functions.

Both these trends increase steadily up the mammalian scale.

Phylogenetic principles five through nine, following, depart from not only the data included in Table IB and Herrick's summary, but also from such standard neurophysiological references as J. F. Fulton's textbook (56); they identify comprehensive *trends* in neural phylogenesis.

Phylogenetic Principle 5. The overall direction of nervous system phylogenesis has been towards increasing structural differentiation of parts and specialization of function, together with increasing interdependence of the parts on the whole and on each other — that is, towards increasing degrees of organization.

Phylogenetic Principle 6. The principle of "encephalization" has obtained, both in structure and in function: new phyletic structures have been added on progressively at the head-end; as each new structure is added on, there is a tendency for functions originally performed by lower, more primitive parts of the central nervous system to be transferred cephalically to the new structure. (Also see Principle 10)

But on the basis of neurophysiological knowledge not included in Table IB, it is necessary immediately to supplement the classic

TABLE I NERVOUS SYSTEM PHYLOGENESIS (continued)

B. Phylogenesis of the Vertebrate Brain Above the Medulla[2]

Neur-axial Center	Fish	Amphibia	Reptiles
Cere-bellum.	Presence of paleo-cerebellum, which has connections with cord and vestibular nuclei of medulla. Cerebellar cortex large in active fishes (180).	Cerebellum is inconspicuous. In lower vertebrates, it receives sensory relays from nose; also, muscle-movement information originates in midbrain (156).	Neocerebellum emerges, along with differentiation of motor and sensory areas of the neocortex (78).
Mid-brain.	The tectum is the chief site of integration of sensory and motor impulses. The mid-brain and diencephalon both show up together clearly for the first time in cyclostomes (primitive fish) (78).	Together with the thalamus, is still the chief site of integration for sensory and motor impulses (78). In lower vertebrates, consists of a rather diffuse series of nerve-cells and fibers of the reticular system (156).	Subtectal, tectal and tegmental regions present. Optic ventricles and nucleus isthmi present. Several reptiles have a parietal eye (156).
Dien-ceph-alic Centers.	Divisible into hypo-thalamus, epithalamus, and a poorly developed thalamus. The hypothalamus is a visceral center throughout the vertebrate scale. In modern, bony, fishes, it shows a regulatory effect over lower autonomic centers.	Skin sensibility begins to prevail over olfactory and gustatory sensibilities. Large dorsal thalamus first evident, as well as the first olfactory projections from it.	The hypothalamus is more developed than in Amphibia. Together with the corpus striatum, the diencephalon acts as the highest sensory-motor integration system. Dorsal thalamus differentiates into internal and external portions.
Corpus Stri-atum	The paleostriatum is inconspicuous. It assists in coordination of motor activities which are constantly rhythmical in character.	Neostriatal area emerges between the archicortex and paleocortex (see below; it becomes the third part of the cerebral hemispheres in later forms); exercises an inhibitory effect on the paleostriatum.	Neostriatal area is larger than in Amphibians. Provides for highest-level instinct-associated movements.

[2]Except where otherwise indicated, abstracted from (8).

TABLE I NERVOUS SYSTEM PHYLOGENESIS (continued)

B. Phylogenesis of the Vertebrate Brain Above the Medulla[2]

Birds	Mammals
Cerebellar cortex large and elaborately constructed.	The cerebellar hemispheres, the lateral portion of the middle lobe or neocerebellum, enlarge markedly. In man, this section has extensive sensory and motor connections with the neocortex via the pons (180). As the mammalian scale is ascended, lesions of the neocerebellum cause increasing seriousness and endurance of ataxia and hypotonia; the worst effects are evident in man (28). Its control of postural reflexes decreases up the mammalian scale — this function is taken over by the cerebral cortex (159).
Similar development to that in Reptiles, but gravistatic and photostatic centers are more developed. Optic lobes are large.	All cranial nerves except those for the eye and ear originate in the medulla and mid-brain (156). In lower mammals, its superior colliculi mediate visual and other reflexes; in higher mammals, only *light* reflexes. Tracts connecting higher to lower centers increase up the mammalian scale, as do tracts of the substantia nigra. Most of its lower-vertebrate functions have been transferred to the neocortex. Well-defined nuclei such as the ruber emerge in the reticular mesh (156).
Similar thalamic development to that in Reptiles. In both Reptiles and Birds, the diencephalic centers serve as the highest coordinating centers, together with the corpus striatum and old cortex.	The dorsal thalamus reaches its highest development in Mammals and increasingly so up the mammalian scale; it is most highly developed in man. The phylogenetic growth of the temporal, parietal and frontal lobes of the neocortex is *directly associated with a similar growth in thalamic lateral and medial nuclei* (90). The mammillary bodies emerge in the hypothalamus. Data integrated in the cerebellum synapse in the thalamus before going on to the neocortex (156).
Archistriatum clear. Neostriatum (concerned with stereotyped reflexive and instinctive behaviors) is the dominant association center; has large number of ascending thalamo-striatal fibers.	The various basal ganglia emerge along with the neocortex. The neocortex in mammals takes over many of the functions previously exercised by brainstem and striatal centers.

[2]Except where otherwise indicated, abstracted from (8).

TABLE I NERVOUS SYSTEM PHYLOGENESIS (continued)

B. Phylogenesis of the Vertebrate Brain Above the Medulla[2]

Neur-axil Center	*Fish*	*Amphibia*	*Reptiles*
Old Cortex	Cerebral hemispheres have only two parts, the olfactory bulb and the hemisphere. Few if any fibers come to this area from the brainstem. The paleocortex is better developed in Fish than is the archicortex.	Amphibia have only a functionally important olfactory area. Only two cortical fields: olfacto-visceral and olfacto-somatic. The hollow cerebral hemispheres of matured lungfish and Amphibia are similar to the human brain in its second month of fetal life (78).	The archicortex is better developed than the paleocortex in reptiles. Lateral olfactory tracts are well developed. Have three cortical fields to the amphibian two: addition of a neocortical area. In the turtle, the hippocampus is concerned with olfacto-visceral functions, the piriform (limbic) lobe with olfacto-somatic functions, and the neocortex with non-olfactory functions (78).
Neo-cortex.	Not present.	Not present.	A rudimentary but clear neocortex appears; it is not dominated by olfactory influences. Beginnings of sensory-dominated functional localization. Hamilton (68) points out that this rudimentary cortex appears in the (eventual) parietal area and states, "If this priority has any significance in the interpretation of function, it may be assumed that general body-sense . . . rather than sight or hearing has been the predominant influence in determining the establishment of the neocortex" (p. 299).

[2]Except where otherwise indicated, abstracted from (8).

neural principle of encephalization with two additional principles, following directly.

Phylogenetic Principle 7. The first supplementing principle may be termed the "principle of successive lowest-center duplication." As each new "head part" is added on phyletically, the oldest neuraxial part's basic segmental or topological-organization pattern is reduplicated on each newly evolved sensory or motor center. That is, the basic segmental organization pattern of the lowest motor center, the spinal cord, is successively duplicated on each new motor center when it differentiates phylogenetically.

TABLE I NERVOUS SYSTEM PHYLOGENESIS (continued)

B. Phylogenesis of the Vertebrate Brain Above the Medulla[2]

Birds	Mammals
The paleocortex is clearer than in Amphibia and Reptiles, but the archicortex is still better developed.	The olfactory connections of the hippocampus are reduced in Mammals and almost eliminated in primates. Lower mammals have very large hippocampal areas, large but less differentiated piriform (limbic) lobes, and a much smaller neocortex; in higher mammals, these proportions are reversed (78). In Mammals, the paleocortex (or mesopallium; limbic areas in man) is related to the expressions of internal states; both its size and such behavior expands up the mammalian scale (36). In man, the six-layered cingulum, phylogenetically part of the mesopallium, is relatively and absolutely larger than in any other mammal (36).
Similar degree of development to that in Reptiles.	The neocortex is greatly expanded beyond that of Reptiles: has more separately localized sensory and motor areas, greater amount of associational tissue, and an increased number of layers. The corpus callosum emerges and increases from front to back in direct proportion as the neocortex develops phylogenetically. The higher the animal, the greater the extent of functional impairment from equivalent cortical lesions (159). As the mammalian scale is ascended, the neocortex takes over many of the functions exercised by brain-stem and strital centers in lower mammals; also, newer and higher correlation and association functions emerge (156).

[2]Except where otherwise indicated, abstracted from (8).

Similarly, the segmental or topological organization pattern of the first receiving center for the particular sensory-modality is successively duplicated on each new sensory center as it differentiates phylogenetically.

Phylogenetic Principle 8. The "principle of hierarchical dominance" is also a necessary supplementation of Principle 6. As new structures are added on at the head-end, they tend to assume functional dominance over the older sections which have the same type of function, sensory or motor.

Phylogenetic Principle 9. But in spite of their functional dominance, phylogenetically newer parts tend to be both highly

TABLE I NERVOUS SYSTEM PHYLOGENESIS (continued)

IC. Structural Phylogenesis of the Mammalian Neocortex[2]

Index of Phylogenesis	General Trends	Lower Mammals
1) Size of the four lobes:	The higher the animal, the greater the proportion of the brain is neocortex. In the frontal lobe, the pre-frontal section (association functions) increases most in size.	The proportion of the total cortical area taken up by the pre-frontal area is: 3.4% in the rabbit;
2) Number of cellularly distinct areas:	Increases steadily up the mammalian scale.	On the basis of cellular characteristics, Tilney counts 13 neocortical areas in the albino rat (178).
3) Degree of localization and specialization of sensory and motor functions, together with #4:	Increases steadily up the mammalian scale (78). (Viz. Lashley's reversal of his earlier postulation of lack of cortical differentiation.)	Of the sub-human forms studied, the degree of overlap of the two basic somatosensory areas of the parietal lobe is greatest in the rabbit (61).
4) Multiplicity of connections with lower centers:	Increases steadily up the mammalian scale.	
5) Proportion of neocortex which is associational in function:	Increases steadily up the mammalian scale (78 and 197). Also see #1 above.	In rodents, 90% of the neocortex is sensorimotor in function, and 10% has association functions (197).
6) Thickness and number of neocortical layers:	As the mammalian scale is ascended, the neocortex thickens, the number of layers increases, and their cellular composition becomes more complex.	An additional, supragranular, layer is added to the submammalian granular and subgranular layers (which continue to be typical of the archicortex). The meso- or paleo-cortex also adds the supragranular layer.
7) The fissuration pattern:	The higher the mammal, the larger the number of cortical fissures.	All mammals have at least three fissures.
8) Number of unmyelinated areas at birth:	Increases as the mammalian scale is ascended.	

[2]Abstracted from (8), except where otherwise indicated.

TABLE I NERVOUS SYSTEM PHYLOGENESIS (continued)

IC. Structural Phylogenesis of the Mammalian Neocortex[2]

Middle Mammals	Lower Primates and Man
and 7% in the dog.	The proportion of the total cortical area taken up by the pre-frontal (PF) association area is: 11% in the macaque; 17% in the chimpanzee (about half the frontal lobe) ; and 29% in man (¾ of the frontal lobe) .
Tilney counts 36 neocortical areas in the adult cat (178) .	Tilney postulates at least 52 neocortical areas in man (178) .
	Of the subhuman forms studied, the degree of overlap of the two basic somatosensory areas of the parietal lobe is least in the monkey (61). There is much greater impairment of function in man than in rodents, e.g., when specific cortical areas are destroyed.
In cats, 70% of the neocortex is sensorimotor and 30% is association in function (197) .	In the monkey, 40% of neocortex is sensorimotor and 60% is association in function. In man, 15% is sensorimotor and 85% is association (197) .
The supragranular layer increases steadily in thickness up the rest of the mammalian scale. The granular layer's thickness increases variably; the subgranular's remains about the same.	In man, the supragranular layer differentiates into the upper three layers of the six-layered neocortex; these "outer three layers are much better developed than in lower forms" (68, p. 300). In man, the middle granular layer thickens and the subgranular layer divides into the two bottom layers.
	The fusiform gyrus, on the underside of the occipital lobe, emerges in primates. The secondary and tertiary sulci are peculiar only to the human brain and serve to increase markedly the size of the association areas of the neocortex.
	In man, *no* cortical areas are myelinated at birth.

[2]Abstracted from (8) , except where otherwise indicated.

vulnerable to external influences and unstable in their functioning, as compared with the older-lower centers. See especially Himwich (80) for documentation of this point. Principle 8 is complicated still further by other concurrent functional-organizational patterns of the human nervous system; these are described in Part C.

As the vertebrate scale is ascended, the size and the complexity of the brain-part of the primitive neuraxis increase, as we have seen; the part of the brain which increases most in size and in complexity is the cerebral cortex. As the *mammalian* scale is ascended, the part of the cerebral cortex which increases most in size and in structural complexity is the cerebral *neo*cortex.

Table IC provides concrete evidence that the mammalian neocortex has made what Eiseley and other anthropologists call a "quantum jump" in its development from the lower primates to man. Structural evidences of such a quantum jump of the neocortex include the following:

(1) its prefrontal section increases markedly in proportional size from chimpanzee to man;

(2) its supragranular layer, which emerges in mammals, increases markedly in further stratification and in cellular complexity in man;

(3) its proportion of total area which is associational in function increases markedly from chimp to man. Zubek and Solberg's proportions, cited in Table IC, bear repeating in the form of a small sub-table:

Mammal	Sensorimotor Neocortex	Associational Neocortex
Rodent	90%	10%
Cat	70	30
Monkey	40	60
Man	15	85

Note the almost complete reversal in proportions in man from the rat, comparative psychology's favorite experimental animal!

Phylogenetic Principle 10. Several functional shifts have accompanied the continuous cephalic development highlighted in Table IC:

(1) the visceral and olfactory senses predate the other senses in functional importance phylogenetically (for vertebrates in general and mammals in particular) ; then the skin and proprioceptive senses follow; and then the distance-receptor senses and kinesthesis, which are of major functional importance only in mammals;

(2) the capacity for refined movement develops in direct proportion to provision for exactness of sensory reception and sensory localization;

(3) emancipation from chemically (i.e., hormonally) and external-stimuli-dominated behavior is in direct proportion to the size and complexity of the cerebral neocortex;

(4) structurally innate factors in the determination of behavior decrease relatively up the mammalian scale, while the role of individual experience and learning increases.

Phylogenetic Principle 11. The infant's period of immaturity and dependence upon older members of the same species increases steadily up the phyletic scale, and makes a marked jump from lower primates to man. This circumstance, together with principle 18, following, suggests an evolved-physical basis for our species' strongly social nature.

Nissen has addressed himself to the enumeration of phylogenetic changes in behavior; principles 12 through 16, following, draw on his discussion (140) .

Phylogenetic Principle 12. Ability to adapt to a constantly widening range of external situations increases up the phyletic scale, and is accompanied by a repertoire of adaptive responses which increases steadily in range and complexity and flexibility — that is, in degree of individual control.

Phylogenetic Principle 13. Cognitive capacities and types of behavior increase steadily up the phyletic scale, and most of all in man. This increase is at least partially related to the circumstance that the length of delay of response to an external stimulus is by far the greatest in man, and as a result: abilities to abstract, generalize, transfer, transpose, all increase steadily; sensory discrimination increases variably; an organism's "influencing environment" expands both temporally and spatially; the period of perceptual-growth improvement becomes longer; the gap between initial and ultimate perceptual ability increases; ability to perceive a relationship between objects appears earlier, phylogenetically, than does the ability to perceive the intrinsic properties of an object.

Phylogenetic Principle 14. The complexity of what can be learned, the limits of training, and the capacity to form complex habits, all increase up the phyletic scale.

Phylogenetic Principle 15. The number, range and complexity of an organism's needs and motives increase up the phyletic scale; the proportion of these needs which are psychogenic — including curiosity or desire to perceive, exploration, play, ethical-esthetic-altruistic motives, anticipation, goal-orientation, need to "make sense" of what is perceived, prudent foresight or capacity to direct one's behavior toward delayed goals (with the exception of the first three, all are peculiar only to man) — increases most.

Phylogenetic Principle 16. The incidence of conflict, frustration and guilt is much increased in man, as well as vulnerability to derangement of his "higher" behaviors. (See also principle 9.)

Finally, four characteristics which are unique in man and so cannot be termed either "carryovers" or "trends"; rather, they represent *departures* from man's phylogenetic heritage.

Phylogenetic Principle 17. The data in Table IC imply a most fundamental development, one so obvious, it is easily overlooked: the genetic endowment of our species includes uniquely human neural structures, apparently superimposed upon the more basic mammalian structures. Just how this dual genetic endowment expresses itself in human ontogenesis becomes an important focus of inquiry in light of this departure. (See also principle 18, following.)

Phylogenetic Principle 18. In man, it is only after birth that those neural centers which mediate all uniquely human behaviors begin to function, as subsequent embryological data will further document; further structural and functional development of these centers occurs after birth. That is, *the "human principle" in our species' genetic endowment* (see principle 17) *is present only as potential at birth.* This species characteristic implies not merely that such behaviors do not develop within a stable, physiologically regulated environment; it further means that *they are subjected throughout the course of their postnatal development to an increasingly variable and complex physical and social milieu.* It is this species characteristic that makes man, to a far greater degree than any other biological form, dependent upon his opportunities for experience subsequent to birth, not only for the degree to which his implanted potentialities for behavior will be developed, but beyond sheerly somatic and vegetative development, even for the *form* many of his behaviors will take. (See also principle 20.)

Phylogenetic Principle 19. Ability to become an object within one's own perceptual field — self-awareness — is peculiar only to man. It is an interesting idea to interpret the biblical story of Adam and Eve symbolically, as the point in phyletic time when this awareness emerged: "And the eyes of them both were opened, and they knew that they were naked" (21).

Phylogenetic Principle 20. "The great basic innovation among all varieties of mankind was the production of the sociocultural world itself," and once having created this "second, invisible environment," man's behavior was thereafter fundamentally and irrevocably influenced by it (47). The qualitative aspect of the difference between man and all other animals may well stem from just this "great basic innovation." Although the structural differences between man and other forms may indeed be conceived as ones only of degree, *once certain of these structural developments made self-awareness and symbolization* (among other uniquely human potentialities) *possible, man developed cumulatively a highly complex emotional, moral and symbolic learning-environment* — and subjects each new generation to it.

This postulation implies that if this complex learning environment were not made directly available to any one new human generation of a particular society as a result of a complete interruption in interpersonal communication (in the subtlest sense) between it and members of the parent-generation, the new generation *if* it survived physically (which is highly doubtful) would, at physical maturity, have at best a behavioral repertoire akin to that of other primates. At worst, it would be so emotionally disturbed as not to be able to produce another generation, as the work of Harlow and others strongly suggests (71). Indeed, it is possible to conceptualize most emotional, including personality, disorders as the product of some sort of interruption in especially the early mother ⟷ child communication process. This possibility will be further developed in Chapter 12.

If it *is* this complex, species-self-made learning environment, rather than the structural changes in and of themselves, which puts man's behavior on a qualitatively different plane from that of other animals, then to answer "yes" to the third question posed at the beginning of this chapter, "Are the differences between lower mammals and man essentially ones only of degree, not of kind?" is to give the less significant part of the answer. The other part must consist of these two additional questions:

What changes in which behavioral capacities made possible the emergence of human culture?

What structural changes within the primate organism, neural and otherwise, provided for these changed behavioral capacities?

When comparative-experimental psychologists frame investigations explicitly designed to answer such questions as these, perhaps then the gap between the way of thinking of traditional comparative psychology and the way of thinking of those who believe that the primary datum of psychology should be those behaviors unique to man will begin at last to be firmly bridged. Psychology needs to emulate modern anthropology in recognizing the width of the gap in neural evolution between man and his mammalian relatives — and the implications for the study of man's behavior of that gap. As anthropologist Eiseley has put it:

> The fact that close on to another century [since 1876] we are only now beginning to bestir ourselves over this question of the curious uniqueness of the human brain, shows how long we have been silenced with the idea that the step from an ape to a man is as simple as the first evolutionists imagined or even wished it to be. . . . The fortunate thing . . . is that we now know the disparity between man and ape is great, not small (47, pp. 65 and 75).

Chapter IV

THE HUMAN NERVOUS SYSTEM'S FIRST TEN MONTHS

PATTERNS OF PRENATAL NEURAL DEVELOPMENT

PHYLOGENETIC DATA IN AND BY themselves cannot satisfy our curiosity about the precise nature of the structural and functional-organization legacy of previous evolutionary stages in the human nervous system. Schneirla's cautionary reminder concerning the phyletic roots of behavioral development also applies in this context, reinforcing Novikoff's analysis of levels of function, cited in Chapter I:

> Behavioral development on any phyletic level is not so much a retracing through the stages and levels of successive ancestral forms as a new composite leading to a new pattern distinctive of that level (163, p. 102).

The first relevant and detailed source of data about the human neural "new composite" is the prenatal phase of neural ontogeny. To arrive at an answer to the question previously put, "Do phylogenetic trends provide any clues as to how previous evolutionary stages express themselves in the form and functioning of the human nervous system?" this phase of neural development must also be examined.

There is yet another reason for a careful restudy of human prenatal development. The richness of available prenatal data on neural development is in sharp contrast to the paucity of postnatal data. Perhaps an examination of the developmental trends of the *pre*natal phase will, in accordance with the well-established ontogenetic "law of anticipatory development," provide clues to *post*natal developmental patterns.

Material on the embryological phase of neurogenesis is therefore being presented and analyzed as an additional source of information relevant to the concerns of this inquiry. Table II presents in summarized fashion material on human ontogeny

TABLE II

HUMAN PRENATAL ONTOGENY

A. From Two and One-Half to Seven Fetal Weeks[1]

Age in Weeks	Nervous System	Exteroceptive Sense Organs	Muscular System	Glands
2½	Neural groove indicated.			
3½	Neural groove prominent and rapidly closing. Neural crest a continuous band. Both the first and the second flexures appear by twenty days. Heartbeat, which is independent of neural control, begins.	Optic vesicle evident in fore-part of neural tube. Auditory placode present. Acoustic ganglia appearing.	Mesodermal segments appearing. Older somites show myotome plates.	
4	Neural tube closed. Third flexure appears between the first and second by thirty-two days, demarcating the three primary vesicles of the brain. Spinal ganglia and nerves forming. Germinal, mantle and marginal embryonic layers present.	Optic-cup and lens pit forming. Auditory pit closes; detached otocyst. Olfactory placodes arise and differentiate nerve-cells.	All somites present.	
5	Fourth flexure appears and all five brain vesicles are demarcated. Cerebral hemispheres are beginning to bulge. Spinal nerves and ganglia better represented. First intracord nerve tracts (viscero-sensory), appear. The twelve pairs of cranial nerves appear during the fifth and sixth weeks.	Chorioid fissure of eye prominent. Lens vesicle free. Vitreous anlage appearing. Olfactory pits deepen.	Premuscle masses present in head, trunk, limbs.	Otocyst enlarges and buds endolymph duct. Suprarenal cortex accumulating. Thyroid gland begins to form.

6	Diencephalon large. Nerve plexuses present. Epithalamus and hypothalamus recognizable. Sympathetic ganglia of spinal cord forming segmental masses. Meninges of brain indicated. Primordium of hippocampus appears, the first part of the cerebral cortex to differentiate. Elements necessary for a spinal reflex-arc present.	Optic cup shows nervous and pigment layers. Lens vesicle thickens. Eyes set at 160°. Modeling of external, middle and internal ear under way. Vomeronasal organ evident. Olfactory bulb formed.	Myotomes, spread into a continuous column, grow ventrad. Muscle segmentation largely lost.	Nasolacrimal duct formed.
7	Cerebral hemispheres becoming large. Hippocampus fully evident. Corpus striatum and thalamus prominent. The six to twelve week period is vital in CNS development: slow-down in n. s. growth during this period — is first evidence of Mongolism; — if due to oxygen lack, results in brain-damage, which may show up after birth as cerebral palsy (16).	Chorioid plexuses, which later secrete cerebrospinal fluid, appearing. Chorioid fissure closes, enclosing central artery. Nerve fibers invade optic stalk. Lens closes cavity by elongating lens fibers. Eyelids forming. Fibrous and vascular coats of eye indicated. Olfactory sacs open into mouth cavity. Olfactory nerves apparent, growing centrally in direction of cerebrum.	Muscles differentiating throughout body and assuming final shapes and relations.	Suprarenal medulla begins invading suprarenal cortex. Male sex-glands form and begin to secrete. Pineal body, closely associated with epithalamus, emerges.

[1]Adapted from (6) except where otherwise indicated.

TABLE II HUMAN PRENATAL ONTOGENY (continued)
B. From Seven and One-Half to Fifteen Fetal Weeks[2]

Age in Weeks	— — — — — — Structure	Nervous System: Elicited Responses #	Spontaneous Function #
7½–8	Cerebral cortex begins to acquire typical cells. Limbic lobes visible. Dura- and pia-arachnoids distinct. Spinal reflexes completely formed and elicitable.	First spinal reflex at seven and one-half weeks: contra-lateral flexion of neck when area near mouth touched lightly. Quick arm, leg, trunk movements when amniotic sac tapped. Characteristic reflex is stereotyped and mechanical.	
9–9½	Anterior commissure (connecting the limbic cortices) evident, followed by emergence of the hippocampal commissure; these are the first two of the intercortical commissures to differentiate.	At nine and one-half weeks, limb flexes when it is stretched: means end-organs in muscles, tendons, joints are capable of function.	Slow, uncoordinated general movements appear.
10–11	Spinal cord attains definitive internal structure. First cells of the neocortex (parietal area) appear: a primordial cortical-gray layer. Two sets of swellings (paired) are the forerunners of the cerebellar vermis and cerebellar hemispheres.	Localized movement in any part of whole extremity when part touched. Reflexes often complex. Trunk extension. Muscular twitch of foot when sole touched lightly (plantar reflex); also grasp reflex when palm touched lightly.	Brain-wave pattern (bipolar, frontal occipital) irregular and slow from higher levels, with superimposed fast waves at greater depth (24).
12–13	Brain attains all its general structural features. Spinal cord shows cervical and lumbar enlargements; also its cauda equina and filium terminale are appearing.	Slight movement of eyelid when it is touched, also eye movements underneath lid. Movement at every joint. Withdrawal of head from point stimulated. Sectioning of spinal cord indicates elicited reflexes are mediated by it.	
13	Fibers from neocortex to dorsal part of hippcampal commissure evident. Also habenular complex (closely associated with epithalamus) and corpus callosum.	Contralateral reaction of limb on opposite side of body stimulated. Entire skin area except back of head sensitive to stimulation.	First respiratory (rhythmic chest movements: via "law of anticipatory function."
14	Flocculonodular lobe of cerebellum emerges. Corpus cerebelli and posterolateral fissure of cerebellum also. During third month long association tracts appear: ascending-sensory, from spinal cord to higher centers, and descending-motor, from mid-brain and hindbrain to spinal cord.	Dorsal flexion of toes when sole of foot touched lightly. Reflexes and movements more flexible and fluid. Has most of the behavioral repertoire of the neonate.	First spontaneous movement of the whole fetus: cerebellar involvement.
15	Dentate nucleus appears in the cerebellum.	Fingers close and stay closed when touched with a hair.	Fetal activity not affected by removal of cerebral cortex.

[2]Except for the columns marked #, *and* where otherwise indicated, adapted from (6). Column

TABLE II HUMAN PRENATAL ONTOGENY (continued)

Structure	Sense Organs: Function	Muscular System	Glands
Eyes converging rapidly. External, middle and inner ear assuming final form. Vestibular apparatus (organ of body balance) already formed in inner ear. Taste-buds indicated. External nares plugged.	Pressure-sensitive: responds lightly to touch. Pressure sensitivity shows a cephalocaudal gradient; also a trend from generalized to specific responses to local stimuli. Temperature sensitivity "early in fetal period."	Definitive muscles of trunk, limbs, head well represented, and fetus is capable of some movement.	Female sex-gland (ovary) formed by eighth week.
Iris and ciliary-body organizing. Eyelids fused. Spiral organ begins differentiating.		Perineal muscles developing.	Lacrimal glands budding.
Characteristic organization of eye attained. Retina becomes layered. Nasal septum and palate fusions completed. Taste receptors more widely distributed. Outer and inner parts of ear fully formed by third month.	Elicited eye-movements seem to be related to functioning of vestibular apparatus: a general postural reaction to movement of body in space.	Smooth-muscle layers indicated in the hollow viscera.	Adrenal medulla begins to secrete lightly.

‍rked # are adapted from (30) unless otherwise indicated.

TABLE II HUMAN PRENATAL ONTOGENY (continued)
C. From Sixteen Fetal Weeks to Birth[3]

Age in Weeks	Structure	Elicited Responses #	Spontaneous Behavior #	Sense Organs
16–20	Hemispheres conceal much of brain. Cerebral lobes delimited by first fissures. Corpora quadrigemina appear in mid-brain. Cerebellum assumes some prominence. During the fourth and fifth months, the first evidence of a layering organization of the neocortex emerges: the primordial grey divides into an outer and an inner band, separated by the primordial internal-granular layer (144). Ventral roots (motor function) in cord begin to show myelin (102).	Sluggishness of previously lively responses.	Muscular movements detected.	Eye, ear, nose, approach neonatal appearance. Kinesthetic sense-organs differentiating.
20–24	Hemispheral commissures completed. Myelination of sensory pathways in cord begins. Calcarine and parieto-occipital fissures appear in neocortex during fifth and sixth months (144). The corticospinal tracts, which allow for eventual voluntary motor control, begin to grow downward from the motor cortex during the fifth fetal month. Inner layers of cortex are developing earlier than outer layers. Evidence of a discontinuous-vertical, striated, cellular organization emerges in the cortex (38).	Big toe extends and other toes flex (Babinski reflex) when sole touched. Respiratory movements when medulla stimulated. Grasp and "trot" reflex readily elicited.	Generalized body activity. Hiccups fifteen to thirty times a minute (medullar involvement).	Nose and ear ossify. At five and one-half months, all retinal layers are present, but rods and cones are very small and immature. Eyelids separate at twenty-two weeks but do not open spontaneously.

Weeks				
24–28	Cerebral neocortex becomes typically multi-layered: during the sixth and seventh months, the inner band of primordial grey divides into two layers, followed by the outer band's similar division into two layers (144). Infant can survive outside of womb at twenty-eight weeks.	Knee-jerk, Achilles-tendon, and sucking reflexes all elicitable.		Vascular trunk of lens at height. Retinal layers complete and light-perceptive. Eyelids reopen. All parts of ear well-defined.
28–32	Cerebral fissures and convolutions appearing rapidly. Rubrospinal tract myelinated. Final general configuration of cerebellum achieved (but neocerebellum's development not completed until well after birth).	Reflexes more pronounced and intense.	Crying occurs during seventh through ninth months. (Fetus' own internal environment may afford it vague pressure sensations as it moves; it may also receive sensory stimulation from contact pressures (14)).	
32–36	The secondary and tertiary sulci, peculiar only to the human brain, develop during the "final fetal months."	Toe reflex more variable. Spreading of toes occurs.		Taste-sense present. Loud sounds elicit fetal movements during the last two months.
36–40	Myelination of "old cortex" begins at forty weeks, just before birth (?).	Still no neocortical control.	The birth-cry is essentially a respiratory reflex.	Mastoid cells still unformed at birth. Ear deaf at birth. Insensitive to smell until after birth (?). Insensitive to pain throughout fetal period and until about six hours after birth.

³Except for columns marked # and where otherwise indicated, adapted from (6) and (197). Columns marked # are adapted from (30).

70 Human Neural and Behavioral Development

drawn from authoritative secondary sources, covering from two-and-one-half postconception weeks, when the neural groove is indicated, to birth. Table IIA, from two-and-one-half to seven postconception weeks, organizes the data under four headings: nervous system, (exteroceptive) sense organs, muscular system, glands. Table IIB, covering seven-and-one-half through fifteen weeks, expands to seven headings: three for the nervous system (structure, elicited responses, spontaneous function), two for sense organs (structure and function), and muscular system and glands.

Table IIC, covering sixteen postconception weeks through birth, is organized much like Table IIB. Electroencephalographic data, although available, have not been included in it, since up to one month after birth, the electrical activity of the brain is so minimal as to require only brief mention. According to Dreyfus-Brisac (42), brain-wave activity is not recordable before five fetal months, and from five to eight fetal months, such activity is entirely sub-cortical in origin. At eight months, cortical activity emerges for the first time and does not appreciably change in its patterning until the end of the first postnatal month; details of this pattern are included in Table IV, on the Neonate. Orientation to the electrical activity of the brain and to the electroencephalograph (EEG) as a means of recording it, is given in the next chapter.

To recapitulate the high points of Table II, the neuraxis makes its ontogenetic beginning as a minute, compact, almost undifferentiated neural tube which emerges by four postconception weeks. The neural tube develops a series of four flexures as it lengthens, the first two emerging even before it has become a sealed tube: the first or cervical, and the second or mesencephalic, flexures have appeared by twenty postconception days, apparently simultaneously. The third or pontine flexure appears by thirty-two fetal days *between* the first and the second flexures, and the fourth or telencephalic flexure shows up in the upper portion of the tube at the end of the fourth fetal week. Note that the numbering of the flexures approximates the time-order of their emergence. Figure 2, following, depicts the development of the four flexures, and is included by courtesy of W. Heffer & Sons Ltd.,

Cambridge, England; it is based on Figures 288-291 and 293 in reference 68.

These four flexures have major neurogenic significance: five sections of the neural tube are demarcated by them and each of these subsections acts as a discrete growth-focus for the differentiation of each of the major nerve centers of the human central nervous system (as outlined in Orientation Supplement 2). Thus, the part of the neural tube below the first flexure differentiates into the spinal cord, the lowest functional level of the mammalian neuraxis, as well as the oldest phylogenetically. The section of the tube just above the first flexure becomes the medulla oblongata or "bulb." That section just above the third flexure becomes the pons and cerebellum, and that just below the second flexure is the mid-brain; that is, *two* sections emerge between the third and the second flexures. The section between the second and the fourth flexures differentiates into the diencephalic centers, and the part of the tube above the fourth flexure becomes the cerebral hemispheres.

The circumstance that the eventual mid-brain section is the only part of the matured brain above the cord that emerges without further subdivision from the primary, neural tube, stage of neural development, and the further circumstance that it is demarcated at the same time as the spinal cord, the most primitive section of the neuraxis, are alike most suggestive. Does this dual circumstance have some special developmental and/or functional significance?

Even at the very early period of five fetal weeks, the fourth or telencephalic flexure is much more marked in the human than in other mammals at a parallel stage of development. The eye begins its structural development as an outgrowth of the forepart of the neural tube in the third fetal week (6).

The discussion of Table II is interrupted at this point to present Figure 3, which gives a composite analysis of the developmental timing of the several neuraxial centers; this analysis is derived from the information in Table II. Figure 3 is so organized as to allow for both a horizontal inspection-perspective, i.e., the time-pattern of development for each neuraxial center (spinal cord and neocortical development are especially fully indicated) ; *and* a vertical perspective, i.e., the developmental status of the various CNS centers at particular prenatal ages.

A quick inspection of Figure 3 along its vertical dimension yields these highlights:

(1) At thirty-two days, the spinal ganglia are forming, at the

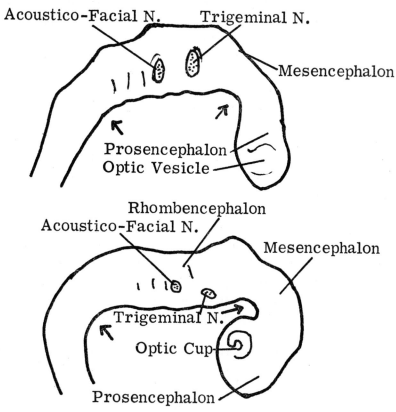

RECONSTRUCTIONS ILLUSTRATING THE DEVELOPMENT AND DEVELOPMENTAL ROLE OF THE FOUR NEURAL-TUBE FLEXURES

Figure 2A. Reconstruction of the external form of the right half of the cranial portion of the CNS in a 3.5 mm human embryo. The left arrow indicates the position of the *cervical* flexure, the right arrow of the *mesencephalic* flexure.

Figure 2B. Reconstruction of the external form of the right half of the cranial part of the CNS in a 5 mm human embryo. Arrows as in 2A.

same time that the pontine flexure appears (which sets off the section of the neural tube in which the pons and cerebellum eventually develop, from the section where the medulla is already differentiating).

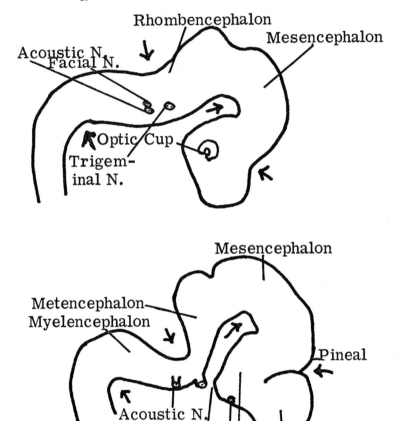

Figure 2C. Reconstruction of the external form of the right half of the cranial part of the CNS in a 9 mm human embryo. The upper arrow indicates the position of the emerging *pontine* flexure. The *telencephalic* flexure is showing signs of emerging at the far lower-right.

Figure 2D. Reconstruction of the external form of the right half of the cranial part of the CNS in an 11 mm human embryo. Arrows as in 2C.

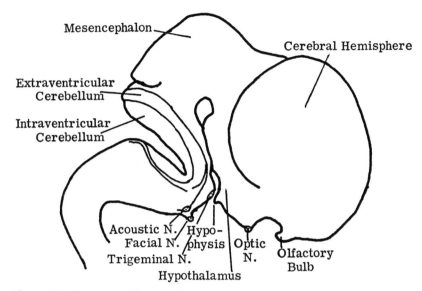

Figure 2E. Reconstruction of the external form of the right half of the cranial part of the CNS in a 27 mm human embryo. The five parts of Figure 2 are magnified in decreasing order: 2E is the least magnified of the five.

(2) At five weeks, the first spinal nerve-tracts emerge, at the same time that the telencephalic flexure appears in the upper section of the neural tube.

(3) At six weeks, the elements necessary for a reflex-arc emerge in the developing spinal cord, at the same time that the hypothalamus and epithalamus of the diencephalon first become evident and the cerebral hemispheres are beginning to bulge.

(4) At seven to seven-and-one-half weeks, spinal reflexes are fully formed and elicitable, just a few days after the thalamus, the hippocampus and the basal ganglia (corpus striatum) first emerge.

(5) At ten-and-one-half weeks, the spinal cord attains its definitive internal structure, with localized fetal movements appearing as a direct consequence, *at the same time* that the primordium of the cerebral neocortex differentiates.

(6) At fourteen weeks, intersegmental sensory tracts appear in the cord, at the same time that the flocculonodular lobe of the cerebellum first appears.

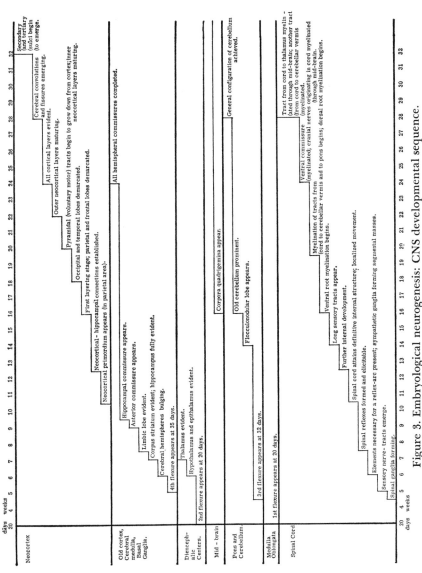

Figure 3. Embryological neurogenesis: CNS developmental sequence.

(7) At sixteen weeks, ventral-root (motor function) myelination begins in the cord, at the same time that the old cerebellum is prominent, the corpora quadrigemina (auditory and visual tracts) appear in the mid-brain, the first neocortical layering stage begins, and the parietal and frontal lobes of the neocortex are demarcated by the central fissure.

(8) At twenty weeks, dorsal-root (sensory function) myelination begins in the cord, a few days before the pyramidal tracts, which eventually play a key role in voluntary behavior, begin to grow down from the motor neocortex.

(9) At twenty-four weeks, the cranial nerves which originate in the spinal cord are myelinated up through the mid-brain, at the same time that all hemispheral commissures are completed and all neocortical layers become evident.

(10) At twenty-eight weeks, a second tract from the cord to the cerebellar vermis is myelinated, and the tract from the cord to the thalamus is myelinated through the mid-brain, at the same time that the full configuration of the cerebellum is achieved and neocortical convolutions and fissures are beginning to appear.

Table II and Figure 3 together show that the differentiation of the respective neuraxial centers follows this time-order:

(1) Although the (a) cervical and (b) mesencephalic, flexures emerge at the same time, marking off the areas of the neural tube which proceed to differentiate into (a) the spinal cord and medulla and (b) the mid-brain and diencephalon, the spinal cord and medulla differentiate much more rapidly than do the mid-brain and diencephalic centers, and attain their definitive internal structure much earlier.

(2) The pontine flexure emerges next, initiating the differentiation of the pons and old cerebellum.

(3) The telencephalic flexure emerges next, initiating the differentiation of the old cortex, and subsequent hippocampal differentiation precedes limbic lobe differentiation.

(4) The first, primordial, cells of the neocortex appear next, and shortly thereafter,

(5) The neocerebellum begins to differentiate.

This time-sequence of the embryological emergence of the respective structural derivatives of the neural tube parallels closely enough the phylogenetic emergence of the respective neuraxial centers (see Table I in Chapter III), the lowest centers, phylogenetically, differentiating first and the highest centers last, that structural ontogeny would indeed seem to recapitulate phylogeny; and this conclusion may be counted as *the first,* not too surprising, overall *developmental pattern* derivable from the data in Table II and Figure 3.

Although all sections of the tube are developing concurrently, *neuraxial differentiation clearly follows a tail-to-headward (caudocephalic) gradient*: the spinal cord, the lowest and oldest CNS center, begins to differentiate first and fastest, and completes its internal structural development earliest, well before birth; while the cerebral neocortex, the highest center, begins to differentiate last, and remains largely undifferentiated and entirely nonfunctioning at birth, although its major structural components are present — with the differentiation of intermediate centers falling between these two extremes. As has already been pointed out, but is worth repeating, the spinal cord achieves its definitive internal structure at the same time that the first cells of the cerebral neocortex emerge: at ten-and-one-half postconception weeks. This lower-to-upper time pattern holds even *within* the cerebral cortex: the phylogenetically oldest parts of the cortex, the hippocampus and the limbic lobe, begin to differentiate before the neocortex. And as for the neocortex, once the three "basic mammalian" layers have emerged, during the second layering stage the lowest layers mature first, and of the various lobes, it is the eventual parietal area, somato-viscero-sensory in function, which differentiates first and most rapidly, and to which can be traced the first thalamo-cortical fibers. Hamilton attributes a special significance to this latter circumstance, as already indicated in Table IB.

The *second developmental pattern* deducible from these data and directly related to the first pattern, is that the overall embryological pattern of development of the central nervous system follows an almost consistent *tail-to-head* growth-gradient (the neo-cerebellum, which differentiates along with the motor neocortex, appears to be the single major exception to this generalization).

If the reader has had a "startle reaction" to the foregoing two paragraphs, he has justification: developmental patterns 1 and 2 appear to contradict flatly the *cephalocaudal* pattern of development of somatic differentiation *and* of voluntary motor behavior, both emphasized in textbooks of developmental psychology. As we shall see later in this chapter, the simply formulated "cephalo-caudal trend of development" has for many years been concealing a far more complex developmental process than its original enunciators were in a position to realize.

Third, this caudocephalic pattern of overall neuraxial development foreshadows the pattern of development of spontaneous functioning of the nervous system, both prenatally (clearly documented by the behavioral data included in Table II and Figure 3) and, hypothetically for the present, postnatally. However, the spinal cord, *as a discrete subunit within the CNS,* is the one — and a most significant — exception to the overall tail-to-head ontogenetic gradient: *within itself, it develops along a head-to-tail gradient,* repeating the overall gradient of somatic development, especially in its pattern of growth of localized nerves and intra-spinal nerve-tracts. Its sensory dermatomes and early muscular myotomes reveal a regular body-segmented, topological organization: the upper parts of the cord subserve the upper parts of the body, the intermediate sections subserve the middle sections of the body, and the lower parts subserve the lower parts of the body. A variety of developmental anatomy data, some of them already presented, indicate that structural differentiation and onset of spinal cord functioning and consequent body-area reactivity also follow an upper-to-lower growth gradient. For example, Langworthy's myelination data (Table III, following) show a consistent head-to-tail developmental pattern in the cord. And concerning the differentiation of the spinal nerves into mature nerves, Arey points out that "The spinal nerves more cephalic in position maintain a slight advance over those of the lower levels" (6, p. 502). This spinal cord subpattern is being counted as *developmental pattern 4A.*

The importance of the implications of this cephalocaudal sub-pattern of development of the spinal cord within the overall caudocephalic neuraxial developmental pattern is in direct proportion to the extent to which it has heretofore been overlooked — not merely by standard textbooks of child and developmental psychology, but by the proponents of one or the other "side" of the now dormant Coghill-Windle controversy. The behavioral concomitants of this subpattern-within-an-overall-pattern will be gone into later in this chapter.

Localized nerve-tracts within each neuraxial center or level develop as part of the process of structural differentiation of each level; at a certain point in a particular center's development, nerve-tracts start to develop out from it. The direction of development — up *or* down — of nerve-tracts connecting the successive levels of the neuraxis with one another depends on whether the tract is sensory or motor in function. Sensory tracts grow out of a particular center up towards the next higher center at a certain point in the lower center's differentiation and play an important role in the acceleration of development of the next higher center. Arey states this role succinctly:

> The hollow brain molds its shape as the result of differential growth-rates; the local rate is influenced by the ingrowth of sensory nerve-fibers which brings on cell-division and differentiation in the centers penetrated (6, p. 478).

And, as a specific example of this process:

> Afferent systems arising from the vestibular mechanism, muscles, bones and joints, are the prime factors in so far as the emergence of the cerebellum and pons are concerned (p. 485).

Local, intracenter motor tracts also differentiate along with a particular center as it develops. In the spinal cord, the peripheral processes of the sensory ganglia begin to link up with the cord's motor tracts by the fifth fetal week — which is why it is possible to elicit discrete, localized muscular reactions early in fetal development. But motor connections *between* neuraxial centers — culminating eventually in neocortical connections with spinal motor cells — follow a *reverse* pattern to that of the interconnecting sensory tracts. Only *after* the mid-brain and hind-brain (pons and cerebellum) centers have differentiated do their motor tracts go downward and link up with spinal motor cells. This pattern is repeated as each higher center having a motor function differentiates, until the pyramidal (voluntary-motor) tracts from the neocortex grow down to the successively already-linked sub-cortical motor centers — and the structural basis for eventual voluntary, refined motor behavior is established. Such behavior can begin only when the cells of the motor neocortex being to transmit impulses — which does not occur until after birth. It is significant in this connection that *both the segmental organization and the developmental direction of the spinal cord is repeated on the motor neocortex* (in line with Phylogenetic Principle 7, page 55), *so that the pattern of development of voluntary motor behavior follows the spinal cord's segmental pattern of head-to-tail.* This highest-center duplication of the lowest-center pattern is being counted as *developmental pattern 4B.*

Myelination of a particular tract — appearance of a fatty white coating on it — is an index of development, since it is considered a sure sign not only that the tract has begun to function but also that the two centers which the tract connects are functioning — even though some nerve-tracts remain unmyelinated (yet functioning, albeit slower conducting) throughout the life of the individual. Patten points out that the myelination ontogenetic sequence is directly related to the phylogenetic age of a particular connecting tract (144, p. 339). Thus, ascending sensory tracts of the cord which transmit tactile and proprioceptive impulses are the first sensory tracts to show myelination (at the end of the fourth month of fetal life), with the spinal intersegmental motor fibers showing myelin at about the same time; then the sensory tract connecting the organ of body-balance, the vestibular apparatus, with the spinal cord (vestibulo-spinal tract — sixth fetal month) ; then the motor tract connecting the mid-brain with the spinal cord (rubrospinal tract — seventh fetal month). All these tracts are pre-mammalian in phylogenetic origin. The corticospinal (pyramidal) motor tract that emerges phylogenetically only with mammals remains unmyelinated until after birth; the latter part of the first year and the first part of the second year, while controlled motor behavior is progressing apace, is *its* period of most rapid myelination. Patten's more recent analysis largely corroborates Langworthy's earlier myelination-pattern data (102), which are presented in an adapted form in Table III, following.

TABLE III

MYELINATION DEVELOPMENT PATTERN OF
MYELINATED NERVE TRACTS[1]

Tract	(Myelin first evident at:)	Fetal Age in Weeks
1. Ventral roots of spinal cord (motor)	)	16
2. Dorsal roots of spinal cord (sensory).	)	
3. Three cranial nerves originating in medulla and pons show myelin up to the mid-brain. (V-motor, VI, VIII-vestib.); also III.	)	20
4. Tracts from cord to cerebellar vermis and from cord to pons.	)	
5. Ventral commissure of cord.	)	
6. Seven remaining cranial nerves originating in spinal cord, medulla and pons show myelin through the mid-brain (V-sensory, VII, VIII-cochlear, IX, X, XI, XII); also IV.	)	24
7. Tracts from cerebellum to cord and from pons to cord.	)	
8. Tracts from medulla to thalamus show myelination through mid-brain.	)	
9. Tract from cord to cerebellar vermis.	)	
10. Tract from cord to thalamus myelinated through mid-brain.	)	
11. Tract from epithalamus to mid-brain.	)	28
12. Intra-medulla, intra-mid-brain and intracerebellar tracts.	)	
13. Vagus complex (cranial nerves IX, X, XI) myelinated through mid-brain.	)	

(The fetus can survive outside the womb beginning at twenty-eight weeks)

Tract	(Myelin first evident at:)	Fetal Age in Weeks
14. Tracts from a basal ganglion to sub-thalamus.	)	
15. Tract listed under 8 now myelinated through lower thalamus.	)	
16. Tract from ruber nucleus of mid-brain to cord shows myelin through medulla only.	)	32
17. Intra-mid-brain tract connecting the optic chiasma.	)	
18. Rest of cranial nerves not listed under three and six myelinated through mid-brain.	)	
19. Tracts from mid-brain to cerebral cortex myelinated into thalamus	)	
20. Tract from medulla to thalamus entirely myelinated.	)	36
21. Optic nerve and pathways; (olfactory (?) nerves and pathways still unmyelinated).	)	
22. Tract from cerebellum to ruber nucleus of mid-brain.	)	
23. Tract from basal ganglion to ruber nucleus of mid-brain.	)	
24. Increase of myelin in thalamic fibers: in ventrolateral nucleus and in optic geniculates.	)	
25. Spinal cord now uniformly myelinated, although somewhat less so in the lumbar segments. Ventral columns well myelinated except where the corticospinal fibers terminate. No lateral myelination of pyramidal tract and little here of the rubro-spinal tract.	)	40
26. Tract listed under 8 shows myelin to its termination-point (ventro-lateral nucleus) in the anterior thalamus.	)	
27. Tract from the ventrolateral nucleus of thalamus to posterior and anterior central gyri (central fissure area) of cerebral cortex.	)	

[1]Adapted from (102).

From the data in Table III, it is evident that the spinal cord pattern of the motor neurons and tracts being ahead of the sensory ones in development does not hold for the brain: above the cord, sensory tracts are ahead of motor tracts in myelination, and, presumably, in onset of functioning. Langworthy explicitly states,

> Whereas the primary motor neurons in the cord acquire their myelin earlier than the primary sensory neurons, in the cerebral cortex the afferent pathways are medullated before the efferent (102, p. 32).

As for peripheral nervous system development, the skin receptors for pressure, warmth, cold, develop earliest of the exteroceptive sensory structures; their central tract connections in the cord are clearly evident at only five fetal weeks. Dorsal-root visceral-interoceptive tracts appear shortly before this time. The peripheral mechanism for olfaction is formed at six fetal weeks and its cerebrally directed nerve-tracts are evident at seven weeks. The vestibular apparatus of the inner ear, the eventual function of which is related to the body's orientation in space, develops by the end of the second fetal month, before the ear. The outer and inner parts of the ear are fully formed by the third fetal month. By the end of five-and-one-half fetal months, the whole eye is formed, including the retinal layers, but the rods and cones are very small and immature (all from 197). In general, then, the ontogenetic order of sense-organ structural development parallels their phylogenetic order. (See Phylogenetic Principle 10, page 59.)

The *fifth developmental pattern* revealed by prenatal ontogeny is taken so much for granted by embryologists and at least some developmental psychologists that it is seldom explicitly enunciated. It is that the central nervous system is hierarchically organized structurally, with the time sequence of the emergence of the respective structural derivatives of the neural tube directly corresponding to this hierarchical organization: the lowest levels in the hierarchy develop first and the highest levels last.

The *sixth developmental pattern* can be stated only as a reasonable hypothesis at this point, pending examination of the scanty data on the development of postnatal neural functioning in Part D, and of the functional-organization principles characteristic of the matured human nervous system (part C) — although it is also taken for granted by modern neurophysiology. It is that the structural hierarchy postulated in the fifth developmental pattern is directly related to the functional organization of the matured nervous system. Just how it is so related will be gone into in the next chapter. For the present, Jackson's principle of the "continuous reduction of succession to coexistences," referred to in Chapter III, offers a major clue.

Developmental pattern 7, a further elaboration of pattern 6, is not derived primarily from analysis of the prenatal phase of human ontogeny, and is the most hypothetical in character of the patterns heretofore postulated. It is that the coherent, unified functioning of the physiologically mature nervous system represents the end-product incorporation of a progressive series of organized functional patterns which develop in an hierarchic (i.e., vertical) ontogenetic sequence, prenatally and postnatally. Although Hughlings Jackson's more rudimentary formulation of a successive series of postnatal functional-dominance levels put the writer on the mental track that eventually led to this postulation, she must take responsibility for it as here stated and as it will be further elaborated in later sections of this monograph. These sections will attempt to outline the approach and the data that provide for its presentation as a reasonable hypothesis begging for direct investigative checking by experimental neuropsychology and physiology.

THE BEHAVIORAL REPERTOIRE OF THE HUMAN NEONATE

To return to the material on the human individual's first ten (lunar) months of development, summarized in Table II. In spite of the detailed data on the structural development of the nervous system and the bits and pieces of functional and behavioral information included in it, Table II gives an essentially static picture of the infant who emerges into so different an environment after several months of rapid and complex growth. What *is* the actual behavioral repertoire of the tiny being which has achieved the level of structural development described in Table II?

Fortunately, we do not have to wait for a future study of

TABLE IV
THE HUMAN NEONATE

A. Behavioral Status[1]

Physiological

1) There is great lability in the breathing-rate after birth, decreasing toward the end of the neonatal period. Also a very high and labile pulse-rate, imperfect temperature-regulation, low blood-pressure and metabolic-rate. High tolerance for anoxia because brain metabolism is still chiefly anaerobic.
2) The hunger pattern is very unstable. Regurgitation and hiccuping are typical. Digestive processes of salivation and gastric secretion occur during the feeding-act only. Urination is frequent, with wide variation in its frequency.
3) Sleeps twenty hours a day in discontinuous periods of three hours or less.

Sensorimotor
Spontaneous

1) Sneezes, coughs, primitive yawning. Sucks and swallows. Strength of sucking increases during the first month. Finger-sucking. Head and mouth orientation when hungry. Rooting reflex before feeding. Highly sensitive oral area, including lips and cheeks. Lip reflexes. Mouth a primitive orientation device.
2) Protective reflexes present: eyelid, pupillary, mouth-ejection, spinal and abdominal withdrawal. Movement of arm, hand, leg toward locus of contact; strong escape reactions when hands confined.
3) Involuntary hand-grasp reflex. Foot-grasping reflex. Babinski plantar reflex: toe-extension more frequent than toe flexion. Moro and startle responses.
4) Only conditioned responses mediated by the autonomic n.s. occur during the first month; natural CRs are more sure to develop than experimental CRs.
5) Can and does actively resist a feeding and passively resist being waked up.
6) Alert when awake; no other evidence of "intelligence."
7) All behavior is involuntary and nonintentional.

Elicited

1) Sensitive to light, girls more so than boys. Eye and head pursuit of moving visual spot in visual field. Pupillary reflex perfects itself during first week; no convergence, binocular fixation, nor focusing of image on retina.
2) Undifferentiated response to auditory stimuli: the louder, the more general the bodily involvement in the response; girls react faster than boys.
3) Only rudimentary olfactory and taste sensitivity.
4) Thermal sensitivity present, more so in leg and foot areas than in hand and head areas. Warm sensations elicit adient movements; cold, avoidance reactions.
5) Reactive to changes in body posture.
6) Pressure the first somatic sensitivity to appear; pain sensitivity emerges several hours after birth. Face, hands, soles of feet most sensitive; shoulders, back, chest, abdomen least sensitive: a head to foot gradient (197).
7) Chin up and crawling movements when laid on a flat surface. During the first week, shows a passive kneel with flexor dominance; both arms and legs are sharply flexed while face is turned and cheek contacts surface (63).

Emotional

1) From two to three weeks, shows generalized reactions to restraint and to prevention of breathing.
2) Cries only in response to inner needs, not mimetically. Crying in response to a withheld feeding was an octave above the female-adult speaking voice and two octaves above the male adult's.
3) Facial responses, including smiling, are not mimetic, but due to inner and sensory factors.

[1]From (152) except where otherwise indicated.

TABLE IV: THE HUMAN NEONATE (continued)

4) No differentiated emotions, just a general agitation. Evidence of two basic emotional attitudes: of accepting or rejecting an external stimulus.
5) Very little overt response to being suddenly dropped two feet.
6) Different cries for pain, hunger, discomfort.

Vocalization

1) Vowel sounds are five times as frequent as consonants. Produces 7.5 sounds at one month compared with the thirty-five sounds of the adult. Sequence of emergence of vocalization: vowels from front to back, consonants from back to front. One thousand vowels are uttered up to ten days (117).
2) Differentiable cries of hunger, pain, discomfort.
3) The organs of speech are first used for establishment of breathing and feeding, the two most vital physiological processes. (If early handling and feeding experiences are responsive and satisfying and give the infant feelings of security, vocalization is established normally.)

At One Month

Physiological

1) Blood-pressure goes up to 80 mm Hg (systolic) at one month, from 40 mm at birth (197).
2) Rapid decrease in heart-rate during the first few months, from 130 beats per minute at birth (197).
3) The breathing-rate decreases after the first month, from 34-45 inspirations during the first month (197).
4) From two to eight weeks, hunger contractions begin three hours and forty minutes after nursing, compared with two hours and fifty minutes at two weeks.
5) Temperature regulation is acquired by the end of the first month.

Sensorimotor

1) Fixates on light at four weeks. Begins really to look or "pay attention" visually towards the end of the first month.
2) By one month, can lift head when in prone position; tonic neck reflex the typical waking posture.
3) At four weeks, shows passive leg extension, with arms still flexed and head lifted slightly. Also active kneel: draws one leg up at a time spontaneously by unilateral flexion (63).

Emotional

1) Active signs of pleasure and of displeasure at four weeks.
2) Emotional preoccupations and drives are chiefly directed towards physiologically dominated experiences of hunger, nursing, satiation, elimination.

newborn babies to get an answer to this question. K. C. Pratt has already provided a thorough answer in his chapter in the indispensable Carmichael manual (152). These behavioral data are incorporated into Table IV (pages 84-7), together with other relevant structural and functional information.

Table IV will be analyzed in Chapter IX. The following summation somewhat anticipates this later analysis.

TABLE IV THE HUMAN NEONATE (continued)

B. Neural Status

Structure

A. At birth, according to Conel's nine histological criteria (38):

1) The lower three layers of the neocortex are most developed; the cells in the upper three layers are very little differentiated.

2) The primary-motor and primary-somesthetic areas (front and back of the central fissure) are the most advanced areas in development. In both these areas, the subarea of trunk and shoulders is most developed, those for legs and hands less so, and those for the head are minimal. Areas next in order of development (in decreasing order): the primary-visual, a hippocampal area, a limbic area and a temporal-auditory area. The frontal lobe anterior to the primary-motor area is least advanced in development of all other parts of the cortex. Subsequent development in each lobe radiates outward from the first focal area. According to Conel, all parts of the old cortex are behind the primary-motor and primary-somesthetic areas of the neocortex in development.

3) Vertical exogenous fibers (from subcortical levels) and horizontal ones (from other cortical areas) are present in all areas, but almost entirely in layers six and five only; they go up to layer three only in the most advanced areas. Myelin is present on these fibers only in the lowest layer. Vertical fibers in the primary-motor area have the most myelin; horizontal fibers in the primary-somesthetic area have the most myelin. In the temporal lobe, myelin shows only in fibers in the acoustic radiation. There are only a few myelinated fibers in the gyrus cinguli, gyrus hippocampus, gyrus dentatus.

4) There were wide individual differences in all aspects of development in the several brains studied.

Function

A. The rate of brain metabolism advances with CNS growth, shifting from dominance of anaerobic metabolism in the embryo to dominance of aerobic in the fully grown system; this rise in oxidations proceeds from lower to higher neuraxial levels. (In the puppy, the highest metabolic rate during the first week of life is in the medulla, during the second week in the midbrain, from five to seven weeks in the striatum. Compared with the rate at birth, the medulla's rate remained the same, while the rate in all other parts increased.) (82).

B. The flicker electroretinogram (ERG) is not recordable on the first day of life (197).

C. *Electrical Activity*

1) Up to eight fetal months, all patterns appear to come from subcortical levels. At eight fetal months and continuing through the first month of life, a difference appears between the deep-sleep and waking EEG and there is some functional adaptation evident in a time-succession of response (42).

2) Brain-waves have been recorded from the primary sensorimotor areas almost entirely during the first month; the parietal (somatoviscereosensory) area is the most active at birth (197).

3) There are no steady frequencies and no 9-10 cps alpha-waves. Most activity is in the delta band ($\frac{1}{2}$-2 cps), is irregular, and about 20-50 microvolts in amplitude. (64).

4) Premature infants have slower and more irregular waves than full-term normals (64).

5) There is a greater variability of amplitude of evoked responses during the neonatal period than later; also a long latency of evoked occipital responses, "probably due to the low conduction rate of the still-immature optic nerve" (48). The latter varies with the type of neo-

TABLE IV THE HUMAN NEONATE (continued)

B. 1) At birth, these tracts show myelin: optic nerve and pathways; tract from cerebellum to ruber n. of mid-brain; tract from globus pallidus (basal ganglion) to ruber n.; spinal tracts, but less heavily in lumbar segments and below; tract from medulla to thalamus; tract from ventrolateral n. of thalamus to primary sensorimotor areas.

2) During the first month, these additional areas and tracts show myelin: the primary sensorimotor area, the primary-visual (calcarine) area, the pyramidal and tectospinal tracts, two pontocerebellar tracts, the tract connecting the amygdala and hypothalamus (stria terminalis), tract connecting a basal ganglion and thalamus (stria medullaris); cerebellar-thalamic tracts, the corpus callosum (102).

nate: prematures have the longest latencies, full-terms' are intermediate, and post-matures' are shortest (49).

6) Focal spikes and/or paroxysmal outbursts of the epileptic type occur normally during the first month (49).

7) Wide individual variations in dominant frequency and in other electrical characteristics are typical: some have frequencies of from 1-3 cps, some 5-6 cps, some 7-8 cps, and some 12-14 cps (170).

At One Month

Changes in Cortical Cells Between Birth and One Month (38):

1) The primary-motor area has advanced most, with the sub area of the hand having developed more than the others. The primary-somesthetic area has the most exogenous fibers; some cells in layer three show development here.
2) The cells in layer three of the primary-visual area have advanced more than any other area. Cell processes in the motor area which mediates contralateral eyeball movements have advanced.
3) The cells in layer five of the gyrus cinguli have also developed. Myelination has advanced very little in the old cortex since birth.
4) The chromophil substance in the cells of the primary-auditory area is more advanced than in the primary-visual and primary-somesthetic areas; but the last area has the most myelin. The chromophil substance forward of the primary-motor area remains in the same undeveloped state as at birth.
5) Some nerve-tracts from the thalamus to the occipital and temporal lobes have acquired myelin; the corona radiata and internal capsule also have a good deal of myelin.
6) There were wide individual differences on all criteria on all brains studied.

Electrical Activity

At one month, the waking record becomes differentiated from the deep-sleep record, and some functional adaptation appears. During waking periods, there are brief intervals of complete cessation of electrical activity, and during deep sleep there is a discontinuous delta rhythm in the occipital sections (42).

The picture of neonatal behavior and nervous system functioning given in Table IV, when considered as an extension of the data in Table II and matched against the functional data included in Orientation Supplement 3, implies that at birth, human behavior is mediated primarily by hind-brain and mid-brain centers, with probably some forebrain (chiefly diencephalic) participation; and that toward the end of the first month of postnatal life, forebrain involvement increases, including some participation of the primary-sensorimotor and primary-visual areas of the neocortex. Anticipating the data and discussion of Part C, following, it can be further concluded that coordinated forebrain—lower brain feedback circuits have not yet established themselves, especially the integrating, reinforcing, inhibiting, controlling, stabilizing, refining roles of the higher, intraforebrain centers of thalamus, hypothalamus, old cortex, basal ganglia and neocortex. That is, the data in Table IV make clear that at birth, the mammalian legacy in human development referred to in Phylogenetic Principle 17, page 60, is dominant, and that the human endowment, although clearly indicated structurally, is functionally present only as potential. This datum constitutes the *eighth developmental pattern* deducible from the prenatal period of neurogenesis.

Pratt's behavioral data also clearly suggest a sex difference of major implication for the personality psychologist: the developmental status of the male nervous system is less advanced at birth than is the female's.

This examination of the prenatal phase of human neural development has yielded a partial answer to the question posed earlier: Do phylogenetic trends provide any clues as to how previous evolutionary stages express themselves in the form and functioning of the human nervous system? Of the eight neural-development patterns which have emerged, four suggest that prenatal neural ontogeny represents an almost unqualified continuation of established phylogenetic trends, *viz*:

(1) The time sequence of the embryological emergence of the respective CNS centers shows that, on the whole, neural ontogeny does indeed recapitulate neural phylogeny.

(2) The overall gradient of development of the neuraxis is from tail (spinal cord) to head (neocortex).

(3) This structural growth-gradient foreshadows the pattern

of development of spontaneous functioning of the neuraxis, which also proceeds from the tail to the head.

(4) However, (a) the spinal cord within itself, as a discrete subunit of the CNS, develops *and* becomes functional in a head to tail direction; and (b) the pattern of development of voluntary motor behavior, which is dependent upon the onset of functioning of the motor neocortex, repeats the spinal cord pattern, i.e., the onset of voluntary motor behavior also reflects a head to tail gradient.

An additional three patterns reflect the influence of a phylogenetically derived organizational principle, *viz*:

(5) The neuraxis is hierarchically organized, with the centers first to develop lowest, and the centers last to develop highest, in the hierarchy.

(6) This developmental hierarchy is directly related to the functional organization of the matured nervous system — a proposition to be examined further in Chapter V.

(7) The coherent functioning of the fully matured nervous system represents the end-product incorporation of a progressive series of organized functional patterns which develop in a vertical-hierarchic ontogenetic sequence — another proposition to be examined subsequently. But precisely how this influence expresses itself in the fully matured human nervous system is not clear at this point, since all three patterns involve projections into the as yet unexamined postnatal phases of neural ontogeny.

The last developmental pattern postulated, number eight (page 88), introduces an extraphylogenetic factor; understanding of how this new, human species, principle (a) expresses itself and (b) influences other neurogenic patterns, must also await examination of pertinent post-natal data.

A RE-EXAMINATION OF THE COGHILL-WINDLE CONTROVERSY

Concerning the basic pattern of development of behavior in the human being, does behavior commence as a generalized, mass activity from which the specific, localized reflexes eventually differentiate in a cephalocaudal direction — the Coghill position?

Or are the earliest responses to stimuli localized muscular reflexes, and the overall, coordinated pattern of voluntary motor behavior established as a result of the gradual integration of the various discrete reflexes — Windle's position? What light do the data included in Table II, Figure 3, and supplementary material in reputable secondary sources on embryology throw on these questions?

Modern developmental neuro- anatomy and physiology have already revealed Windle to have been much more right than Coghill. To begin with, Coghill's investigations overlooked (apparently completely) the great phylogenetic gap between the nervous system of the amblystoma and the nervous system of higher mammals (37). But there is one important commonality between the two forms: the amblystoma's nervous system happens to be directly analogous in its internal organization and pattern of development to the pattern of development and internal organization and functional inter-relationships of the two lowest levels of the human nervous system, the spinal cord and medulla oblongata. As was reviewed in the preceding chapter, the mammalian spinal cord represents a phylogenetically very early type of nervous system which subsequently became the phylogenetically unchanging "tail end" of more complicated nervous systems becoming increasingly more complex at the head-end. That is, once evolved, this early type of nervous system was thereafter incorporated as a coherent subunit, substantially unchanged and unchanging in its basic internal segmental pattern of organization, into the increasingly complexly organized nervous systems of successively higher forms. Modification of this relatively independent subsystem's functions has come about as a result of its *external* relationships with the neural centers above it — *relationships superimposed on its own inherent pattern of organization and functioning.*

Fairly enough, the cord has in turn influenced the functioning of the higher centers through the neural principle of successive representation of this lowest center's segmental pattern upon the successively higher sensory and motor centers — a phylogenetically derived pattern that must be appended to the better known principle of encephalization (see Chapter III). It is only because the spinal cord (i.e., amblystoma) motor pattern is repeated in the medulla, in the cerebellum, in the basal ganglia and in the motor neocortex that a degree of correspondence exists between the pattern of development of motor behavior in the amblystoma and in man — as I hope to make still more clear shortly.

Windle was quite right when he maintained that localized reflexes and muscle movements were elicitable in lower and higher mammalian fetuses long before overall, coordinated movements were expressed (195). The dual circumstance that the muscle-movement and simple-reflex level of behavior is the spinally mediated level, and that the spinal cord has achieved its definitive internal structure by the eleventh fetal week in man, provides the neurological underpinnings for Windle's findings: note that just such movements are elicitable at seven-and-one-half to eight fetal weeks. But the other half of Windle's postulation — that the overall, coordinated pattern of behavior comes about through the gradual integration of the separate reflexes ("But with progressive development of central reflex mechanisms, more complex and integrated reflexes become elicitable" [196, p. 642]) is, in light of current knowledge of the organization and development of the human nervous system, much oversimplified.

Not one, but *two* patterns of development relevant for the developmental pattern of human behavior, the second actually a complex of several subpatterns, *are occurring independently of each other but overlapping in time,* during embryology. While the spinal cord, the center which mediates localized reflexes and muscle-movements is differentiating *along its own cephalocaudal gradient,* the successively higher centers of the neuraxis and their respective associated nerve-tracts are also developing. As each successively higher motor center differentiates, it establishes motor-tract connections with the already developed, lower, motor centers: medulla and mid-brain with the cord; cerebellum plus pons with the mid-brain, medulla and cord; basal ganglia with the cerebellum and pons, medulla and cord; and finally, after birth, the motor neocortex with the basal ganglia and etcetera. As each of these separate sets of motor connections is established, the lower center (or centers) gradually comes under the functional dominance of the particular higher motor center which has newly differentiated — and more and more complex reflexes and movements emerge progressively. The first spontaneous mass movement of the fetus at fourteen weeks is usually attributed to the "old" cerebellum's having established functional relations with the mid-brain, medulla and cord.

Coghill's postulated cephalocaudal pattern thereafter emerges *only after birth,* after the initiation of yet a third pattern of neural development relevant for the early developmental pattern of human behavior: the postnatal onset of function in the motor and somatosensory areas of the neocortex, which is responsible for the development of controlled-motor behavior. Once the highest motor center, the motor neocortex, has begun to function, it gradually establishes cerebral dominance over the subcortical motor centers. The pattern of voluntary motor behavior which then emerges is superimposed upon a heretofore scarcely coordinated cacophony of movements of varying degrees of specificity and complexity.

Why *does* the postnatal pattern of development of controlled movement, once it begins, proceed along a cephalocaudal gradient and towards increasingly refined-yet-coordinated movements, even though it represents the end-stage of an overall-neuraxial *caudocephalic* growth-gradient? For two reasons. First, because the topological pattern of the lowest motor center, the spinal cord, is reduplicated on the motor neocortex, and the onset of function in both the motor and the somatosensory areas of the neocortex echoes the head-to-tail bodily order in which the spinal cord develops and becomes functional: *Coghill's amblystoma in a phylogenetically updated location!* Second, because until both sensory and motor aspects of the nervous system begin to work smoothly together through the mediation of the highest CNS centers, stable and coordinated and focused highest-center control over successively lower and localized-in-function centers cannot be achieved — and this is a lengthy and complicated process, extending well into postnatal life.

PART C
THE POINT OF DEPARTURE:
THE MATURED HUMAN NERVOUS SYSTEM

Chapter V

THE HIERARCHICAL-REDUPLICATIVE FUNCTIONAL ORGANIZATION PATTERN

PREAMBLE TO PART C

THE HUMAN NERVOUS SYSTEM as a physical entity has been studied from many different perspectives: structurally, histologically, early cellular growth, physiologically — including its biochemistry, electrical activity, overall and unit-level functional characteristics, embryologically, neuropsychologically, as well as other aspects not mentioned. Every one of these approaches is rich in complex data. Since this monograph is not intended to be a textbook of neurology, even to begin to describe the matured human nervous system as a coherent organismic entity necessitates the deliberate making of choices — choices as to which data to include and which data to ignore.

It is already evident that the central nervous system has been made the major focus of this discussion, with peripheral mechanisms included more or less incidentally. The basic structural characteristics of the CNS have already been presented in the orientation materials, as well as a somewhat superficial overview of the functional contributions of each major neuraxial center below the cerebral cortex. To provide a basis for comparison with the neonatal nervous system, as well as to lay a foundation for later speculation on the stages between birth and maturity, this section will concentrate on the functional organization of the matured, *in situ* human nervous system, and will tend to place its major emphasis on the CNS macroscopically approached, on the thesis that the CNS and the macroscopic level together have the most immediate relevance for behavior.

When an entity as complex as the human nervous system is the subject under discussion, it would betray the influence of an overly specialized orientation to speak of *the* overall functional-organization pattern of the nervous system. At least three such patterns seem to be so basic as to necessitate their analysis in some depth; they include the following:

(1) The hierarchical-reduplicative phylogenetic legacy pattern;

(2) The neuropsychological functional sub-systems pattern, and

(3) The triple-system phylogenetic legacy pattern.

Analysis of these three patterns requires a more detailed anatomical picture of the subneocortical human forebrain than has as yet been provided in the orientation materials. Orientation Supplement 4, The Human Forebrain, is therefore included at this point: 4A covers the diencephalic centers of thalamus and hypothalamus, and 4B the cerebral medulla, in which are embedded the basal ganglia. The cerebral neocortex will be dealt with later in this chapter, the old cortex in Chapter VI.

ORIENTATION SUPPLEMENT 4

THE HUMAN SUBCORTICAL FOREBRAIN[1]

A. Diencephalic Centers and their Connections

Thalamus

Consists of about twenty-five nuclear groups, plus the Subthalamus and Epithalamus.

Anterior Nuclei: (2)	(Receive fibers from the mam (millothalamic tract and pro (ject to the gyrus cinguli of (the mesocortex.	Midline Nuclei: (4)	(Include the reticular (N.; all have hypo (thalamic connections.
Posterior Nuclei:	(N. pulvinaris: to parietal asso (ciation area of neocortex. (the Genic- (Corpus genicula (ulates: (tum lateralis: (from the optic (tract to the (visual cortex. (Corpus genicula (tum medialis: (to the auditory (area of the (temporal lobe.	Medial Nuclei: (5)	(Medialis dorsalis: (projects to hypo (thalamus and (frontal lobe. (Centrum medianum ((Luys) : no direct (cortical connections. (Intralaminar nuclei.

---

[1]Based on 160 and 180 except where otherwise indicated.

Lateral   (N. ventralis anterior: connected with the basal ganglia.
Nuclear   (N. ventralis lateralis: receives fibers from the superior cerebellar
Mass: (peduncle and projects to the motor cortex.
            (N. ventralis posterior — arcuate N. plus ventralis postero-lateralis:
            (project to the postcentral gyrus of the neocortex.
            (N. lateralis dorsalis   )
            (N. lateralis posterior) both project to the posterior parietal lobe.

Subthalamus (Corpus Luysii) : well-defined only in man; related to proprioception.
Epithalamus: composed of the Pineal body or Epiphysis, Habenular Ganglion, and
   the Striae Medullaris nerve-tract.

On the basis of their connections, there are *three* types of thalamic nuclei:

A. Those with subcortical connections: midline nuclei (paleothalamus), intralaminar nuclei, and the centrum medianum, and N. ventralis anterior. All three
   groups project to the neocortex via the nonspecific thalamocortical projection,
   a slower, diffuse, multi-synaptic route, considered to be the upper part of the
   BSRF. (See Chapter VI.)
B. The cortical relay nucleus: N. ventralis posteromedialis, which has somesthetic
   functions and is topographically (body-surface) organized. *From* trigeminal,
   medial lemnisci and spinothalamic tracts; *to* postcentral gyrus of neocortex. A
   "specific" thalamocortical projection nucleus.
C. Association nuclei: all receive impulses from type A nuclei (with sub-cortical
   connections) , and project to the association areas of the neocortex, as follows:
   N. dorsomedial: to the prefrontal area; N. dorsolateral and N. posterolateral: to
   posterior parietal lobe; N. pulvinar: to the T-O-P posterior-association area.
   There are also specific thalamocortical projection nuclei.

Hypothalamus

Consists of nine (so far identified) nuclear groups. The pituitary gland or
hypophysis is functionally closely associated with it.

Anterior	(N. paraventricular	Middle or	(N. ventromedial
Nuclei:	(N. preoptic	Tuberal	(N. dorsomedial
	(N. supraoptic	Nuclei:	(N. posterior
			(hypothalamic
	Caudal or	(N. medial mammillary	
	Mammillary	(N. intercalated mammillary	
	Body Nuclei:	(N. lateral mammillary	

Connections with centers below:

Afferent	*Efferent*
From spinal and tegmental (upper mid-brain) structures *into* N. lateral mammillary (via the mammillary peduncle) .	1) *To* the lateral and medial reticular nuclei in the tegmentum from the medial mammillary nuclei, via the mammillotegmental tract.
	2) *To* tegmental reticular nuclei of mid-brain, into dorsal longitudinal fasciculus, *to* brain-stem parasympathetic nuclei and, through relays, *to* spinal sympathetic preganglionic neurons, *to* spinal levels, *to* dorsomedial nuclei; all via the periventricular system, from supraoptic, posterior and tuberal nuclei.
	3) *Into* the posterior lobe of the pituitary, from the supraoptic, tuberal and paraventricular (water metabolism) nuclei, via the hypothalamo-hypophysial tract.

Connections with centers parallel or above:

Afferent	*Efferent*
1) *From* ventromedial area of old cortex to preoptic, lateral hypothalamic, and mammillary nuclei, via the medial forebrain bundle.	*To* anterior thalamic nuclei (thence

2) *From* the hippocampus to the mammillary nuclei via the fornix.
3) *From* the amygdaloid nuclei to anterior hypothalamic nuclei via the stria terminalis.
4) *From* frontal cortex, globus pallidus and thalamus to various hypothalamic nuclei via other, less well-defined pathways.

to cingulate gyrus) from the medial mammillary N., via mammillo-thalamic tract of Vicq d'Azyr.

B. Cerebral Medulla

Nerve Tracts (white matter)

On the basis of their connections, tracts are of three types; those connecting:

1) cortex with lower centers (projection fibers) :
   afferent — thalamocortical and rubrocortical;
   efferent — corticospinal, corticobulbar, and to pons, thalamus, hypothalamus, striatum, mid-brain centers.
2) cortical areas of the same hemisphere: intrahemispheral subcortical association fibers, which are both short (arcuate) fibers connecting adjacent convolutions, and long fibers interconnecting cortical lobes.
3) the two cortical hemispheres (interhemispheral commissures) :
   — the corpus callosum interconnects the two neocortices;
   — the anterior and hippocampal commissures interconnect the two old cortices.

Basal Ganglia and their Connections

Amygdaloid nuclei (2)   )   not uniformly considered basal ganglia.
The claustrum   )

Caudate N.   )   the neo-
(separated by the Internal Capsule))
Putamen   )   striatum

Globus pallidus (or pallidum)   (lateral portion: afferent
   (the paleostriatum)   (medial portion: efferent

Afferent connections: from midline and medial thalamic nuclei (intralaminar, centromedial, smaller midline) .
Efferent connections: to subthalamus and the brain-stem nuclei of substantia nigra, ruber, and the reticular formation.
Other: Lateral pallidus — afferent; receives fibers from thalamus and neocortex, forming this circuit: thalamus → motor cortex → pallidum → thalamus.
Medial pallidus — efferent; projects to the lateroventral N. of the thalamus (thence to motor cortex), via the ansa and fasciculus lenticularis.

THE HIERARCHICAL-REDUPLICATIVE PHYLOGENETIC LEGACY PATTERN

The principle that the CNS (spinal cord and brain) is functionally hierarchically organized in a complex, lowest-center-reduplicative fashion, with the highest centers functionally dominant over the lower centers, has been a basic assumption of biologists such as Weiss and Tinbergen and neurophysiologists such as Fulton and Himwich for some time. The phylogenetically (and ontogenetically) oldest parts of the CNS are lowest in this functional hierarchy, its phylogenetically (and ontogenetically) youngest parts are highest, and there is a successive re-representation at each ascending level of each level below. The functional corollary of this anatomical arrangement is the emergence, with each reduplication, of a greater degree and scope of functional coordination, along with a greater degree of refinement of functioning.

This pattern must, however, be considered in conjunction with the two subsequently discussed functional-organization patterns, and *be qualified by them.*

The hierarchical-reduplicative pattern is especially relevant for psychology because it provides the framework for the *over-time* (phylogenetic and ontogenetic) investigative perspective, which has hitherto been slighted by behavioral theory and without which the complex behaviors of the matured organism during a particular *moment-in-time,* the typical psychological and neurophysiological experimental design, cannot be adequately conceptualized.

Reference to the hierarchical-reduplicative pattern necessitates the re-introduction of the far-ahead-of-his-time thinking of Hughlings Jackson, the later-nineteenth century English neurosurgeon-psychiatrist. Although many of Jackson's anatomical specifics have since proved inaccurate because of the relatively primitive status of neuroanatomy during the second half of the nineteenth century (papers published from 1874 to 1898 are being used), his prolific theorizing, based on keen observation of his patients, has proved to be so heuristic, he has been periodically rediscovered by neurophysiology — and is now considered to be one of the three "patron saints" of modern neurophysiology, along with Ramon y Cájàl, formulator of the neuron theory, and Sir Charles Sherrington, the great experimentalist. The newest, methodologically most impeccable research keeps discovering with almost disconcerting regularity that Hughlings Jackson was "already there." Since the concept of a hierarchical-reduplicative functional pattern in the human CNS is primarily Jackson's, and since all his writings are accessible in early volumes of British medical journals, as well as in a recent two-volume collection of his publications (174), this pattern will first be presented as Jackson originally postulated it, in the table of excerpts from his writings, following. Seven modern restatements of his thesis will be cited thereafter.

ORIENTATION SUPPLEMENT 5
EXCERPTS FROM THE WRITINGS OF
J. HUGHLINGS JACKSON

Excerpted Passages*

(1) "The higher the centre, the more numerous, different, complex and special movements it represents, and the wider the region it represents, equals *evolution*. The *highest* centres represent innumerable, most complex and most special movements of the whole organism, and . . each unit of them represents the whole organism differently. In consequence, the higher the centre, the more numerous, different, complex and special movements of a wider region are lost from a negative lesion of equal volume, equals *dissolution*."

(2) "The higher nervous arrangements inhibit (or control) the lower, and thus, when the higher are suddenly rendered functionless, the lower rise in activity."

(3) "There is no localisation in the sense that each unit of the [highest-motor] centre represents only a part of the muscular region; each unit represents, or coordinates, the whole region. And there is no localisation in the sense that every unit of the centre represents the whole region similarly; each represents, or coordinates, the whole region differently."

(4) "The nervous system is a representing system, and even the centres 'for mind' represent parts of the body. My doctrine of 'evolution' repudiates all schemes which make piebald divisions into ideational, etc. centres, and sensory and motor centres — *all* centres are sensory or motor or both. Nor does it divide motor centres into centres for representation of movements, and centres for coordination of movements; the two things — representation and coordination — are really one. The whole nervous system is a sensori-motor mechanism, a coordinating system from top to bottom." [The purely association sections of the cortex had not been identified in 1882.]

(5) A lowest motor centre is "one which represents some limited part of the body most nearly directly; . . is one of simplest yet compound coordination . . The sum of these representations in detail is the first, most direct representation of the whole body." "A middle [motor] centre represents over again in still more complex combinations what many or all of the lowest have represented in comparatively simple combinations, and thus represent a *less limited* part of the body. The middle centres are re-representative; they are centres of doubly compound coordination. . The sum of these representations is . . a doubly indirect representation of the whole organism." "The highest [motor] centres are . . re-re-representative; they represent parts of the body triply indirectly. They are centres of triply compound coordination. The sum of their representations is the third and triply indirect representation of the whole of the body." "The highest motor centres of each half of the nervous system represent both sides of the body." In each higher centre, there is "increase in complexity of representation of parts of the greater range represented, and increase in speciality of representation." Thus they have *range* — i.e., impression and movements of all parts of the body are represented; *complexity* — i.e., each unit represents the whole organism; *speciality* — i.e., each unit represents the whole organism differently from all other units.

Excerpted Passages†

(1) "*Evolution* is a passage from: 1. The most to the least organised," "from centres comparatively well organised at birth to those, the highest centres, which are continually organising throughout life." 2. "The most simple to the most

---

*From *Medical Press and Circular*, Vol. II, 1882.
†From Croonian Lectures, 1884. Printed in *Lancet, Brit. Med. J.,* and *Med. Times and Gazette.*

complex." 3. "The most automatic to the most voluntary." Thus, the highest centres "are the least organised, the most complex and the most voluntary."

"Dissolution is the reverse of the process of evolution." "It is a 'taking to pieces' in the order from the least organised, most complex and most voluntary, towards the most organised, most simple and most automatic." "The symptomatology of nervous disease is a double condition; there is a negative and there is a positive element in every case. Evolution not being entirely reversed, some level of evolution is left. . . 'To undergo dissolution' has the same meaning as 'to be reduced to a lower level of evolution.' " "I submit that disease only produces negative emotional symptoms answering to the dissolution, and that all positive mental symptoms (illusions, hallucinations, delusions, and extravagant conduct) are the outcome of activity of nervous elements untouched by any pathological process; that they arise during activity on the lower level of evolution remaining." As a concrete example, take Aphasia (speechlessness) ; it consists of loss of intellectual or more voluntary language, but persistence of emotional, the more automatic, language, including gesticulation.

(2) My doctrine of evolution implies that "there is a gradual 'adding on' of the more and more special, a continuing adding on of new organisations. But this 'adding on' is at the same time a 'keeping down.' The higher nervous arrangements evolved out of the lower keep down those lower. If this be the process of evolution, then the reverse process of dissolution is not only a 'taking off' of the higher, but is at the very same time a 'letting go' of the lower." Thus, "over-activity in epileptic mania and in other cases mentioned, is not caused, but is *permitted*; on cutting across the pneumogastric, the heart is not caused to go faster, but is permitted to go faster."

(3) "The activities of the highest, least organised nervous arrangements, during which consciousness, or most vivid consciousness arises, are determined by activities of lower, more organised nervous arrangements, I firmly believe. . . Roughly speaking, the highest nervous states are determined from below, and not by autocratic 'faculties' acting upon the highest parts of the highest centres." [JHJ here anticipates the ARAS, one of neuropsychology's most recent findings!]

Excerpted Passages‡

JHJ cites T. A. Ribôt as saying in his book on personality, "Le moi est une coordination."

"The centres of the lowest level are much more strongly organised than are those of the highest level. . A man [deeply comatose from sucking spirits out of a cask] whose highest level . . is rendered functionless by much alcohol rapidly taken, recovers because the 'vital' centres of his lowest level are very strongly organised and go on working, although imperfectly, when the comparatively weakly organised centres of his highest level have 'given out.' If the 'vital' centres of the lowest levels were not strongly organised at birth, life would not be possible; if the centres of the highest level ('mental centres') were not organised *and therefore very modifiable,* we could only with difficulty and imperfectly adjust ourselves to new circumstances and should make few acquirements. . . The highest layers are most easily rendered functionless by injurious agencies, such as alcohol, by great heat in febrile diseases, etc."§

‡From *J. Med. Sci.,* 1887.
§From *Lancet,* 1898.

Whether or not Nicholas Tinbergen was acquainted with Jackson's writings when he wrote his *Study of Instinct* (179) , I do not know, but his statement following tends to provide independent corroboration of Jackson's hierarchical principle since it is based on ethologists' observations of the behavior-patterns of chiefly fish and birds, forms which have the hypothalamus and striatum as the highest controlling motor centers. Tinbergen notes that the neural mechanisms underlying innate reactions of varying levels of complexity are arranged in a hierarchical schema with various associated levels of integration, and then he goes on to say,

> There is a hierarchical system of Innate Releasing Mechanisms and of motor centers. . . . Each motor center controls a *configuration pattern* of muscle contractions (p. 103). (Italics EM's.)

B. M. Patten, an embryologist, echoes ethologist Tinbergen's postulation in a table presenting the levels of the somatic-motor nervous system in the human being (144, p. 318):

Level	*Highest Mediating Center* (read up)	*Function or Behavior* (read up)
Arc 6:	Neocortex.	Voluntary and regulatory control.
Arc 5:	Basal ganglia (striatum).	Automatic associated control.
Arc 4:	Cerebellum plus mid-brain.	Synergic control (automatic control of muscle-movements).
Arc 3:	Cerebellum plus medulla plus cord.	Equilibratory control.
Arc 2:	Several spinal segments acting in co-ordination.	Intersegmental reflex.
Arc 1:	Only one spinal segment.	Intrasegmental reflex.

Denny-Brown postulates a slightly different neuraxial schema of integration of motor performance (41):

Level	*Mediating Center*	*Function or Behavior (read up)*
5	Neocortex.	Dominates the whole; *selects* items of behavior and modifies them in terms of projected reactions.
4	Hypothalamus.	Adds the elementary drive and internal-milieu homeostasis that results in total response in coarse, automatic form.
3	Cerebellum plus mid-brain plus subthalamus.	Reactions of level 2 modified by tactual and contactual responses from body surface.
2	Pons plus medulla.	Domination of level 1's reflex pattern in terms of wider postural reactions.
1	Spinal cord (segmental level).	Anatomically fixed synaptic coordination of agonists and antagonists.

His analysis of the behavioral implications of such an hierarchical arrangement of motor centers will be included in the next chapter.

J. F. Fulton, in the seventeenth edition of Howell's famous textbook, refers to the "levels of function" of the central component of the autonomic nervous system (56, p. 246). Each autonomic level above the spinal cord (medullary, pontine and hypothalamic) not only dominates level(s) lower; it also expresses more complex functions which depart from the reduplication and integration of lower-level functions. The progressively more complex ANS functions of spinal cord, medulla, mid-brain and hypothalamus have already been incorporated into Orientation Supplement 3A, but Fulton's table, page 460 in his book, is here reproduced separately in somewhat modified form.

Research in connection with schizophrenia strongly suggests that *another level should be added to Fulton's table*: the ANS is apparently also reduplicated on the cortex; more specifically, on a six-layered mesopallial area, number 24, the anterior cingulate gyrus, which is a powerful autonomic effector region and which has connections with a supplementary body-representation motor area (160, pp. 268 and 489). The anterior thalamic nuclei project to it, and it in turn projects back to them via the caudate nucleus, one of the basal ganglia (34).

Levels of Autonomic Function in the Central Nervous System
(after Fulton, 56)

Level	Function
Spinal cord	Autonomic reflexes (sweating, blood pressure, evacuation, sexual, vasomotor) will all return after spinal transection, eventually — but are more sluggish.
Medulla Oblongata	When the brain-stem is severed at the intercollicular level, decerebrate rigidity ensues, but many well-organized autonomic integrations continue, including: maintenance of blood pressure at normal level, responsiveness to reflex mechanisms such as those controlled by the carotid sinus, less sluggish vasomotor responses to heat and cold than in the spinal animal — but there is still limited capacity for heat regulation. Also, the individual can sneeze, cough, vomit and swallow, all of which involve simultaneous sequential discharge of the somatic and autonomic divisions.
Pons	If the brain-stem is severed so as to leave the mid-brain intact, ocular reflexes are retained: the pupil constricts in response to light; there is also consensual reaction of the pupils to light.

Hypothalamus The hypothalamus is the principal focus of integration of the entire autonomic system. In its forepart is primary parasympathetic representation; in its posterior part, sympathetic representation. Through interaction between these two areas, many complex integrations are carried out: heat regulation, regulation of water metabolism, other phases of general metabolism.

As for somatic-motor functions, Fulton's discussion of the increasing complexity and integration of spinal cord, cerebellum and basal ganglia have also been incorporated into Orientation Supplement 3, as was the same principle for the sensory functions of spinal cord, medulla, mid-brain and thalamus.

H. E. Himwich, a thoroughgoing Jacksonian who specializes in the chemical aspects of nervous functioning, has reported on the behavioral effects of insulin shock as higher to lower CNS centers are progressively "knocked out" (81, pp. 115 to 118):

(1) Elimination of the neocortex:

    (a) Negative symptoms: Distortion and waning of activities of the special senses, resulting in impairment of perception and retardation of recognition. Concentration is difficult. With loss of perception, recognition and attention, go memory and orientation. Coordination necessary for normal movements can no longer be mustered: awkwardness and ataxia occur, along with, for example, the inability of the hand to locate a desired object. Speech is also disturbed (a motor disturbance). The patient becomes increasingly somnolent, and environmental contact is lost.

    (b) Positive symptoms: The sensory thalamus, visceral hypothalamus, subcortical motor nuclei (basal ganglia) are the next highest layer left unaffected; *as the cortex goes out, their activity is released.* Hypothalamic release shows in a preponderance of sympathetic responses over parasympathetic: flushing of the skin, dilation of pupils, increase in heart-rate, rise in blood pressure. Somatic and visceral activities become endowed with an excessive affective tone — much like reaction to painful stimuli when the cortex is present. Effects of sensory-thalamus release are the same as for hypothalamic release. Liberation of subcortical motor nuclei results in motor restlessness, pursing of lips as in kissing, protrusion of the tongue, forced sucking, forced grasping, choreiform movements, fine myoclonic muscle-twitching.

(2) Elimination of basal ganglia, sensory thalamus and hypothalamus:

    (a) Positive symptoms: Release of mid-brain centers results in increase of tonus coming on in spasms, with flexion of arms and extension of trunk and legs. Acceleration of heart-rate, rise of blood pressure, dilation of pupils, occur during each spasm. The next phase starts with extensor spasms: the trunk is rigid, arms and legs are in maximal extension, but fingers, ankles and toes are flexed — the classical picture of decerebrate rigidity. The spasms are short and accompanied by a temporary preponderance of the sympathetic system.

(3) Elimination of neuraxis down to (but not including) the medulla:

    (a) Positive symptoms: Release of medulla is indicated by preponderance of parasympathetic activity over sympathetic — slow heartbeat, slow and shallow breathing, pallor, myosis, fall of body temperature. The muscles are profoundly relaxed, tendon jerks are depressed, the corneal reflex is lost. This phase is very risky: it should not be continued for more than fifteen minutes, since life cannot be maintained if the medulla is eliminated.

Intravenous glucose restores the activities of each of these "layers" in a *reverse* direction. Himwich concludes his report with the statement that the cerebral neocortex may be regarded as that part of the brain which contains the highest sensory re-representation which is necessary for environmental contact.

As already indicated in Chapter III, Herrick also accepts Jackson's concept of successively higher functional levels in the neuraxis, but incorporates it into a more complex organizational schema of his own. He divides the nervous system into two basic functional systems, "analytic" and "integrative" (each subserved by structurally different types of neural networks, referred to in Chapter III also), and postulates six levels of structural and functional complexity for the two roles of the latter system. His schema has already been presented. (Please see pages 48-9.)

Arieti utilizes Jacksonian concepts to account for the symptomatology of schizophrenia, *viz.*:

> In schizophrenia there is an altered functionality of the [old cortex]. . . . If we follow again Hughlings Jackson's principles, a *hypo*functionality of neopallic areas should be accompanied by a release and *hyper*functionality of the archipallium. Such a syndrome presents negative symptoms, caused by hypofunctionality of highest levels, and positive symptoms, caused by the prominence of released lower centers. . . . Dysencephalization, the reverse of encephalization, seems to occur in schizophrenia (9, p. 422-3) .

Jackson's hierarchical thesis is so taken for granted by neurophysiologists that the adjective "Jacksonian" is routinely used to refer to this principle in the literature.

A major factor contributing to the hierarchical-reduplicative schema is a consistent patterning of nerve-tract connections in the neuraxis. Each of the major nerve centers, with only minor exceptions:

(1) sends impulses *to* centers above (if any) via ascending (sensory) nerve-tracts and *to* centers below (if any) via descending (motor) tracts;

(2) receives projections *from* centers above (if any) via descending tracts and *from* centers below (if any) via ascending tracts;

(3) within each major nerve-center, a specific nucleus (or neocortical area) sends impulses to other nuclei (or areas) of the same complex nerve center, and receives impulses from other nuclei (or areas) of the same center, via interconnecting tracts.

Each of the nine major CNS nerve centers — spinal cord, medulla, pons and cerebellum, mid-brain, hypothalamus, thalamus, basal ganglia, old cortex, neocortex — may thus have anywhere from three to six of these categories of connecting tracts, not allowing for the two kinds of sensory and motor tracts, diffuse and specific.

This intra-CNS formulation should not be interpreted as either overlooking or excluding those nerve-tracts which connect various central loci with the periphery. The recent discovery of modifying-in-effect efferents from the mid-brain to the various receptor cells provides a specific example of how much more complex than previously conceived are central-peripheral interconnections. These connections are further gone into in the next chapter.

Nor does this formulation mean to ignore the existence of both myelinated and unmyelinated connecting tracts, within the CNS as well as between the CNS and the PerNS. The discovery of diffuse afferent and efferent unmyelinated connecting systems, existing side by side and/or overlapping with the more specific-in-distribution myelinated motor and sensory pathways indicates what is in actuality another type of phylogenetically derived duplication, one which Herrick anticipated in his functional division of the nervous system into integrative and analytic systems. The older, diffuse nerve-net type of structure and electrical transmission has been retained by the human nervous system along with the more recently evolved, more focused, more specialized and directly highest-center-associated connections.

This dual diffuse and specific pathways arrangement, and the key role played in its activity and coordination by the brain-stem reticular formation (BSRF; to be gone into under Pattern 2), have together led Livingston, the neurophysiologist, to group the interconnecting neural pathways into a different sort of schema than heretofore presented. He identifies the following six conduction systems in the CNS (111):

(1) the classical, lemniscal, myelinated ascending sensory pathways to the primary-sensory receiving areas of the neo-cortex;

(2) the parallel, extralemniscal, unmyelinated ascending sensory pathways via the BSRF to more widespread regions of the cerebral cortex;

(3) centrifugal, "sensory control" motor mechanisms which seem to involve fibers going in reverse direction to (1) and (2)

and which may implicate, through the BSRF, projections from cerebral and cerebellar loci;

(4) the brain-stem reticular formation as such, which exerts modifying influences upward upon both cerebral and cerebellar hemispheres and downward upon both sensory and motor synaptic relays;

(5) the classical pyramidal (corticospinal) myelinated descending motor pathways, projecting directly from neocortex to lower moto-neuron aggregates;

(6) the parallel, extra-pyramidal, unmyelinated motor pathways, descending to the motor nuclei indirectly — by way of basal ganglia and the BSRF.

In Herrick's terminology, systems 1, 3, 5 subserve analytic functions, while systems 2, 4, 6 subserve integrative functions. All six conducting systems are interdependent and are knitted together at subcortical levels in the BSRF. This circumstance was discovered only recently because of previous experimental use of central anesthesia; also, the usual staining techniques do not make the fibers of the diffuse networks visible.

It is this exceedingly complex maze of interconnecting nerve-tracts, here merely pointed to, that contributes to one of the two necessary qualifications of the hierarchical-reduplicative functional-organization pattern — and possibly to both. Such qualifications comprise functional-organization patterns 2 and 3, discussed in the two following chapters. Also, Jackson's ontogenetic dictum, already cited in Chapter III, of the "continuous reduction of succession to co-existences," must be applied when the hierarchical-reduplicative pattern is related to neural functioning *at any one moment in time.*

At the top of Jackson's functional hierarchy is the cerebral neocortex. So much more is known about this most recently evolved part of the neuraxis now than at Jackson's time, an updated description of key aspects of its structural and functional characteristics must be added to this heretofore Jackson-dominated discussion.

THE CEREBRAL CORTEX

Brain-mapping of cortical functions is no longer the simple topological matter it was considered not long ago to be because of:

(1) The high degree of functional interdependence of every level of the neuraxis with every other level and with the peripheral nervous system; and of the nervous system with the organism's chemical order of functioning (these findings are serving to re-emphasize how unsatisfactory a word "psychosomatic" continues to be, with its reification rather than elimination of the old mind-body dichotomy) ;

(2) A much greater degree of cortical-area overlap of sensory, motor and association functions and of visceral and somatic sensory projections, than was earlier appreciated; mapping of sensory areas is now approached in terms of termination-points of nerve-tract projections from specific sub-cortical centers, especially the thalamus (11).

Two cautionary reminders by Hebb are especially germane at this point:

> [When] reference is made to "cortical processes," [it is] usually a brief way of saying "higher processes in which the cortex is essentially involved." The cortex, in other words, is not a functional system in itself; and when we speak of cortical processes, what we mean is cortico-thalamic processes (or cortico-subcortical), since there are probably other subcortical structures also involved (75, p. 83).

> No psychological function can exist within a segment of the cortex by itself. We commonly say that vision is located in the visual area, a part of the occipital lobe; but this does not mean that the whole process of seeing (or even of visual imagery) can occur in the occipital lobe. What it means is that *an essential part of the process occurs there, and only there.* Speech is "localized" in the cerebral cortex on the left side (for most persons). This again does not mean that the mediating processes of speech can occur in that tissue alone; it does mean that their organization depends on it (p. 83).

Well, then! *Which* functional principle obtains in the cortex, localization *or* equipotentiality?

Before answering this misleadingly phrased question, a brief overview of the apparently contradictory findings which made it for many years a major neuropsychological issue is in order. On the one hand, a high degree of equipotentiality is indicated by these characteristics of the matured cortex: (1) there is a marked capacity for the specialized function of injured or extirpated sections to be taken over by the remaining cortical tissue, and (2) there is, as we have seen, a far greater degree of cortical-area overlap of sensory, motor and association functions and of visceral and somatic projections from the thalamus, than the earlier, precise-boundary brain-mappers had realized. Also, Lashley's early emphasis on equipotentiality was based on extirpation studies on the far less complex rat cortex (See cortical phylogenetic trends, summarized in Table 1C.)

On the other hand, localization of function is indicated by these findings: (1) injury to certain primary-sensory and primary-motor areas eliminates entirely its behavioral correlate — e.g., blindness when the primary-visual area is damaged, and (2) if a cortical area having a specialized function is injured or extirpated before, during, or shortly after birth, the sensory or motor or association behavior dependent upon that area does not emerge as the cortex matures.

As might be anticipated from the circumstance that — continuing to use Herrick's terminology — the analytic system and the integrative system are closely intermingled in the neocortex, the former with its delimited and specialized functional style and the latter with its general and diffuse modus operandi, the long-standing argument as to whether there is localization *or* equipotentiality of function is being resolved in the classical manner pointed to by Tinbergen: *both* principles, localization *and* equipotentiality, obtain! It is now correct to speak of a few foci of functional specialization, supplemented by concepts of statistical probability of neuronal excitation within homogeneous regions (166; 72).

Recourse to the developmental perspective also helps to resolve the old contradiction. Initially, the intact presence of the various function-specific areas of cortical tissue is essential for its particular sensory or motor or association function to emerge as neocortical maturation proceeds. But after that specialized bit of cortical tissue has begun to function and has as a result established a complex network of interconnections with all layers, with other areas of the cortex, and with sub-cortical centers, both these interconnections *and* the overlap principle provide for the spread of its function well beyond its own originally delimited focus.

Maps of cortical-area function would accordingly seem to have their greatest applicability to the young child's cortex. Certainly, speculation as to behavioral implications is provoked by such interesting topological findings as the following (8, pp. 1620-57) :

(1) the areas mediating the sensibility of the corner of the mouth and of the thumb are directly adjacent to each other;

(2) the areas which mediate touch overlap with visual areas, and

(3) the areas which mediate handedness and the motor aspects of speech are directly adjacent to each other.

As for the functional arrangement of the two cerebral hemispheres, a similar argument has gone on, this one related to specialization versus duplication: does each half of the cortex have a unique function or do the two halves duplicate each other, functionally? The evidence is that, again, *both* principles obtain: certain functions are specific to only one side, while other functions are represented on both sides.

The two parts of Figure 4, following, together show the gross sensory, motor and association functional "divisions" of the neocortex. The most frontal section of the frontal lobe in both diagrams should be designated the prefrontal - PF - area.

The four basic anatomical divisions of the neocortex are the frontal, parietal, occipital and temporal lobes. The central fissure, which runs across the top of the two hemispheres almost from ear to ear, is the usual point of departure for discussing cerebral functions, both because it provides the anatomical demarcation of the frontal lobe from the parietal lobe and because its front and back walls and long strip-areas immediately to the front and the back of it are the first cortical areas that begin to function after birth.

Parietal Lobe. Its overall function is to provide a picture of what is going on in and on the body. It is primarily somatosensory, viscero-sensory, and sensory-associative in function. It receives projections from the thalamus; and the primary somatoviscerosensory area, like the thalamus, has a dermatomal representation of the whole body.

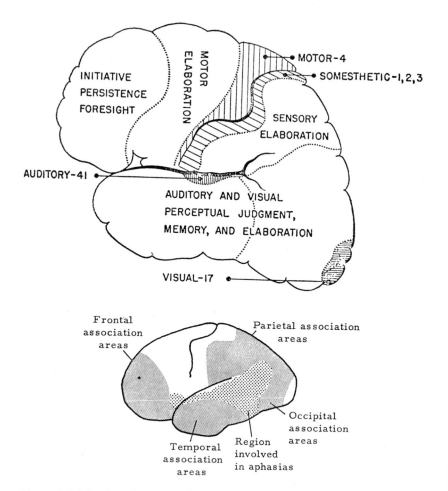

Figure 4. Major functional divisions of the human neocortex. Two diagrams of the lateral surface of the left cerebral neocortex highlighting the association (or "elaboration") areas. In Figure 4B, with the exception of the frontal striped area, all shaded areas both striped and stippled comprise the "T-O-P association area."

Figure 4A is from 78, page 417, and is reproduced by courtesy of the University of Texas Press. Figure 4B is from 59, and is reproduced by courtesy of W. B. Saunders and the author, Ernest Gardner.

Frontal Lobe. (a) Posterior sections. The first two areas directly forward of the central (Rolandic) fissure mediate all voluntary motor behavior. The body is represented part by part in the motor cortex; the size of cortical area devoted to each part is proportional to the discreteness and exactness of the movement involved rather than to the size of the part's muscle-mass. Another area makes speech possible. Another area mediates movements of the eyeballs and acts as a visual association area, integrating stimuli from the eye muscles and from the retinae (projected to it from the visual cortex), and appears to play a role in the focusing and maintenance of attention. Two further body-projection motor areas have been located recently in the frontal lobe.

(b) Pre- (*or* orbito-) frontal sections. A prefrontal area is the primary respiratory center of the cortex, along with other autonomic-integration functions; it is one of the two neocortical areas entering into the "limbic system," to be discussed in the next chapter. The gyrus cinguli is usually grouped with the frontal lobe, although it is meso- (*or* paleo-) cortex, not neo-cortex; it is also part of the limbic system, and is reciprocally connected with the anterior thalamic nuclei. The prefrontal (PF) association area performs life-essential autonomic regulations, mediates affective reactions to pain, is the seat of recent memory. Its ablation or injury results in impaired learning ability as well as in a number of personality changes which vary from person to person. Foresight and the pursuit of long-term goals seem also to depend upon the PF area.

Occipital Lobe. It is necessary for seeing the external world and for recognizing what is seen. It is primarily visuosensory in function; the reaction of the pupil to light is the only visual function not mediated by the visual cortex.

Temporal Lobe. It is necessary for hearing, for understanding what is heard, for maintenance of body-balance in space, for speech comprehension (left lobe), and for visual appreciation and discrimination and manipulation of form and spatial relationships (right lobe) (123). Penfield has located "stream of consciousness" affective-memory centers in it (145); it also has other complex intellectual and emotional activities yet to be fully identified.

Since determining the functions of the neocortex, especially of the sheerly association areas, is currently an active research frontier, the foregoing summary (originally drawn from a variety of sources but ultimately checked against 160) cannot be taken as definitive.

For the purpose of future reference, another, more detailed, brain-map diagram — of the monkey brain — is here inserted as Figure 5. It combines incompletely both of neurophysiology's customary ways of referring to specific areas of the cortex: the Brodmann number system and the Campbell double-letter system (in which the first letter stands for the lobe). It is taken from reference 160, and is reproduced by courtesy of the publisher.

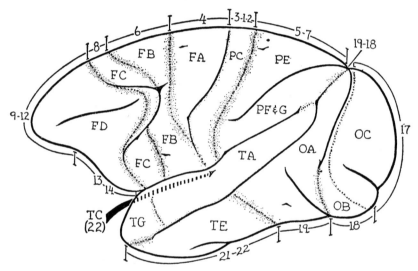

Figure 5. Cytoarchitectural map of monkey brain. This diagram is a copy of Figure 138 in 160, and is reproduced by courtesy of W. B. Saunders, Philadelphia.

Herrick's description of the entire amphibian brain *vis à vis* the intimate structural and functional relationships between the integrative and analytic networks applies with only slight modification to these same relationships *within* the human neocortex; this description provides a good introduction to a discussion of *the cortex's internal pattern of organization* (especially significant passages have been italicized) :

> The nervous elements concerned with the analytic functions are generally recognizable, and among these nerve cells and fibers there are others that are integrative in function. The latter form a very closely woven fabric of interlaced thin naked fibers, the neuropil. *The bodies of all nerve cells and their widely spread dendritic branches are embedded within this fibrous mat and closely enveloped by it.* . . . This web of neuropil permeates the entire [neocortex] and acts as a nonspecific conducting system which puts every part of the brain into physiological connection with every other part. It is the primary integrating mechanism, but it is much more than this. *It is germinative tissue with potentialities for further differentiation in an endless variety of ways* (78, p. 249) .

Second only to the dual cellular arrangement to which Herrick points, the most obvious intrastructural characteristic of the neocortex is its horizontal, multilayered organization, each layer distinguishable on the basis of distinctive cellular characteristics. Although six is the consensus, there is some disagreement in the literature as to the exact number of layers, perhaps because they vary in thickness and in relative degree of development in different sections of the cortex (160, page 248) . These layers have both a phylogenetic and an embryological history, as data in Tables IC and IIC have shown. By convention, the numbering of each layer departs from the surgeon's or dissector's perspective and so proceeds from the outside in. That is, the layer closest to the skull is designated 1, and the deepest layer, directly contiguous with the cerebral medulla, is numbered 6. However, the gradient of layer development is in diametrically reverse direction to this numbering order; the layers will be discussed here in their *developmental* sequence.

Motor tracts originate in the two deepest layers (6 and 5), as do association fibers and the hemispheres-connecting fibers of the corpus callosum (8, p. 1570). The two latter types of fibers are now thought to terminate in several layers (160, p. 251). The axons of the spindle-shaped cells in layer 6 go down into the cerebral medulla and their dendrites go up into layers

3 and 2. The axons of the large and medium pyramidal cells in layer 5 (which also has many of the star-shaped cells typical of layer 4) also go down into the cerebral medulla (160, p. 250). Layer 4 is composed of many multipolar cells with short branching axons which give them a star-like appearance. It is a receptive layer, receiving the endings of specific thalamic afferents in sensory sections of the cortex (160, p. 250). This layer is especially rich in its blood supply and in oxydase ferment and is a major matrix for cell-connecting proliferations (8, p. 1572).

Experimental evidence "suggests strongly that the upper [three] cortical layers form a unit in themselves" (8, p. 1571). These are the layers which differentiate from the supragranular layer during embryology; this layer is by far the thickest in man, as pointed out in Table 1C. Layer 3 is a thick layer in most parts of the cortex and is made up of large pyramidal cells. It is frequently subdivided; for example, Conel, whose material is extensively drawn on in Part D, refers to layers 3a, 3b, 3c. In this designation arrangement, 3a is the highest subsection, directly contiguous with layer 2, and 3c is the deepest section, directly contiguous with layer 4.

Layer 2 is made up of both small pyramidal cells and the small starlike cells with short branching axons which are also present in layers 4 and 5. The apical dendrites of the cells at the lower boundary of layer 2 go upward into layer 1, "forming the basis of intracortical association;" the basal dendrites go down to the cerebral medulla (160, p. 250). Layer 1 has few cell-bodies, being made up chiefly of dendrites and axons from neurons deeper in the cortex; there may be significant functional ramifications from the circumstance that layer 1 receives many fibers from layer 5, which in turn receives many fibers from the cingulum, which plays a major role in man's affective life. Layer 1 also receives collaterals from the nonspecific thalamocortical afferents, which terminate in blocks of cortex and then run horizontally through the layer (160).

Very many vertical and horizontal fibers originating both outside and inside the cortex are found in the various layers. Horizontal fibers, which are believed to be concerned with higher associative functions, have been estimated as continuing to increase up to at least thirty-eight years of age (8, p. 1576).

There are a great many cells with short axons in the human neocortex; Cájàl's assumption that such cells provide for the delicacy of function of man's brain is now taken as fact (160, p. 252).

The distinctive functional contributions of the multiple-layering pattern has not yet been firmly determined. Such suggestive speculation as the following does exist, however:

> Studies on the development of the cortex and reviews of clinical cases indicate that the outer layers of the cortex are those most particularly concerned with the highest associative activities of the cortex, since failure of these layers to develop or their softening, is accompanied in man by a marked decrease in the intelligence coefficient of the individual (8, p. 1665).

My own speculations are in line with Jackson's principle of repeated re-representation up the neuraxis together with a "continuing adding-on of new organizations" with each reduplication. That is, the six-layered neocortex adds not one, but *six* more functional levels to the human neuraxis: layer 6 re-represents all *sub*cortical levels, layer 5 re-represents layer 6, layer 4 re-represents layer 5, and so on up to layer 1, which re-represents all representations below it. This schema would account for a number of heretofore puzzling cortical characteristics. It helps explain the brain's remarkable ability to recover functionally after damage. If the re-representation is not isomorphic, that is, topographically precisely duplicated from bottom to top layer, which I believe it is not, then the overlapping of functional areas that has been consistently observed would also be explained.

Goody's criticism of the point by point stimulation technique as a means of ascertaining localization of function becomes especially germane in this context; he points out that this technique reveals only isolated "bits" of a particular unit of behavior, never the whole, integrated behavior-pattern that is actually what occurs *in situ*. For example, speech involves the coordination of many cortical foci, both vertical and horizontal; the point stimulation technique has evoked sounds but never speech (65).

Phylogenetically, the supragranular layer (from which layers 3 and 2 and possibly also 1 are derived) is an exclusively mammalian acquisition, while its further sub-division into layers 3, 2, 1? is an exclusively human characteristic. Is alert conscious awareness mediated by layers 3 and 2? This functional role does not exclude subcortical contributions to alert consciousness, specifically the ascending reticular activating system (ARAS), to be described in the next chapter.

This conception of the functional role of the layering pattern would also provide for the successively higher levels of adaptive behavior that emerge as postnatal development proceeds — from the first sensorimotor coordinations of the first months of life, to ideation and ideational integration at neural maturity. It is tempting to speculate that Piaget's postulated stages in the development of "intelligence" (148) are directly correlated with the postnatal onset of functioning in the various ascending layers of the neocortex. This possible relationship will be kept in mind when postnatal neural and behavioral developments are examined in Part D.

It is also tempting to speculate that *vocalization* is mediated by the three lower layers (6, 5, 4) of the cortical speech areas, while *verbalization,* i.e., speech, is mediated by the upper layers. Both phylogenetic and clinical data suggest this possibility. This question will also be kept in mind for later reference: does speech emerge postnatally as layer 3 becomes functional? It may also be that sensorimotor coordinations are mediated by the lower layers of the T-O-P association area, while the upper layers of the same area make possible increasingly refined perceptual discriminations.

Concerning layer 1, the circumstance that it receives many connections direct from layer 5, which in turn receives many projections from the cingulum, the part of the mesopallium which is six-layered and which Cobb describes as important in the human individual's affective life (36), becomes most suggestive within the re-representation schema here hypothesized. If layer 1 mediates the fully conscious, "willing" and "feeling" self, may the phenomenon of hypnosis be explained as the hypnotist's temporarily taking over the functional role of the top cortical layer?

Conel points out that the layering or horizontal organization of neurons in the neocortex is supplemented by striation, a discontinuous-vertical cellular arrangement at direct right angles to the horizontal pattern and with no direct contact between the horizontally and vertically arranged cells anywhere in the cortex (38, Vol V). Although this dual pattern is clearly evident by six fetal months (the layering pattern emerges a month earlier, at five months), Conel does not refer to the striation arrangement as being a dominant neocortical characteristic until fifteen months after birth, in Volume V of his so far seven-volume histological investigation of the postnatal cerebral cortex. He goes on to speculate, concerning the functional correlates of this horizontal cum vertical structural arrangement,

> It suggests an adaptation to diametrically opposed forces, as in an electro-magnetic field (38, Vol. V, p. 202).

It it possible that the vertical cellular organization provides for a kind of "sedimentation" process, whereby recent experience, which is originally mediated by higher layers and registered, in Hebb's terminology, as a phase-sequence (72), gravitates down to the bottom layers, *spreading in locus as it does so?* Such a process would mean that layers 6 and 5 serve as a memory "reservoir" for current functioning. If a current experience is frequently repeated, or if, even though happening only once, it has great affective meaning for the individual, the higher-to-lower connections become well established and such experiences later are readily accessible memories. If the experience occurred only once or a few times and at the time was affectively neutral, connections between higher and lower layers would be tenuous and not readily accessible, memory-wise. Interestingly enough, the deepest layers are the only ones which continue to function during (lighter) sleep: "To sleep, perchance to dream . . "?

The remarkably complex cellular organization just described means that functionally, every part of the cortex can both originate and receive impulses, and is in potential contact with every other part of the cortex, as well as with all subcortical centers. A particular cortical afferent can relate to a cortical efferent in a variety of ways: it can go directly via one fiber to one cortical efferent; it can effect multisynaptic connections with an efferent; it can form, through recurrent collaterals from both afferents and efferents, circular chains capable of reexcitation or reverberation, i.e., "feedback circuits" (104). Although more extended analysis of the important behavioral correlates of the last functional mode itemized is being reserved for the second functional-organization pattern, it is evident from the description already given why the physiological and the behavioral universes of discourse, until recently kept rigidly separate, have begun not merely to come closer together, but to overlap.

The electrical activity of the neocortex is another of its unique characteristics. Berger's invention in 1925 of the electroencephalograph, an electronic device which records that activity, has provided a valuable new technique for studying the *in situ* nervous system. Several references have already been made to data derived through use of the EEG. Since some degree of technical knowledge of electrical activity as an index of neurophysiological, and especially of neocortical, functioning is necessary for the appreciation of such data (and there are more to come), the last in this monograph's series of orientation supplements is here inserted.

ORIENTATION SUPPLEMENT 6

ELECTRICAL ACTIVITY, INDEX OF
NEUROPHYSIOLOGICAL FUNCTIONING

A. The physiological index of neural functioning is, at the single-unit level, the nerve impulse, and at the macrophysiological level is the record of potentials arising from myriad neurons. It is the latter record, usually obtained through the electroencephalograph (EEG), an electronic brainwave recording device, which is significant for behavioral purposes. A brief overview of the key characteristics of both levels, and their respective methodological considerations, follows.

B. *The Microphysiological Level* (chiefly from 45)

   (1) The individual neuron is functionally specialized, like so:

   (Sensory)   (cell-body)   (Motor)

→   Dendrite   →   Soma   →   Axon   →   [Synapse → next neuron]

That is, the dendrite and the soma have a receptive function, and the axon and its branching collaterals have a motor, effecting function. Note that one neuron is not in direct physical contact with the adjoining one: there is an intervening, microscopically small gap between, termed the synapse (*viz.* Cájàl's neuron theory).

   (2) It is the very thin surface-membrane of the neuron which is functionally significant. This membrane has high electrical resistance and capacity and low chemical ionic permeability. The membrane-ionic hypothesis, following, is the currently accepted explanation for the propagation of the nerve impulse along a neuron and for its transmission across synapses. The nerve-membrane is polarized in such a way that its inner surface is negative to its outer surface in the resting cell. Potassium and sodium, and apparently also calcium, are the

chemical ions involved in this opposite polarization and in the selective permeability of the membrane to the propagation of the nerve impulse. An "adequate stimulus" initiates the reversal of this polarity and an electrical current is set up which causes polarity reversal in the immediately adjoining membrane area. That is, each area of polarity-reversal acts as a stimulus to successive sections of the nerve-membrane. This self-propagating, chemically mediated electrical change along the nerve-cell membrane is the *nerve impulse*. The potential difference between the external and internal surfaces of the membrane at the moment of reversal of polarization can be technically recorded; this difference is termed the *spike potential*. A *negative after-potential* succeeds the spike potential, and a *positive after-potential* succeeds the negative after-potential; all these potentials are recordable. These three phases of the nerve impulse together constitute a neuron's *action-potential* — a process involving the use of oxygen, formation of carbon dioxide and liberation of heat. Summary table:

Action	1.	spike potential)	in
Poten-	2.	negative after-potential)	ser-
tial	3.	positive after-potential)	ies

(3) The transmission of the nerve impulse across a synapse occurs not through the direct spread of electrical current from the activated cell, but by liberation of chemical substances from the pre-synaptic membrane, initiated by the nerve impulse itself. These chemical substances affect the ionic permeability of the sub-synaptic membrane, which in turn initiates ionic fluxes across the gap, which in turn cause the postsynaptic currents in the next cell.

(4) At the synapse, the nerve impulse may be passed on unchanged or augmented in strength — termed "excitatory synaptic action"; or it may be weakened in strength or even suppressed — termed "inhibitory synaptic action." Which one it is, is determined by the type of chemical substance which is liberated from the presynaptic membrane. Acetylcholine (Ach) is an excitatory substance in some CNS synapses only; none of the inhibitory substances had been isolated in 1959. It is currently believed that there are only two types of CNS nerve cells on the basis of the substances they release — excitatory or inhibitory.

(5) Nerves conduct at differential rates which depend upon: nerve-fiber diameter (larger — faster) and myelination status (unmyelinated — slower) (59).

(6) Some sensory and motor neurons *initiate* in autogenous fashion a series of rapid, repetitive impulses; such neurons are termed *pacemakers*. (173)

C. Subcortical CNS Mass Neuronal Activity

(1) Autogenous activity in addition to individual "pacemaker" neurons in the PerNS and spinal cord, is also evident in some brain centers. The respiratory center in the medulla, which emits periodic bursts of impulses, is one example; "activating" nuclei in the brain stem reticular formation, affecting the individual's degree of consciousness and alertness (through influence on the neocortex) is another example; the pain and reinforcing centers at various points in the neuraxis, including the old cortex, are additional examples.

(2) The neocortex apparently does not contain any of its own autogenous centers: nerve-tract interruption between neocortex and sub-cortex rapidly results in the elimination of characteristic electrical activity in all neocortical centers (i.e., the neocortex is the "driver," while lower centers are the "engine").

D. Neocortical Electrical Activity

Methodological (Electroencephalographic) Aspects

(1) Synchrony, a feature of the slow component of neuronal activity, is detectable by macro-electrodes, while asynchronous spikes are detectable by micro-electrodes. Hence micro- and macro- electrodes serve as complementary recording devices (51).

(2) Progress in EEG engineering are summarizable historically as follows (25):

Two electrodes placed on uncut animal cortex: Caton, 1875.

Recording of the human brain's action potentials through the intact skull through use of the vacuum tube in electronic amplifiers: Berger, 1925.

Design of instruments for automatic frequency analysis: Walter, the 1940s.

More refined analyzing and recording techniques which have permitted detection of slow fluctuations of steady potential, previously obscured by circuits with resistance-capacitance coupling: the 1950s.

EEG reordings are still based on the two-electrode principle, but now, multi-electrode placements on several locations permit simultaneous recording from several brain-areas. Eight-channel recording was adopted during the late 1940s (the latest machines are 16-channel), permitting a wide variety of brain-maps or "montages." Recording technique is a major factor in evaluating the adequacy of research utilizing the EEG: accurate placement of "leads" on the skull-surface is most important. Usual lead locations: two hemispherically matched prefrontals, two motor-frontals, a vertex, two parietals, two occipitals, two anterior and two posterior temporals, one mid-forehead (optional), lobe of each ear, ground lead to mastoid bone (46).

Galambos states flatly, concerning the use of the EEG in animal research, "Wires implanted upon or in the brain are for several seasons far superior to scalp electrodes, and when such eletrodes are permanently glued to the skull and attached to a suitable plug through which connection to an EEG machine can be used at any time the experimenter desires, the most reliable preparation for brain-wave recording will be achieved" (58).

(3) Overbreathing, photic stimulation, induction of sleep, use of drugs, are the various techniques which have been used deliberately to induce electrical changes in the brain; each one yields different types of clinical information (25).

Its Characteristics

(1) The intrinsic electrical activity of the brain can be classified into three types (25):

Shifts in potential evoked by nerve impulses (which are initiated by changes in the organism's internal and/or external environment). The two types of sensory pathways to the brain, direct, and indirect via the BSRF, produce different EEG patterns when they reach the cortex.

A difference in potential between the grey cortical surface and the white matter below it, always present.

The oscillating potential of the brain-surface itself — brain-waves — recorded by the EEG. This is the type of electrical activity which has been most investigated. Brain waves and potentials are indicators of fluctuation in excitability of cortical neurons and are therefore related to neuron metabolism. Changes in the electrical patterning of the cortex appear to be dependent upon the meaning of the sensory stimuli to the subject (91).

(2) Brain waves have been classified into four types according to their frequency in the adult (186):

(a) *Alpha* rhythms: frequency of 8-13 cycles-per-second, with 10 cps the mode. They are most pronounced in the occipital (visual) area of the neocortex, are believed to be synchronous discharges of occipital-lobe neurons, and do not become the dominant rhythm until after six years of age for most persons. They show up most strongly when the eyes are closed, excluding external visual patterns, and are "associated with the inattentive state, occurring in regions of the brain which are playing no part in mental activity because attention is directed elsewhere" (91). Attention to visual processes which are meaningful to the individual arrests the A-rhythm. There has been a good deal of research done on the characteristics of the A-rhythm, and the reader is referred to Walter's article for further data.

(b) *Theta* rhythms: frequency of 4-7 cps. They are prominent in the parietal and temporal regions, are associated with the early and middle childhood developmental periods, and also show up during states of emotional stress in some adults.

(c) *Delta* rhythms: frequency of less than 1½-3 cps. They are associated with infancy, with deep sleep in adults, and with organic brain-disease.

(d) *Beta* rhythms: frequency of 14 cps and higher. They are associated with activation and muscular tension. Walter describes them as the "faster components of theta waves" and as "common in tension, whether acute or in the form of chronic anxiety states" (184). The B-rhythm is blocked by tactile stimulation or voluntary movement (91).

(3) The apical dendrites of pyramidal cells going from the deeper to the upper layers of the neocortex have been found (a) to be significant in the EEG, and (b) to behave electrically not at all like the peripheral n.s. nerves. Their normal activity consists chiefly of nonpropagated, *graded* potentials spreading decrementally from the point at which the stimulus is received. These non-propagated potentials are of long duration, have no refractory period, reflect the strength of the initiating stimulus — that is, are *not* all-or-nothing in character, and can sum with any consequent potentials before they die away. This is the reason why "no experience finds the organism in the same condition twice" (25).

(4) Spike discharges from cortical dendrites are characteristic only of infancy and of the excessive discharge of epilepsy, not of the normal brain. Their absence in the normal brain is due to the presence of certain inhibitory-in-function interneurons, as well as to sub-cortical influences (25).

(5) All EEG workers have noticed that changes in states of consciousness are accompanied by alterations in electrical potentials. Electrical stimulation of the central reticular core of the mid-brain has an arousing effect similar to the alerting evoked by stimulation of peripheral sensory receptors, and this transition from sleep to arousal is invariably accompanied by an EEG shift from slow waves of high voltage to fast waves of low voltage. This diffuse ascending reticular activating system acts to keep the cortex in an "appropriate state of facilitation or inhibition for processing of the impulses received via specific sensory routes." The recruiting response — the evocation of a successive increase in amplitude of response over widespread areas of the neocortex — appears as the result of repeated stimulation of the nonspecific ascending diencephalic system at a rate close to that of the brain's intrinsic rhythms (25).

(6) Several parameters of the electroencephalogram in addition to dominant frequency show consistent changes with development. These developmental changes are summarized in Chapter VIII, Table VI.

E. *Gross Behavioral Correlates*

(1) D. B. Lindsley has provided a succinct summary of the EEG patterns associated with various psychological states and gross behavior patterns; this table is here reproduced in slightly modified form (109, 110).

Behavioral Continuum	State of Awareness	Behavioral Efficiency	EEG Patterns
Strong, excited emotion: fear, rage, anxiety.	Restricted awareness, divided attention; diffuse, hazy; "confusion."	Poor: lack of control, freezing up, disorganized.	Desynchronized: low to moderate amplitude; fast mixed frequencies.
Alert attentiveness.	Selective attention, but may vary or shift; "concentration," anticipation; "set."	Good: efficient, selective, quick reactions: organized for serial responses.	Partially synchronized: mainly fast, low-amplitude waves.
Relaxed wakefulness.	Attention wanders — not forced; favors free association.	Good: routine reactions and creative thought.	Synchronized: optimal alpha rhythm.

Behavioral Continuum	State of Awareness	Behavioral Efficiency	EEG Patterns
Drowsiness.	Borderline partial awareness; imagery and reverie; "dreamlike" states.	Poor: uncoordinated, sporadic, lacking sequential timing.	Reduced alpha and occasional low-amplitude slow waves.
Light sleep.	Markedly reduced consciousness (loss of consciousness) ; "dream state."	Absent.	Spindle bursts and slow waves (larger); loss of alphas.
Deep sleep.	Complete loss of awareness (no memory for stimulation or for dreams) .	Absent.	Large and very slow waves (synchrony but on slow time bases) ; random, irregular pattern.
Coma.	Complete loss of consciousness; little or no response to stimulation; amnesia.	Absent.	Isoelectric to irregular slow waves.
Death.	Complete loss of awareness as death ensues.	Absent.	Isoelectric: gradual and permanent disappearance of all electrical activity.

Chapter VI

THE FUNCTIONAL SUBCIRCUITS
PATTERN

Recent research of both neurophysiologists and physiological psychologists, independently and in collaboration, provides the basis for the second functional-organization pattern. The mammalian nervous system is now seen as made up of countless overlapping unilevel and multilevel functional subsystems or "circuits," many of them closed-loop or reverberatory in character, each of which functions as an organized whole *and* with the rest of the nervous system in an instantaneous and coherent manner. Although these subsystems are primarily central in locus and regulatory in function, the essential contributory role of peripheral neural structures is expressly acknowledged.

If one were able to observe directly the functioning of the entire *in situ* nervous system — that is, the passage of nerve impulses — for a limited period of time, one would see a bewilderingly complex series of spatially overlapping patterns of activity: a clustering of activity in one or more delimited regions of the central and the peripheral nervous systems; an extremely rapid series of impulses darting up and down the full length of the neuraxis in patterns too complex for the eye to follow; intense and sustained activity involving two or more neuraxial centers — a picture made famous by Sherrington's often-quoted "magic-loom" portrayal.

Certainly there is nothing under our observation to suggest the hierarchical organization pattern that has just been presented! But another kind of pattern *is* evident upon closer, more discerning inspection of the loom's activity: there are many, many, both discrete and overlapping subsystems or circuits of activity, a large number of them of a reverberatory or feedback nature. A nerve-impulse darts from a specific nucleus in the thalamus to a particular section of the parietal neocortex, thence to a particular section of the frontal lobe, thence to the hippocampal formation,

125

back to another thalamic nucleus, whence it goes to the original one — and the cycle is repeated many times before the activity-cycle ceases (159). The sensory nerve-cell in a muscle-spindle of the PerNS sends its signal to the reticular formation of the brain-stem and the reticular formation promptly sends a modifying impulse back to the muscle-spindle in a constant, never-ceasing circuit which is subject to higher-center influences (27). In a similar manner, receptor-cells in the retina send impulses to the BSRF and it promptly sends a modifying impulse back to the retina (66). The motor neocortex sends a chain of impulses to the neocerebellum via the corticopontine tracts, the pontine nuclei and the middle peduncle of the cerebellum; the neocerebellum sends a chain of impulses right back to the motor neocortex via the superior cerebellar peduncle and the ventrolateral nucleus of the thalamus — and *this* circle is repeated several times before activity ceases (159).

There appear to be two general types of functional subsystems: (1) those of a relatively limited scope, involving either only one CNS center *or* more than one *sub*cortical level; and (2) those of a more complex character, involving either several neuraxial levels, one of which is neocortical, *or* interaction between the CNS and the PerNS. *The autonomic nervous system is an example of the second type of functional subsystem*; this point needs explicit restating because of the continuing error in conceptualization of the ANS still appearing in some psychology textbooks.

SOME COMPLEX SUBCIRCUITS

Because some of the more complex of these functional subsystems have been traced out relatively recently, and because they have major behavioral implications, a few of them will be described in some detail, while a few others will be referred to only briefly.

The first example of a complex functional subsystem comprises the diverse connections centering in the reticular formation of the brain-stem, i.e., the medulla oblongata, pons and mid-brain sections of the neuraxis — ordinarily abbreviated to BSRF. According to Brodal, the BSRF's motor connections are of two types: those going to different parts of the cerebellum, and those going to the spinal cord and to higher centers (27). The reticular nuclei in which these projections originate also receive diffuse *afferent* fibers from the spinal cord and from higher centers; and the nuclei subserving the second type of motor connections just cited also receive collateral connections from the specific sensory pathways on their way from the spinal cord to the thalamus. There are many reticular-formation intraconnections (via internuncials), so that several basic reverberatory circuits become possible. Here are three examples:

(1) BSRF → medulla → spinal cord → medulla → BSRF.
(2) BSRF → pons → cerebellum → pons → BSRF.
(3) BSRF → thalamus → sensory neocortex → thalamus → hypothalamus → BSRF.

Circuit 1 provides for facilitation or inhibition of either cortically or reflexly induced movements; for effects on muscle-tone of a constant, "tonic" nature; for such basic autonomic functions as modification of inspiration and expiration, pressor and depressor effects on the circulatory system and gastro-intestinal functions, complex protective reflexes and temperature control and pupillary reactions; for influence on muscle spindle discharge; for a depressant effect on ascending sensory impulses. Circuit 2 provides for an inhibitory and a facilitating influence on the functioning of the cerebellum. Circuit 3 provides for the BSRF's alerting function, so basic to the behavioral phenomena of wakefulness-consciousness and attention: it traces out a central mechanism generally termed the ARAS — the ascending reticular activating system. This circuit also provides for neocortical influence on the functioning of the BSRF — that is, for cortical "feedback."

Magoun attributes additional, even more complex functions to the BSRF than those already given (116). He cites it as the route by which stressful stimulation leads to the hypothalamic-pituitary overactivity postulated by Selye and others; it also seems to be involved in normal activation of hypothalamic influence on other glands such as the thyroid, and on ovulation. The BSRF also affects the functioning of the hippocampal formation, which, together with cortical and diencephalic centers, plays a major role in emotional expression (see the "limbic system," following). The BSRF's functioning influences the brain-wave patterns of the neocortex in indirect ways. Another investigator, Gastaut, believes it also plays a role in the conditioning sequence (60).

There are three delimitable regions of the unspecific sensory pathway of the reticular formation: the medullary or caudal end, the mid-brain section — its major part, and the thalamic or upper, rostral, end (157). The functioning and functional role of the upper section of this diffuse sensory pathway, termed the "unspecific thalamocortical integrating system" (UTCIS) by Jasper (91), is sufficiently different from that of its brain-stem section to warrant its explicit discussion.

The reticular complex appears to be one of the most stable systems within the mammalian thalamus. It is easily identifiable in opossum, sloth, rat, rabbit, bat, pig, sheep, cat, dog, monkey and man (157, p. 458).

All the direct sensory projections from thalamus to cortex and from cortex to thalamus "pass through the meshes of a screen formed by the reticular neurons" (157). The thalamic reticular complex is closely related functionally with the dorsal thalamic nuclei and has many intrathalamic connections. Jasper's UTCIS does not project directly from the thalamus to the neocortex, as do the specific sensory pathways; rather it projects first to the putamen, a basal ganglion, and thence, diffusely, to the neocortex. The neocortex, in turn, projects back to the thalamus via the striatum, and so the UTCIS appears to be a reverberatory system. The cerebellum also projects to the thalamic reticular system as well as to the BSRF, and there are many connections between the old cortex and the UTCIS. It makes connections with the specific sensory-projection systems, not only at three successive levels in the neuraxis —medulla, mid-brain and thalamus, but also inter-relates with these sensory systems by means of: collaterals from the major sensory pathways, intrathalamic connections, overlapping projections in nearly all areas of the neocortex, projections radiating out from the neocortex. Cortical electrical activation takes two forms, phasic (rapid onset and brief duration) and tonic (slow onset and prolonged duration); the phasic form is characteristic of the thalamic reticular system (and the tonic of the BSRF). Since the thalamic system typically affects more delimited areas of the neocortex than does the brain-stem system, Jasper suggests that localized processes of attention may be in part mediated by it; it also connects with the limbic lobe through specific thalamic nuclei (90). Its diffuse nature suggests its function is integrative, to use Herrick's terminology.

Functionally, the UTCIS constitutes the upper or rostral portion of the ARAS, already referred to. It acts as a general mechanism for the regulation of the spontaneous electrical activity of the cortex as a whole. It joins the BSRF in maintaining a general level of cortical excitatory state and so is related to behavioral processes of attention, alerting, general excitement, sleep. In sensory areas of the neocortex, there seems to be a "competitive interaction between the specific and unspecific projection systems for the control of cortical electrical activity" (92). The UTCIS's activity affects sensory neocortex response in very specific ways, and some investigators have suggested that these cortical influences may be related to subjective sensation or perception (92).

Not as unanimously accepted by neurophysiological investigators as the connections, characteristics, and functions of the BSRF and the UTCIS, is another highly complex and functionally important subcircuit, termed variously the "limbic system" and the "visceral brain." The human clinical evidence appears to be more conclusive than animal experimentation, where phylogenetic differences have resulted in equivocal findings: an excellent example of the handicapping effects of lack of recognition of the relevance of differing integrative levels. The basic circuit involved is a reverberatory one and was first pointed to in 1937 by Papez. Old cortex centers figure largely in it. Structurally, it is composed of an "inner ring" and an "outer ring" of limbic cortex (160, pp. 486-9), thus:

inner ring:	(Part of the hippocampal formation.
(projects to	(Archicortex.
septal region,	(Olfactory structures: olfactory tubercle, prepiriform
hypothalamus	(cortex, periamygdaloid cortex, corticomedial nuclei.
and mid-brain,	(Structures with thalamic and hypothalamic connections:
via the fornix)	(entorrhinal area and hippocampus.

outer ring:	(Cingulate gyrus.)	six-
(projects to subcortical centers, mostly	(Orbito-insulo-)	layered
via the striatum; is closely associated	(temporal cortex.)	meso-
with the septal nuclei and the baso-	(Presubiculum.)	pallium
lateral amygdalar nuclei) .		

The various parts of the limbic cortex are closely interconnected, but, except for the gyrus cinguli, are poorly connected with the neocortex. Also, it may be significant that the recently discovered body-projection supplementary motor area is half in the outer-ring mesopallium and half in the neocortex (160).

Electrical stimulation applied to any component of this circuit is immediately transmitted to all its other components. This subsystem is found in all mammals, according to Broca, as cited by MacLean (114). "Its relative constancy of gross and microscopic structure throughout the phylogeny of the mammal contrasts strikingly with the changes in structure of the neopallium that mushrooms around it" (115). "It seems to set the emotional background on which man functions intellectually," according to Cobb (36). Kaada disputes its emotional role and says it is involved in such "higher psychic functions as memory" (96). [Why not, in man, with both, as a result of feed-ins from the temporal lobe?] Pribram has still another interpretation of its function; he says it is "related primarily to the mechanism of the execution of complex sequences of action" (154a). In short, its precise behavioral role in man has not yet been finally determined.

The circumstance that the gyrus cinguli (area 24) is one of the key components of the limbic system has led to the following speculation. Cobb cites experimental data documenting this area's involvement in autonomic-control functions and its contribution to the suppression of lower motor behaviors associated with emotional reactions (36). The gyrus cinguli is also connected with the entire prefrontal association area, which is by far the most developed in man, and which is part of the A-mechanism of Penfield's "centrencephalic integrating system," discussed below. So it would appear to act as a common factor between circuits subserving affective behavior and circuits subserving integrative functions. Here is a most suggestive circumstance! Recall Jackson's citation of Ribôt's "Le moi est une coordination." Does the gyrus cinguli play a key role in the make-up of the individual self, perhaps?

The functions of other key components of the "visceral brain" include:

The hippocampal formation: modulates the intensity of activities mediated by lower centers related to the basic instincts; it also contributes to control of emotional tension and to the *orientation* of behavior-patterns (26);

The anterior thalamus: acts as a nodal way-station for the limbic system because of its connections with the other thalamic nuclei, with the gyrus cinguli, and with the mammillary body of the hypothalamus; it also influences the sensory information relayed to it by other parts of the thalamus (26);

The hypothalamus: is the principal integrative focus of the entire autonomic nervous system, which serves to mediate the basic life processes.

How singularly inappropriate is the term "psychosomatic," with its reification of the old mind-body dichotomy, in light of the make-up and functioning of the limbic system!

Apparently the anatomical details but not the entire functional interpretation of another complex functional sub-system, Wilder Penfield's "centrencephalic integrating system" — the CIS (146), have been accepted by other investigators. An upper brain-stem subcircuit, made up of the diencephalic and mid-brain centers, with feed-ins from old and new cortex, acts as *the* integrating system for the two cerebral hemispheres according to Penfield — and it, not the frontal neocortex, acts as the neuraxial "highest center" originally postulated by Hughlings Jackson. Penfield separates the CIS into two related mechanisms, one of which can function independently of the other. The "B-mechanism" is the CIS proper, and is used in the integration of the sensory and motor systems, the acquired skills of speech and manual dexterity, and in recollection of past experience. The "A-mechanism" is seen as an adjunct to the CIS and is made up of two subcircuits: (1) the frontal lobe subdivision, involving prefrontal areas, and (2) the temporal pole subdivision; both are used to record one's current perceptions. B-mechanism can function independently of A-mechanism, but A-mechanism cannot function while an epileptic seizure is affecting B-mechanism. However, if the thalamus is involved in an epileptic seizure, the cortex "blanks out" altogether; this circumstance confirms the thalamus' key role as "gatekeeper" of the cortex.

In a slightly later discussion (147), Penfield acknowledges that the neocortex plays a greater role in the CIS than originally postulated by him, and gives this formulation of the functional role of the CIS:

> The hypothesis is suggested that sensory information is integrated within the CIS. A selected portion of this information is then somehow projected outwards to the temporal cortex by that portion of the system which is in functional connection with the temporal cortex of both sides. As it is thus projected, a comparison is made with past similar experiences, thanks to the records of the past that are held there, and judgment with regard to familiarity and significance is made (p. 303).

Penfield's formulation has been referred to primarily because it is based on sophisticated and recent observation of *human* functioning and as such has a potentially major contribution to make to the conceptualization of the overall functional organization of the human *in situ* nervous system.

> Further examples of functional subsystems having apparently major behavioral implications not yet clearly determined include one centered in the thalamus and two centered in the cerebellum, as follows:
>
> (1) Sensory tracts (somatic, visual, auditory) to the receptive nuclei of the thalamus → association nuclei of the thalamus → T-O-P association area of the posterior neocortex
> → cerebellum via pons.
> → hypothalamus via old cortex.
> → BSRF via hypothalamus.
>
> (2) Vestibular apparatus in inner ear (organ of body-balance) → BSRF → Deiters nucleus (near pons)
> → spinal cord via vestimulospinal tract
> → medulla → cerebellum.
> → pons → cerebellum → pons → Deiters nucleus → spinal cord via vesticulospinal tract (28).

(3) Motor neocortex → corticopontine tract to pons → middle
cerebellar peduncle → neocerebellum → dentate nucleus of
cerebellum → superior cerebellar peduncle → ventrolateral
nucleus of thalamus → motor neocortex (159).

In sum, the following are some of the human adult behaviors
which are now known to be subserved by complex, forebrain-
participative neural circuits; 1 through 5 are drawn from (160).

(1) Voluntary motor behavior is made possible by reverberatory circuits connecting motor areas of the neocortex, the basal
ganglia, thalamic nuclei and pons and cerebellum. Ruch has provided a useful summary-diagram of the circuits involved; it is
here reproduced, with permission, as Figure 6.

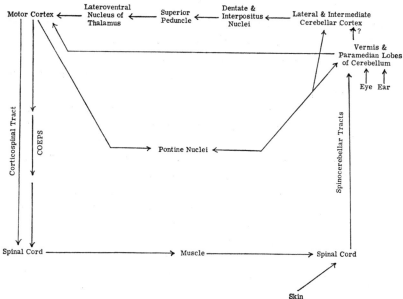

Figure 6. Feedback loops to and from motor cortex. The long loop involves
a return of proprioceptive information from muscle to motor cortex by way
of the cerebellum. A second potential loop is shorter and entirely within
the CNS; it may or may not receive information from the periphery: it does
so only if there are connections between the medial and more lateral cerebellar regions. Note that the arrow connecting the vermis and the para-
median lobe is questioned: as of about 1959, this pathway was known functionally but not anatomically.

This diagram is a copy of Figure 162 in 160, and is reproduced by
courtesy of W. B. Saunders, Philadelphia.

This diagram omits the cortex-basal ganglia subcircuit; for it to be complete, the following addition should be made in the upper left-hand corner, as follows:

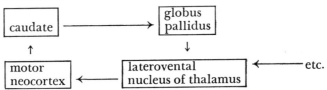

(2) Basic-vegetative, cortex-alerting and emotion-mediating functions are all either centered in the hypothalamus, or heavily dependent on it. These functions depend upon feedback connections with various forebrain centers (detailed in Orientation Supplement 4A).

(3) Almost all information from the external world and from our bodies passes through the forebrain thalamic gateway en route to the neocortex. This information is derived from the exteroceptors of sight and hearing, as well as from the somato-visceral senses.

The important role of the latter — skin, interoceptive and proprioceptive — senses in early development warrants the inclusion of the following data:

(a) Most aspects of visceral functioning reach the cortex via autonomic pathways, and a few via the somatic nervous system. Pain originating in the body-wall and diaphragm is transmitted via the somatic nervous system. The following sensations and reactions involve mostly unmyelinated parasympathetic and sympathetic pathways: hunger, thirst, nausea, sexual sensations, erection, blood flow and blood-pressure, vomiting, coughing, bladder and rectum distention, urination, defecation, visceral pain. Conduction of somatic afferents to the cortex takes priority over visceral conduction: activity in visceral afferents can be blocked by somatic afferents. [Why getting out and taking a walk helps relieve an attack of anxiety!]

(b) Visceral, proprioceptive and skin sensations leave the cord en route to the thalamus by one or the other, or both, of these two tracts:

(1) Sensations served by the *posterior column* include muscle, tendon and joint sensibility (proprioception and

kinesthesis), and touch and pressure; these modalities subserve the perceptual functions of topognosis or localization,
two-point discrimination, spatial functions such as figure-
writing and length and direction of a line; weight-dis-
crimination, appreciation of vibration, stereognosis (recognition by palpation) — i.e., the senses which "give knowledge of the position of the limbs in space and knowledge
of the objects making up the external world" (160, p. 334).

(2) Sensations served by the *spinothalamic tract* include:
pain from skin, muscles, tendons, joints, viscera; cold; sexual
sensations; pressure and touch (partially); tickle and itch;
feelings of muscular fatigue.
These sensations are added to the ascending sensory pathways
at the upper border of the medulla oblongata. These ascending
pathways not only go directly to the thalamus; they also, as we
have seen, give off collaterals to the BSRF.

(c) From the BSRF, there are supplementary, slow, unmyelinated, multisynaptic pathways (including those carrying
somatovisceral sensations) to the thalamus. These supplementary pathways exert some sort of inhibitory effect on central
pain responses; they are in some way connected with pain and
the affective side of sensory experience.

(d) The extensive somatoviscerosensory area of the parietal
neocortex is reached by four different pathways, all of which
synapse first in the thalamus: from the cerebellum, via the
thalamic relay nuclei, via the diffuse thalamocortical projection system, via a short-latency projection to the motor area.
All thalamic nuclei except the geniculates (sight and hearing
functions) project to the parietal and frontal lobes. And each
such thalamic nucleus is projected back to, by the same or a
neighboring cortical area. Thus, complex feedback circuits are
involved.

(e) The affective side of sensation has remained at the
thalamic level with evolution — pleasantness, unpleasantness,
pain. Peripherally, rather than cortically, induced pain is a
strong motivator of behavior.

(4) There are a great many thalamic-hypothalamic feedback
circuits which allow for interaction between the perceptual and
affective aspects of sensation.

(5) The functions of the association areas of the neocortex are dependent upon complex intracortical reverberatory circuits. Foresight and the pursuit of long-term goals are behaviors apparently centered in the PF association area. Damage to this area has resulted in lack of consistency and stability of purpose and behavior (high distractability); incapacity to delay a response; hyperactivity; loss of strong anxiety and other emotional tensions; indifference to pain, and a loss of learned social controls and consideration for others' feelings. Damage to the anterior-temporal section of the posterior, T-O-P, association area in the monkey has resulted in psychic blindness, compulsive oral and manipulative exploratory reactions, docility and unresponsiveness. In the human being, damage to this same area sometimes yields a kind of perceptual detachment from self. Penfield has found "stream of consciousness" memories in it (145).

(6) Hebb conceptualizes learning as dependent upon mediating processes in the cortex; more specifically, upon the reverberatory circuit principle. His "cell assembly" consists of activity in one closed group of neurons, while the "phase sequence" is a series of linked cell-assemblies (75, Chapters 3 and 5). P. M. Milner (no relation!) has added to Hebb's formulation by postulating an inhibitory regulatory system which limits the number of neurons that can fire at once and insures the wide dispersal of these firings (130). Cell-assemblies become "representors of stimuli" and can "be linked together by being fired contiguously." "Perceptual" learning results when the cells newly added to an assembly were primed by sensory input to the cortex; "associative" learning results when newly added cells are primed by the firing of another cell-assembly. Apparently, Milner's formulation does not take into account the two types of cellular structure and associated conduction-modes in the cortex, that of the nerve-net and of the nerve-cell.

With the exception of Penfield's CIS, which was deduced chiefly from his extensive surgical work on persons suffering from epilepsy, most of the neural subcircuits described in this chapter were derived from very exact and ingenious animal experimentation. The findings so far obtained from such experimentation illustrate both the advantages and the disadvantages of such research for the understanding of human behavior. On the one hand, animal work permits operative, dissection, and "sacrifice"[1] techniques which cannot be used with human beings. This use of animals is of course undertaken as a means of attaining the ultimate goal of understanding human behavior; as such it departs from the investigative rationale concerning man as a mammal cited in Chapter I. The typical analytic design of neurological research departs also from this tacit assumption:

> Since the nervous system is essentially a complex physical mechanism, it must, like any machine, be made up of many component parts. The kind of research we are doing permits us to identify the various component bits and pieces of that mechanism. When we have identified enough of the component parts, we should know the nature of that mechanism's make-up and functioning as a coherent totality — and since behavior is a direct function of that mechanism, our basic goal of understanding human behavior will have been furthered.

The volume of data of the "component parts" type that has and is being poured out, and the resulting sharp increase in our knowledge of the mammalian, including the human, nervous system, provides concrete testimony to the value of this methodological approach — and, by implication, provides as well validation for the basic assumptions from which this methodology departs. Attempts to put the fragments of circuitry together according to some theoretical model have begun; Pribram's use of information theory, especially as it has been applied in the construction of computers, is one such coherent attempt (154b). As yet, however, all we actually have "for certain" is a steadily growing number of neural circuits, from simple, functionally limited ones, to some as complex as the autonomic nervous system and the ascending reticular activating system.

Although the contributions of such research to our knowledge have been manifold and genuine — and will undoubtedly continue for some time to be, it is important, on the other hand, to

---

[1]Some time after certain brain areas have been extirpated or neural circuits cut, the animal is killed and the brain carefully dissected to ascertain the pathways that have degenerated.

recognize its limitations. Just as psychology discovered some time ago that more and more intricate chains of S—Rs do not a behaving human being make, so do not bits and pieces of electrical circuitry — even though they can make and have already made some very complex computers (which is what Pribram's TOTE model essentially amounts to). Chapter I attempted to make the point that when we do not keep raising new — and better — questions, we run the risk of continuing to turn out more and more data which persists in answering questions which are now the wrong ones, good as they may at one time have been.

However, both those who are carrying on such research and those who have reservations about its limitations will be able to concur in this hopeful prediction of Ingram's:

> One can perhaps look forward to the time when the interactions of peripheral ganglia, spinal cord, medulla, pons, midbrain, diencephalon, cerebellum and telencephalon will present to the scientist a unified and not altogether incomprehensible picture, not constituted of segmental moieties or theories of emotion or of the laws of learning, but of a system in which the vegetative, somatic and the psychic may be blended in their true proportions. *It will not be a simple picture* (87, p. 975). (Italics EM's.)

Pattern 2, the functional subsystems pattern, is clearly apparent when one observes the functioning of the *in situ* nervous system for any limited period of time. But an hierarchical patterning, in the literal sense of each higher level's functional dominance over lower levels, would definitely *not* be readily apparent. Does not Pattern 2 contradict Pattern 1? How can both apply simultaneously? The necessity explicitly to raise these questions constitutes a reflection on the theoretical limitations of the moment-in-time observational perspective, to which experimental neuropsychology and physiology have hitherto been almost exclusively devoted in the design of their investigations.

The hierarchical organizational principle is clearest when the over-time or developmental observational perspective is resorted to. All lower motor centers and activities eventually subject to neocortical influences cannot be so subject until related primary-motor and association areas have begun to function. Effective sensorimotor relations — that is, refined sensory control over (voluntary) motor activities — can only be established after primary-sensory neocortical areas and related association areas have begun to function. And all the complex cognitive and intellectual functions of the human brain, centered in the neocortex, can emerge only as the neocortex becomes functional. Yet *at birth, the human infant's neocortex* (as well as such lower centers as the neocerebellum) *is simply not transmitting impulses!* This state of affairs means that all functional subsystems which include neocortical centers, or are subject to the influence of such centers, emerge subsequent to birth, in accordance — it is here hypothesized — with an hierarchical organization principle which, in line with Jackson's dictum of the "continuous reduction of succession to co-existences," expresses itself at neurological maturity in vertically organized, functionally coherent and *instantaneous* subsystems.

When the over-time observational perspective is included in this manner, functional-organization patterns 1 and 2 become *complementary* rather than contradictory organizational principles. Future study of the nervous system must, therefore, include not only sheerly structural changes subsequent to birth. It must also include as a major area of inquiry *how, when and under what conditions each one of the more complex functional subsystems emerges, both structurally and functionally.*

SOME BEHAVIORAL IMPLICATIONS

The hierarchical-reduplicative and functional subsystems functional-organization patterns suggest a complex mechanism indeed. The concept of "feed back," borrowed from engineering terminology, approximates only feebly the functional correlates of this staggeringly complex system. The number of neurons in the CNS have been estimated at about 10^{10}, and every one is potentially functionally related with every other. Engineering has had no experience with mechanical systems of this degree of complexity (138). It is, furthermore, a self-sustaining system — a dynamic, constantly active composite of many systems which maintains its activity independent of external stimulation. In the neurologically

mature individual, the entire cortex is a great network of reverberatory circuits, constantly active. When a new stimulus reaches
such an already active system, it produces changes in the overall
excitation pattern (104). Autonomy of pattern, rhythmic automatism and hierarchical organization are the primary attributes
of the human nervous system, as they are of even the simplest
nervous systems (191). It is only in the living organism that this
amazing interconnected network functions as a coherent unity:
no study of functional localization, nor of cellular and chemical
analysis, nor of any part of it in isolation, has yet approximated
the dynamic, coordinated character of its functioning as an intact
system.

Some of the implications for man's behavior of such a complex
system are suggested first in these three excerpts from a wide-
ranging discussion by Gerard (62):

> There is now much evidence that many minutes must elapse
> between having a sensory experience and establishing a
> permanent memory of it. This period for fixation may well
> involve continued reverberation of impulses in the appropriate
> neural nets; and with some hundred thousand repetitions possi-
> ble in the fixation time, a relatively enduring trace is left (p.
> 1947).

> [Even brief inputs may continue to reverberate in closed
> loops] for minutes and hours, during which a transient experi-
> ence produces an enduring memory trace. [Such "unfinished
> business" as anxiety, dreams, unsatisfied drives, would also be
> associated with long-maintained reverberation] (p. 1950).

> With reverberation and feedback and synchrony, much can
> happen within the brain . . . with no immediately correlated
> behavior. . . .Such separation in time and type and locus of
> stimulus and response gives the richness and spontaneity of be-
> havior, experienced as volition and rationalized[2] as free will
> (p. 1952).

And second, in Herrick's application of the newer physical
concepts of electrodynamic fields to cortical organization and
functioning, and the implications of this application for the per-

---

[2]Since we are dealing with a highly advanced, open system, the use of this word
in this context may be questioned.

ceptual process (78) ; these implications are further developed in the next chapter:

(1)   (a)   To explain the observed facts, the new theory of quantum mechanics was developed. . . . The 'quantum field' [is one] in which objects are not . . . regarded as separate entities in fixed positions that react with the field. While still called elementary particles, their properties are identical with those of quanta of energy and *the particles are loci or patterns of energy*. The field can be defined only by its dynamic properties. The particle and its field are inseparably one. . . . [This way of looking at the electromagnetic field directs attention] to the system as a whole exhibited 'in the form of the *relations of the motions of the parts.*' Different individual particles may be engaged from time to time *but the pattern persists* (p. 264) . (Italics EM's.)

(b)   The most characteristic properties of the nervous tissues arise from two types of structural and physiological polarization of the nervous elements. The first type is *structurally* determined by the fact that each neuron is physiologically separated from all the others with which it is in contact by barriers — synapses — which nervous impulses can pass in only one direction. Nerve fibers, accordingly, usually transmit nervous impulses as one-way traffic. The second type of polarization arises from an organization of the nervous tissues such that *electrodynamic fields* may be activated in relatively stable patterns that are not inflexibly bound to any particular arrangement of the nervous elements (p. 269) .

(2)   (a)   So also if mentation is a vital process carried on in a field of metabolic activity, then the mind must not be regarded as an entity separable from its field of operation, a being which somehow pulls the strings that move a mechanical robot. The mind and the field are inseparably one. . . . The field in question is not a structure; *it is a pattern of process*. But such a pattern may occur only in some particular region of the brain with the requisite structural organization, and this region, which has more or less definite boundaries, may be called the field of this particular type of process; that is, a field defined in terms of its relations in space to other parts of the brain (p. 266) . (Italics EM's.)

(b) The distinction which we draw between awareness on the one hand and on the other hand the projection outward of some components of experience as things known about, including objects set in the frame of space and time, all observable behavior of ourselves and others, and all symbols of mental processes — this distinction . . . is a methodological artifact which results from the structural limitations of the human apparatus of perception. *The knowings and the known are intrinsic components of a field of experience within which they are inseparable* (p. 279). (Italics EM's.)

(c) An essential feature of perceptual integration is the polarization of the perceiving subject against the thing perceived, of the self against the not-self (p. 349). [That is] I experience myself in action as immediately as I experience things acted upon (p. 207). This clear-cut conscious polarization of subject and object, [which] arises rather late in human psychogenesis, is basic for perception and all mental processes derived from it (p. 323).

These excerpts from Gerard and Herrick suggest that a picture of "mechanism" adequate to the complexities of human behavior *and* personality is at last beginning to emerge.

It is impossible to resist commenting on comparative-experimental psychology's Stimulus-Response model of behavior — and its subsequent reluctant modifications — in light of the foregoing fascinating complexity.

Historically, experimental psychology's traditional interest in only the overt aspects of behavior has been accompanied by an equally traditional lack of interest in the human nervous system as a physiological entity with its own special functional characteristics — perhaps because psychology made its self-conscious beginnings as an avowed "natural science" at a time when neurophysiology was not only a relatively primitive field of study, but also, to all practical intents, the "kept woman" of the applied profession of medicine. Still extant expository use of the "little black box" by psychologists when theorizing about the role of the nervous system in behavior often reveals a continuing intradiscipline tendency toward the exclusion of the by now extensive body of neurophysiological data and informed speculation on the nervous system as a species-unique biophysiological entity.

Consistent with this traditional concern of psychology-as-a-science with behavior in the most immediately tangible, macroscopic, objectively observable sense, has been experimental psychology's tripartite conception of the basic functional pattern of the mammalian nervous system: STIMULATING-RECEPTIVE-SENSORY-AFFECTING, central-regulatory (in small print, note), RESPONDING-MOTOR-EFFECTING. This psychological functional-organization pattern reflects not only a strict overt-behavioral orientation, but adherence to the moment-in-time observational perspective.

The very simple, very overt, very deterministic-mechanistic stimulus-response schema of the spinal one-segment reflex-arc was experimental psychology's first theoretical behavioral model. So atomistic was it, the early experimentalists fell deeply in love with its preserpentine (i.e., precognitive) perfection, a love-affair so satisfying, it continues to haunt psychology's collective-unconscious with a sort of former-Eden sweetness. The first experimentally derived theory of learning departed from the CR, a learned modification of the reflex-arc or UR. The original version of the theory maintained, to the complete satisfaction of its psychology-must-be-a-natural-science propounders, that all, even the most complex, of human behaviors are no more than chains of such conditioned responses. This stage in psychology's theorizing about behavior is symbolized by the gut-engraved S–R hieroglyphic.

Clear evidence that most of even the most simple mammalian reflexes were *inter*segmental rather than *intra*segmental in character subsequently forced upon psychology the essential role of "connector" neurons, which neither stimulated nor responded. But since it was possible to detect the actual physical presence and activity of such neurons in carefully set up spinal preparations, psychological theorists remained true to their scientific value-system of being governed by objective findings — and S–c–R fairly represents experimental psychology's next behavioral model.

The Gestaltists' experimental demonstrations of something (to the orthodox Behaviorist) almost metaphysical called "insight," as well as the radical finding that sensory stimulus and perception-experience were by no means a one to one matter, provided a further challenge to those whose picture of the human nervous system was that of, at the most, a mid-brain preparation (but more often, only a bulbar, i.e., medullary, one). Hull introduced the revolutionary notion that even if an experimenter couldn't see it tangibly or demonstrate it tangibly, if motor output showed the influence of something other than the sensory input, then it was quite safe, scientifically, to postulate the existence of unknown "intervening" processes. Other theoretical contributions, such as Hebb's cell-assembly, already referred to, have also contributed to this marked break with all that the original Behaviorists held dear — and S—C—R became psychology's next behavioral model, with C now standing for the yet-to-be-determined central mediating processes. This phase initiated the "little black box" as a theorizing device, a device which is proving to be as handicappingly tenacious in its hold on psychology as the old S—R paradigm. (Skinner's R—S variation has not been referred to in this quick Behavioristic overview because his formulation is entirely "operational" — i.e., it is not concerned with underlying mechanisms, neural or otherwise.)

Lashley, Hebb, and recently also Pribram (among others), have been trying very hard to convince their fellow theoretical psychologists that the classical intra- and inter- segmental spinal reflex-arc does *not* provide an adequate mechanistic foundation for most of human behavior. If they and theorizing neurophysiologists such as Gerard and Livingston have their way — and there are encouraging signs that they are, the latest behavioral schema must at the very least be conceptualized, as Ralph Gerard has put it, in the form of "input and output to the CNS" (62) ; that is, as s → C → r, in which C represents the explicitly acknowledged — and increasingly well documented — highly complex role of the central nervous system, and s and r represent the functional roles of the peripheral nervous system, which, as we shall shortly see, not only influences but *is influenced by,* the CNS. This formulation brings us right 'round to the functional-organization patterns just postulated — and indeed, to the objectives of this monograph.

More specific documentation of the validity of the proposed s—C—r model requires that new understandings of the extent to which the CNS influences the functioning of the PerNS be added to the CNS-centered information already presented.

First, the sensory or, rather, *stimulus aspect*. All receptor-cells have a common, truly remarkable function: each type of receptor-organ acts as a highly specialized, high speed "transformer," instantaneously converting a particular kind of *physical* energy (pressure, chemical substances, sound-waves, light-waves) into *neural* energy. We now know they also play a "screening" — and therefore a perceptual — role as a result of central-efferent influences on them: they do not automatically transmit all stimuli impinging on them. Not even the subjective concomitants of higher-level functioning — consciousness, self-awareness, thought — exceed the metaphysical-like complexity of receptor-organ functioning.

The brain-stem reticular formation acts as a second-level "check-point" or modifier of incoming sensory impulses: it receives collaterals from nearly all the sensory modalities and, *under the influence of higher centers,* selects which stimuli will go on to higher levels and which shall not; hence it also plays a major role in the perceptual process. Also, at the same time that higher-order functions are being subserved by thalamic projections to specific sensory areas of the neocortex, the BSRF is responsible for a more fundamental biological function: it determines, through the ascending reticular activating system (described earlier in this chapter) the neocortex's degree of receptivity to the specific sensory impulses being sent to it from the thalamus. Further discussion of this modifying-of-sensory-input motor system awaits analysis of the motor aspects of nervous system functioning which follows.

The thalamus, working in feedback intimacy with the old cortex and hypothalamus, contributes an important preconscious perceptual attribute to those sensations which have survived their previous "inspection points": their feeling-tone associations. Perceptual selectivity and discrimination reaches its greatest degree of refinement at the neocortical level: the neocortex has a recognition-discriminative role, in which memory processes are involved; these in turn involve the limbic system, which appears to have a strong self-referent aspect. When it is recalled that it is the primary somatoviscerosensory (parietal) area of the neocortex which is the first neocortical area to appear in phylogenesis and ontogenesis, and that a number of recognized neurophysiological authorities (Tilney and Hamilton, at least) attribute to the body senses the initiation of the evolutionary development of the entire neocortex, the first experience of self would seem to be provided by the interoreceptors and therefore to be of a primary-physical — gut-level and body-surface — nature. According to this datum, "primary narcissism" has a phylogenetic, mammalian basis! With self-referrent feelings and visceral, muscular, and external-world information all available to it, the sensory-association neocortex, acting through overlapping motor-association circuits, affects conscious-voluntary behavior directly via the primary-motor centers, and unconscious-autonomic levels of functioning via old cortex and hypothalamus.

The highly coordinated, *purposive* nature of all these neural activities is highlighted in this statement of Lord Adrian's:

> It is essential to consider the sense organs not only as groups of receptors excited by particular physical or chemical events, but as organs capable of presenting a detailed report which will enable the event to be compared with others of the same class which have occurred before. The description must be as full as possible, yet it has all to be conveyed by trains of impulses in nerve-fibers (1, p. 366).

The necessary involvement of motor activities in the sense organs' role of "presenting a detailed report" is stressed in another comment by Lord Adrian from the same article:

> All the actions which focus the sense organs on the stimulus will evoke afferent signals of their own to be related to the signals from the sense-organ itself. Thus the full report which comes to the CNS will be far more complex and informative than anything which could be furnished by a sense-organ isolated from the body and controlled by the electrophysiologist (p. 366).

Lord Adrian's cautionary reminder serves as an apt introduction to the *response "side"* of the nervous system. Here we must start where we left off in the quick overview of its sensory aspects:

the highest centers. Not only the highest level of perception and meaning and thought and volition are exercised on the body musculature by the neocortex, but also the organism's emotional reactions to the incoming sensory messages may be transmitted from cortical centers to both skeletal and visceral musculature. In the execution of coordinated voluntary movement, the reverberatory circuit comprising cerebral-striatal-cerebellar-striatal-cerebral centers comes into play. Both autonomic and emotional reactions depend heavily on hypothalamus-centered circuits — *and the hypothalamus, through its close association with the pituitary gland, both affects and is affected by the body's chemical order of functioning.*

Denny-Brown reciprocates Lord Adrian's emphasis on central-motor factors in sensory functioning by stressing the importance of central-sensory factors in motor functioning (41). He posits two basic principles of motor integration (p. 793): (1) Every motor reaction has an adequate stimulus, immediate *or* remote. (2) "The nervous system as a whole contributes to each motor act." He amplifies on the second principle by stating,

> It is not possible to indicate separate mechanisms for posture and for movement: postural reactions are fundamental in neural organization, and movement in its most elementary form is seen as modifications of postural responses. [A salute to the shade of Hughlings Jackson!]

Another statement of Denny-Brown's, stressing the controlling-suppressing function of the highest centers, throws light on the role of the neocortex in the development of voluntary prehension:

> The appropriate contactual stimulus releases an otherwise latent proprioceptive reaction. . . . The proprioceptive system is restrained by the subthalamic system and harnessed to a series of specific contactual triggers or signals in the pattern of body-on-body righting reflexes. Both the subthalamic mechanism and segmental reflex are restrained by the primary-motor neocortex where the specific activation is further differentiated into the delicate contactual pattern of the instinctive tactile grasp reaction and the instinctive placing reaction (p. 794).

And again:

> Suppression with selective facilitation appears to us to be a general principle of neural organization, exemplified not only in the mechanism of prehension but also in the organization of spinal reflexes (extensor thrust), labyrinthine [body-balance] reactions, autonomic facilitation (e.g., urination), learned behavior and Pavlovian conditioning (p. 794).

Livingston has pointed out that unknowingly inadequate investigative methods are partially accountable for the delay in confirming the existence of a sensory-modifying motor system, the lower parts of which were first noticed many years ago by Cájàl and others: a system of connections that permits central influences to "modify sensory-input patterns anywhere from peripheral sense organs to at least the sensory neocortex" (111, p. 741). (Except where otherwise indicated, all direct quotations in this and the next several paragraphs are drawn from Livingston's discussion.) The use of anesthesia and cortical extirpation in investigating motor connections and functions — both of which eliminated cortical influences — had much to do with this oversight. These central processes are tonically active *and usually inhibitory in effect,* acting so as to reduce or eliminate potential sensory experiences in *initial* stages of sensory integration. Since such central influence allows both past experience and the direction of attention to play a part, "central interference with sensory transmission appears to be regulatory *and to constitute a goal-seeking physiological mechanism*" (p. 742). (Italics EM's.)

> The influence of this system at the receptor-organ level has been traced out for the muscle-spindle. The rate of discharge of the muscle-spindle afferent depends not only upon the state of the muscle as a whole but also upon the degree of tension developed by a small intrafusal fiber contained within the spindle, a fiber in turn controlled by small ventral-root or "gamma" efferents. "Thus, the discharge of spindle afferents, which play such an important role in proprioception, is determined both by the state of the skeletal muscle and by the rate of discharge of gamma efferents. . . . This peripheral feedback or loop-gain system provides an exceedingly important measure of central

control over sensory input" (p. 743). In turn, the gamma efferents have been found to be regulated by remote central structures, the brain-stem and diencephalic reticular formation; and these centers are "normally under a tonic inhibitory influence from above" (p. 744).

The principle of central control of afferent activity is also applicable to the special senses, as has already been mentioned for the retina. Anesthesia interrupts this tonic inhibitory effect from above, as is evident from the high amplitude of evoked responses in the main sensory pathways from the spinal cord, regularly recorded in anesthetized animals. Anesthetics appear to owe their effects to their blocking of conduction in certain sensory pathways.

The tonic inhibitory influences from above are also evident in all subcortical sensory-relay points in the spinal cord, medulla, thalamus. Each ascending neural pathway is parelleled directly, on a one to one basis, by a matching descending pathway "which links the same nuclear relay stations from above downwards" (p. 750). This pattern has been so fully documented for the auditory pathways that Galambos has stated "the solution of certain problems of hearing resides as much in the understanding of the function of these descending pathways as in the knowledge of ascending ones" (57).

As for what happens in the neocortex, "not only are input and output patterns modifiable within the cortex, but the cortex itself can also modify activity taking place within the brain-stem and thereby possibly have an indirect influence back upon sensory patterns as these are initiated and relayed at lower levels" (p. 749).

Further evidence of central influences on sensory functioning is shown in the phenomenon of attention. Behavioral signs of attention are directly related to recorded physiological (EEG) reaction to *novel* stimuli. Additional experimentation of this type has led Livingston to conclude that "activity in the auditory and visual and possibly olfactory and somesthetic pathways is vulnerable to systematic intervention according to previous experience (habituation) and shift of attention (distraction)" (p. 754).

And the behavioral concomitants and implications have not yet been covered. Through the sensory-pathway collaterals to the BSRF, most sensory pathways and certain neocortical areas almost surely have "indirect reciprocal relations with the *cerebellum*" (p. 752).

The experimental evidence pushes Livingston even further in his insistence on the complex and fundamental role of central influences on what is experienced:

> The nervous system possesses some mechanism whereby the amplitude of sensory-evoked responses, and hence the number or synchrony of units responding, can be greatly modified. (p. 756).

> This sensory mechanism may be interpreted to be designed to diminish the engagement of higher centers with those signals that have the least significance for the individual. A mechanism operating in this way requires that incoming signals be identified and given significance (p. 757).

> Perhaps 'value' is likewise inserted into the complex at these early stages of sensory integration. Certainly, significance to the organism appears to be a guiding principle with respect to the operation of sensory control mechanisms, hence *a survival of incoming impulses in the unanesthetized brain would appear to be prima facie evidence of their significance*" (p. (758). (Italics EM's.) [They may also be evidence of their nonthreatening character — i.e., anxiety-inducing stimuli may be excluded from awareness by these same mechanisms.]

> Sensory signals appear to be subject not only to error . . . but also to some purposive central control . . . some teleological mechanism is at work (p. 759).

All this from an experimental-research neurophysiologist and therefore, by definition, a "tough-minded" investigator! One thing has been omitted in this thorough documentation of the existence of "purposive central control": giving it a name. Might it be, in the human being, the *self* — that product of highly individualized postnatal experience, Doctor Livingston?

To illustrate the assertion that the updated behavioral schema must indeed be s—C—r at the least, herewith a concrete example of a familiar behavioral sequence which highlights the functional role of the ARAS. A person starts to watch one of his not-so-favorite TV shows. The impulses from his eyes reach mid-brain visual centers, and from there branch out in two streams: one goes to certain thalamic nuclei and thence directly to the occipital neocortex; the other stream maintains the nerve-net of the BSRF at a degree of activity which allows it to signal diffusely to nearly the whole neocortex via the thalamus and striatum: stay awake and alert. But the association areas of the neocortex have by now analyzed the meaning of the more direct, faster traveling visual impulses received by the visual cortex and have found that what the eyes are receiving and transmitting is very dull fare indeed. And so the impulses from the cortex to the BSRF serve to damp down its activity, which in turn leads both to its cutting out many of the incoming sensory impulses *and* its sending back to the cortex a diffuse set of "don't stay so awake and alert" signals. This reverberatory subcircuit keeps up until our not-atypical TV viewer falls into a doze. The 'phone rings suddenly and sharply — and the auditory impulses reactivate the BSRF (as well as the neocortex directly), and a new reverberatory cycle is set up.

Pribram concludes his 1960 review-article with this paragraph:

> Reinforcement by cognition, based on a mechanism of hierarchically organized representations; dispositions and drives regulated by multilinked and biased homeostats; representational organization by virtue of graded, as well as all-or-nothing, neural responses; spontaneously generated, long-lasting intrinsic neural rhythms — organisms thus conceived are actively engaged not only in the manipulation of artifacts, but in the organization of their perceptions, satisfactions and gratifications (154a, p. 32).

S—R (or R—S) indeed! So solidly established is the complexly fundamental role of central nervous mechanisms in behavior, although many structural and functional details of that role yet remain to be deciphered, familiarity in depth and in breadth with the data of modern neurophysiology would seem now to be an essential component of the behavioral *and personality* theorist's armamentarium of knowledge.

Chapter VII

THE TRIPLE-SYSTEM PHYLOGENETIC-LEGACY PATTERN

Logically, the third functional-organization pattern should have been placed second, because both it and the hierarchical-reduplicative pattern are deeply rooted in a phylogenetic orientation. But since it is the most conjectural of the three, and because it departs from data included in the discussion of the other two patterns, it has been placed last.

Phylogenesis has apparently bequeathed not one but three relatively discrete neural-structure legacies to the human species: a visceral, internally oriented subsystem; a sensorimotor, external-environment-interactive subsystem; and a third system which coordinates the first two sub-systems into a coherently functioning whole. Each one is functionally organized along the vertical — i.e., hierarchical — dimension. Close consideration of Herrick's functional division of the neural networks of the vertebrate nervous system into "analytic" and "integrative" *and* of Romer's dual-structure phylogenetic-legacy postulation, which coincides with Herrick's sub-division of the "analytic" conduction system (all referred to in Chapter III), underlies this formulation. It also takes into account the two functional-organization patterns previously enunciated.

First, an overview of all three systems is presented and then a more detailed analysis of each one.

THE PHYLOGENETIC-LEGACY

Romer, in building towards his postulation of a dual system in man, refers to the prevertebrate tunicate larva, a water-form chordate, and comments:

> We see for the first time a body-organization basically comparable to that of vertebrates. . . . This tadpole-like larva is essentially a dual organism (156, p. 59).

He agrees specifically with Garstang's analysis that

> . . . the ancestors of the chordates were sessile [free-floating] filter-feeders; that the actively swimming larva seen here is a new development at or just prior to the attainment of the ascidian [tunicate] level, and that further evolution toward the true vertebrate stage was by paedomorphosis — abandonment of the original sessile adult-condition, and evolutionary elaboration of the larval animal (p. 60).

Having described the chordate's dual — "visceral" and "somatic" — neural structure, already cited in Chapter III, Romer continues:

> This anatomical duality appears to be represented by a duality in behavior-systems: (1) visceral, internal responses, regulated by [autonomic] nerves and endocrines inherited from the ancestral visceral adult, and (2) external responses, brought about by the development of somatic, sensory, nervous and locomotor structures. I suggest that many features in the neurology and behavior of vertebrates may be explained to some degree by this duality of origin; there has been in higher vertebrates a welding together of somatic and visceral structures and functions, but their union is still far from perfect or complete" (p. 61).

The following chart serves to summarize Romer's dual-system conception:

ROMER'S "VISCERAL SYSTEM"

Structure	*Function*
(1) Elaborate food-collecting apparatus. (2) Gut. (3) Gonads. (4) Associated neural and endocrine structures.	Visceral, internal responses, regulated by autonomic nerves and endocrines inherited from the ancestral visceral adult.

ROMER'S "SOMATIC SYSTEM"

Structure	*Function*
(1) Active locomotor apparatus of striated musculature, supported by a notochord. (2) Sensory structures strongly receptive to external stimuli. (3) A relatively elaborate nervous system of "brain," spinal cord and somatic nerves, controlling the locomotor apparatus.	External responses, brought about by the development of somatic, sensory, nervous and locomotor structures.

Herrick's division of his "analytic" conduction system into a visceral-sensory pool and a somatic-sensory pool at both the lowest (salamander) and highest (man) vertebrate levels has also been already referred to in Chapter III. In his description of the three cortical fields — medial, lateral, dorsal — of the reptilian brain, also cited in Chapter III, Herrick identifies the medial field as having functions similar to the first sensory pool of the salamander's medulla (i.e., olfacto-visceral), and as later giving rise to the mammalian hippocampus; the lateral field as having functions similar to the salamander's second sensory pool (i.e., olfacto-somatic), and as later giving rise to the mammalian piriform or limbic cortex; and the phylogenetically new dorsal field as having large thalamocortical sensory connections and a motor cortex and later becoming the neocortex.

The reptile's three cortical fields may be taken as prototypical of the mammalian brain. Utilizing only the sensory side of Herrick's description, and adapting the forebrain-dominated human brain to it, the following diagram was developed:

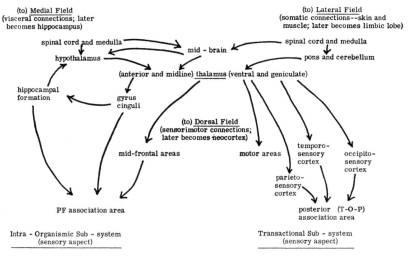

Figure 7. Hypothesized sensory aspect of the intra-organismic and transactional sub-systems.

The left half of Figure 7 indicates the supracord sensory components of an internally oriented system, hereafter termed the *Intraorganismic subsystem*; the right half indicates the sensory components (with the exception of the striatum) of an externally oriented system, hereafter termed the *Transactional subsystem*.

The diffusely organized Integrative system is concentrated not only in various nuclei or centers in the CNS and most especially in the association areas of the neocortex, as Herrick postulates (78, p. 251). The recently discovered network of unmyelinated, slower-conducting, diffusely distributed neural pathways, paralleling in a one to one manner the myelinated, faster-conducting, and function- and distribution-specific motor and sensory pathways, would appear to indicate that it also encompasses a conduction system which overlaps with the pathways of the two mode-specific branches of the "analytic" system. The reticular mesh and nuclei of the brain-stem and thalamus appear to comprise the subcortical aspects of the Integrative system.

The question was raised in Chapter III as to whether there might be some special significance in the dual circumstance that the mid-brain section of the neuraxis is the only part of the matured brain that has persisted without further subdivision from the primary, neural-tube stage of development *and* that this part of the CNS is demarcated at the same time as the spinal cord, phylogenetically the most primitive section of the neuraxis. Such special significance may well be that the BSRF — which has persisted virtually unchanged throughout the vertebrate series and which apparently serves as the first central locus where the three systems interact with one another — is located in the mid-brain. As for the thalamus-centered unspecific thalamocortical integrating system, Jasper makes two suggestive comments, already cited but worth repeating in this context, that (1) there seems to be a competitive interaction in the sensory areas of the neocortex between the specific and the unspecific projection systems for the control of cortical electrical activity, and (2) the UTCIS's influence on the sensory neocortex may be related to subjective sensation and perception.

It is debatable whether the sensory-modifying motor pathways, and the muscle-spindle-modifying sensory-feedback pathways centered in the BSRF should be grouped with the Integrative system or with the Transactional subsystem. The latter arrangement is probably the more accurate, functionally, so long as it is understood that these modifying, perception-related networks are influenced by the functioning of the Integrative system, which incorporates and transmits the accumulated learnings of *both* the Intraorganismic and Transactional subsystems.

At the heart of all three systems is the thalamus. The paucity of information on its prenatal and early postnatal development, including its intra- and inter-functional relationships, is particularly regrettable in light of this circumstance.

Pribram's emphasis on the thalamus in his neural-organization schema makes it noteworthy. He also speaks of two vertically organized systems very similar to those postulated by Romer and Herrick, one made up of an "internally or centrally located core of neural systems," and an "external portion of the forebrain," each of which contains "both old and new formations" (153, p. 143). He concentrates on the forebrain components of each system, especially on the thalamic nuclei which subserve each one. Close examination of his 1958 and later, 1960, analysis (154a) however, reveals that he consistently interjects aspects of the Integrative system into his "internal" and "external" systems conception. Reinterpretation of his figure allocating various dorsal thalamic nuclei to each of his two systems (153, p. 149) according to the three-system arrangement here postulated suggests that (1) the anterior thalamic nuclei subserve the Intraorganismic subsystem; (2) the ventral and geniculate nuclei subserve the Transactional subsystem; (3) the midline, intralaminar, centromedian and medial thalamic nuclei subserve the Intraorganismic forebrain section of the Integrative system, and (4) the posterior thalamic nuclei subserve the Transactional forebrain section of the Integrative system.

Although the precise structural details of each of the systems here postulated, their exact function, the developmental history of their respective structures and functions, and their functional interrelationships all require further experimental verification, enough data and relevant theorizing is already available to warrant the making of some reasonably precise guesses concerning the characteristics of each system. Accordingly, it is here postulated that phylogenesis has bequeathed a triple neural system to the human species: the Intraorganismic subsystem, the Transactional subsystem, and the Integrative system.

THE INTRAORGANISMIC SUBSYSTEM

The first of the two subsystems, called the "Intraorganismic vegetative and feeling-tone subsystem," is conceived as subserving the organism's internal milieu, that is, its basic life processes, *as well as* the organism's orientation to — its feelings about, attitudes towards — self and external world. Such behavioral concepts as organismically-centered drives or instincts (including Freud's id) and emotion can be related to it. The strong possibility that it also subserves a still more complex, subjective, function for the human individual — awareness of one's own reactivity — will be discussed in a later chapter. Its sensory pathway reaches the thalamus via the hypothalamus, and from the thalamus it goes to the cingulate gyrus of the frontal mesopallium (and thence to the PF association area). Its motor pathway goes from the cingulate cortex (with feed-ins from the PF area) to the hippocampal formation, thence to the hypothalamus and the rest of the ANS.

The Intraorganismic subsystem functions through two discrete-yet-overlapping sensorimotor circuits: a short and a long. The "short circuit" subserves the vegetative-homeostatic processes of the body; its highest coordinating center is the hypothalamus. Neurophysiology's updated picture of the autonomic nervous system — that is, as having both CNS and PerNS components, with the hypothalamus at the top of the functional hierarchy — provides the motor aspect of the "short circuit." Significantly, in light of Romer's formulations, the body's chemical order of functioning is closely inter-related with its neural order through the hypothalamus' close functional relationships with the pituitary, the "master gland." Fulton's "levels of ANS functioning" formulation, cited on page 103, documents the hierarchical-reduplicative organization of the short circuit. The "long circuit" entails the connections to the cingulate gyrus and prefrontal association area, thence to the hypothalamus (and the ANS) via the hippocampal formation — that is, it is the "limbic system" described in the previous chapter. The long circuit provides for the "orientation" aspect of the Intraorganismic system's hypothesized functional role: it "transforms" inner, physiologically derived sensations into (psychological) experience, a function analogous to receptor cells' transformation of physical energy into neural energy. It affects physiological functioning via the hypothalamus and influences the motor component of the Transactional subsystem through relevant Integrative system circuits.

THE TRANSACTIONAL SUBSYSTEM

The second of the two subsystems is being termed the "transactional-perceptual" subsystem. It is seen as directly subserving both the organism's interactive transactions with the physical world external to it, *and* its awareness-perception of itself as a physical entity and of the outside world. The posterior, T-O-P, association area is believed to be the core locus of the perceptual process.

The sensory aspect of this subsystem comprises the specific sensory pathways direct to the thalamus, and also the sensory aspect of the cerebellar-striatal-thalamic subcircuit; thence to the sensory neocortex and the T-O-P association area. The motor aspect of the Transactional subsystem has two distinct components: the rapid pyramidal "short circuit" to the skeletal muscles via the cerebellum, which ordinarily functions almost automatically; and the modifying of sensory-input motor pathways which Livingston has described as paralleling every ascending neural pathway on a one to one basis and as providing for central regulation of sensory transmission (discussed in the previous chapter). The cortical processes and centers from which these modifying pathways derive, the pathways themselves, and the incoming-sensory tracts upon which they exert highest-level influences, together comprise the Transactional "long circuit"; its functional role is to "transform" externally derived sensation into (psychological) experience and, via relevant Integrative system circuits, to initiate the purposeful bodily activity that may result.

According to Romer's analysis, the Transactional subsystem is the newer, phylogenetically, of the two subsystems postulated.

THE INTEGRATIVE SYSTEM

At this point, we have two vertically organized, apparently functionally discrete subsystems, except for their convergence in the thalamus. In actuality, there is, *in situ,* much interaction between them — and here is where the slower conducting, diffusely organized Integrative system comes in. The extralemniscal sensory pathways, the BSRF, the UTCIS, the extrapyramidal motor pathways are key components of this system, which will hereafter be termed, collectively, the "central integrating circuits" or *CI circuits* in abbreviation.

Already traced-out integrative circuits are the ARAS, the UTCIS (which is the upper, thalamocortical, aspect of the ARAS), circuit 1 on page 132, and most importantly, Penfield's CIS, which appears to overlap with the ARAS and possibly also with the first circuit described on page 132. Also, there are major concentrations of integrative tissue in the neocortical association areas, in the basal ganglia, in the cerebellum, and in various nuclei of the brain-stem and forebrain. The discussion of the vertebrate integrative conduction apparatus in Chapter III is also relevant. The following schema is derived from the integrative networks which are already known.

The CI circuits comprise six forebrain branches or categories, here listed in their hypothesized *developmental* order:

(1) Those networks paralleling the mode-specific sensory pathways to and from the posterior cortex (these feed into and out of the posterior thalamic nuclei) .

(2) Those networks paralleling the motor pathways from and to the pre-central and mid-frontal cortex (these feed into and out of the basal ganglia) .

(3) Those pathways paralleling the ANS networks of the forebrain — i.e., paralleling the limbic system (these feed into and out of the anterior and midline and centromedian thalamic nuclei) . (Or is the limbic system a CI circuit *in itself,* perhaps?)

(4) The heavy reciprocal connections between the T-O-P posterior association area and the posterior thalamic nuclei.

(5) The heavy reciprocal connections between the temporal pole and the posterior thalamic nuclei.

(6) The reciprocal connections between the PF association area and the intralaminar and medial thalamic nuclei.

In the matured, conscious brain, all "branches" function together as a coherent unit.

Branches 1, 2, 4 collect data from and feed data to the Transactional subsystem from other forebrain centers and from sub-forebrain centers. Branch 3 collects data from and feeds data to the Intraorganismic subsystem. Branch 5 serves both the Intra-organismic and Transactional subsystems.

Branch 6, which develops well after birth, as we shall see, is related somewhat differently to the Integrative system than the other "branches." This CI circuit projects to the PF association area (via the thalamus) data deriving from the ongoing function-ing of the Transactional and Intraorganismic subsystems, and in turn feeds back data via the thalamus to cortical centers involved in the functioning of the Intraorganismic and Transactional sub-systems; thus branch 6 is the most heavily dependent of all the CI circuits upon the accumulated experiences of the individual. It appears not to develop at all in the autistic and early-schizophrenic child, to be defectively developed in psychopaths, and to be min-imally developed in persons with limited mental ability, whether the limitation is due to organic factors or to environmental de-privation or to a combination of both. *It appears to have emerged phylogenetically only with the human species.*

The Integrative system appears to play a key role in creative thought; in all probability, in all types of creative activity. Its linking together of initially isolated T-O-P area neural structur-ings is the process which underlies the emergence of new insights. This rationale fits the personal observation of many that creative insights usually begin to emerge after one has been immersed for a lengthy period in the materials related to the problem or area of thought. It also fits the further observation that it is usually either after a night's sleep or a period of time spent in a completely different activity that the most important new ideas occur. Such an hiatus would appear to interrupt at the thalamic level the blocking dominance of either external stimulation or a related-but-irrelevant neural structuring — or both, and so permit the easily over-powered CI circuits to "come through."

THE T-O-P ASSOCIATION AREA AND THE PERCEPTUAL PROCESS

More thorough discussion of the behavioral correlates of this triple-system schema beyond the generalizations already given is being postponed until the later presentation of postnatal developmental data, since these correlates are more readily constructed within a developmental framework. However, authoritative speculation relevant to some of these correlates already exists and will be referred to here.

The intimate involvement of the posterior, temporo-occipito-parietal (T-O-P) association area in the process of perception appears, by implication, to be accepted by some investigators, Herrick among them. According to Herrick, it may well be the actual locus of the perceptual process. His analysis of the properties of an electrodynamic field, cited in Chapter VI, applies especially well to the cortical association areas, which are especially rich in integrative, diffusely and gradedly conducting neuropil. It is legitimate to assume that in the T-O-P area ". . . analysis and synthesis of experience go on hand in hand and simultaneously. It is therefore not surprising that the sensorimotor and integrative tissue are closely related and intricately interwoven" (78, p. 244). Recall that all sensory data from the external world and from both the surface and the inside of the body are channeled into the T-O-P electrodynamic field. Perceptually, "the knowings and the known are intrinsic components of a field of experience within which they are inseparable" (p. 279). "An essential feature of perceptual integration is the polarization of the perceiving subject against the things perceived" (p. 349) ; that is, "I experience myself in action as immediately as I experience things acted upon" (p. 207). This polarization of "subject" (the knower) and "object" (the known) within the T-O-P field is "basic for perception and all mental processes derived from it" (p. 323).

In Herrick's terminology, perception is an "analytic" neural function, as opposed to the nervous system's integrative functions. He clearly feels that it is important for the distinction between these two basic functions of the nervous system to be grasped, and elaborates upon it at some length. The following excerpts summarize his estimate of the distinction:

The analytic functions, which are primarily concerned with adjustments of the organism to its environment, must of necessity be oriented in space and time with the body of the organism as a fixed point of reference. The integrative processes, on the contrary, are wholly internal to the body and some of the laws of their action are relativistic rather than inflexibly bound to dimensions that can be measured in absolute units of space and time. The analysis of sensory and motor processes must be made (consciously or unconsciously) in terms of spatial and temporal relations that can be numerically expressed. Integration combines the products of this analysis in a constructive process in which space and time may not be separately individuated but retain a primordial unity as space-time defined relativistically and in parameters different from those of Newtonian mechanics (p. 273).

Everything in our objective world is set in a frame of perceptual space and time, but all conceptual [i.e., integrative] processes are more or less independent of this frame of reference. All thinking is now and here (p. 272).

In both phylogenetic and embryological development, unconscious action in four-dimensional space-time precedes our perceptual individuation of three-dimensional space and linear-dimensional time (p. 276). In current mathematical theory a time dimension is added to three-dimensional space, giving integrated four-dimensional space-time. In behavior the integrative processes go on in four-dimensional space-time primordially. If consciousness emerges within the integrative process, then the activity is stepped up to a higher level and a fifth dimension is added to the original four dimensions. It may be argued further that in conceptual thinking, which employs language and other symbols of high-level abstraction, the process is being stepped up to a still higher level, with the addition of still another dimension to the complex (p. 277).

The third functional-organization pattern, which has been presented here in tentative, outline form, is at once the most comprehensive and the most conjectural of the three functional-organization patterns postulated. In essence, it is that the organization of the nervous system at neurological maturity represents the outcome of a continuous, largely — perhaps entirely — postnatal developmental process involving the knitting together[1] of

---

[1]This term is preferred over Romer's "welding," not because the writer is a woman (who doesn't knit), but because it is believed to express more adequately the nature of the complex neural-interconnecting process involved.

the two disparate structural and behavioral legacies here termed the Intraorganismic and Transactional subsystems; the thalamus is a core factor in this knitting process. The details of this neurogenic, chiefly forebrain, process, have yet to be documented by research. It is further hypothesized that (a) each of the three systems has its own developmental timetable, and (b) the integrative process referred to in the second-last sentence is heavily influenced by the growing individual's experiences.

With the postulation of the triple-system functional-organization pattern, we are now in a position to determine from the postnatal data whether the seventh developmental pattern formulated in Chapter IV — that the coherent, unified functioning of the physiologically mature nervous system represents the end-product incorporation of a progressive series of organized functional patterns which develop in a hierarchic (i.e., vertical) ontogenetic sequence — is borne out.

Certainly the hierarchical order of the emergence of mental functions, upon which all authorities appear to be agreed, will be better understood when these four inter-related neural variables are better understood:

(1) The functional and behavioral correlates of the horizontal-cum-vertical organization of cortical nerve cells, nerve processes and endogenous and exogenous fibers;

(2) The pattern and timing of development of the Intraorganismic short and long circuits;

(3) The pattern and timing of development of the Transactional short and long circuits, and

(4) The pattern of integration of the two subsystems, as well as *its* developmental timing.

It may well be that such fundamentally important, still unsolved, neuropsychological problems as the following will also yield to the broader orientation provided by the third functional-organization pattern:

(1) Why is it that only some aspects of an individual's environment constitute CNS "intake"?

(2) Why is it that there can be "outgo" without prior intake?

(3) Why is it that some intake—outgo sequences permanently change the organism's subsequent behavior while others do not?

PART D

**THE SEARCH FOR DEVELOPMENTAL
PATTERNS II:
RELATING OF POSTNATAL NEURAL AND
BEHAVIORAL DEVELOPMENT**

Chapter VIII

APPROACH AND NEURAL OVERVIEW

PREAMBLE TO PART D

In the previous section, the matured nervous system was examined, with the focus primarily on its functional organization as a physical system. This emphasis was an expression of the earlier cited proposition that all human behavior, whether innate or learned or a fusion of both, is directly dependent upon the nature of the given *and* potential neural structure-functioning biologically indigenous to the human species. We are now in a position to compare the status of the human nervous system at neural-behavioral maturity with its status at birth.

Chapter IV, after presenting an overview of the neural structural status and behavioral repertoire of the newborn human infant, concluded with the deduction that at birth, the infant's behavior is mediated primarily by hind-brain and mid-brain centers, with probably some forebrain (diencephalic, striatal and old cortex) participation; and that by the end of the first month of postnatal life, there is also some participation of primary-sensorimotor and visual areas of the cortex. We are not born, Table IV made clear, with the ability for refined and smooth complex motor and eye-hand coordinations and skills, nor for sustained mental manipulation of symbols, nor with the ability to formulate a long-term plan and carry it out, nor for awareness of and strong feelings about self, nor with attitudes and values and ethics and religious beliefs.

If we accept the fundamental assumption of this inquiry that all the uniquely human behaviors just enumerated are directly dependent upon a nervous system which obviously continues to develop after birth, and which makes possible all individual experience, performance and learning, we are confronted with a very wide gap indeed between the status of the nervous system at birth and at neural maturity. This gap prompts these two questions:

167

(1) *What* neural maturative changes occur between birth and maturity, and *when* do they occur?
(2) When developmental trends in behavior are matched against indices of neural development, do relationships between the two orders of data become apparent?

This section (Chapters VIII through XII) will address itself to both these questions.

APPROACH

At the time material for this inquiry was gathered, systematic longitudinal studies deriving both neural and behavioral indices of development from the *same* samples of infants and children had apparently not been done. But a few cross-sectional studies of neural changes with age, some structural and some functional, were found in the neurological literature. The field of developmental psychology has made rich materials on human behavioral development readily available, in reputable secondary as well as primary sources. So an interim, hopefully heuristic, approach has been adopted.

Behavioral data were abstracted from a variety of sources, both primary and secondary but chiefly secondary, systematically collated under age and behavioral categories, and behavioral trends deduced therefrom.[1] These trends will be presented under eight successive age-levels: the first month of life, one to three months, one to two years, two to six years, six to eleven to twelve years, eleven to twelve years to neural maturity. This organization is based primarily on the organization of the data in the literature. Since formulation of generalized developmental trends rather than a specific timetable of development was the intermediate goal, critical examination of the original studies is being dispensed with: it is assumed that readers interested in more thorough documentation will have access to the sources from which the behavioral materials were drawn.

The neural studies located have also been developmentally organized, and will be presented within the same age periods.

---

[1] A listing of these categories *and sources* is included as Appendix A.

Neurological data related to the first few years of life comprise gross-structural, histological (including myelination), and EEG analyses. Beyond four years of age, only gross-structural and EEG studies could be located. It is especially unfortunate, in light of the important role of unmyelinated nerve-tracts in the functional organization of the matured nervous system, that data on the pre- and post- natal development of these tracts appear to be nonexistent. Also, the circumstance that the postnatal neural data to be cited are chiefly neocortical leaves many important lacunae from a developmentalist's point of view: what of postnatal patterns of development of other forebrain centers, especially the thalamus, of the cerebellum, especially the neocerebellum, the time of onset of impulse-conduction in the various interconnecting pathways, both myelinated and unmyelinated, forebrain—sub-forebrain, as well as intraforebrain?

Within each age-level, after both orders of ontogenetic data have been presented in sequence, an attempt will be made to answer Question 2 in the Preamble above. In line with Sellars' points that at our phylogenetic level a second — i.e., subjective — way of knowing has emerged and that therefore it is important to include as essential data the subjective concomitants of objectively observable events, deductions concerning the subjective dimension of behavior will be made from the objective data in positing relationships between the two orders of data, especially when this dimension appears to be playing a key role in objectively observed behavior. Material on the development of the self is constructed chiefly on this basis.

Before proceeding to a more extended introduction to the neural data, it is important to acknowledge explicitly at the outset that behavioral changes which occur with age cannot be ascribed solely to neural maturation. Growth changes in accessory structures — in the receptor-organs, in the bones and skeleton and muscles, in the organ-systems, in the glands and in related biochemical factors — also occur after birth and obviously contribute to behavioral change. Even more complicative is the circumstance that learning enters into the shaping of behavior at every stage of human development, less so in the early months, more and more so as time goes on. How then can behavioral changes which are manifestly due to a multiplicity of factors be justifiably attributed to only one of these factors? More important, how can one with confidence ascribe a particular change in behavior to particular maturative changes in the nervous system rather than to the individual child's experience subsequent to birth?

Such an enterprise is indeed untenable and is not the writer's goal. My goal within this context is more realistic; it is, rather, to be guided by this question: *Can one reasonably conclude from the data that a particular evidence of neural change has contributed to, played a role in, a particular behavioral development?*

"But why can't the relationship be in the opposite direction: may not the child's experience have brought about the neural change?" a not-so-imaginary challenger might further question. The best answer I can give to this difficult question is my present idea of how neural-development factors are related to learning, summarized in these three propositions:

(1) Learning is dependent upon the individual organism's having an experience, either conscious or unconscious. An experience may or may not have an overt-motor component.

(2) An organism's "having an experience" is dependent, as a minimum, upon conduction in central supra-midbrain neural tissue (perhaps even in *cortical* tissue), conduction which is in turn dependent upon two *equally essential* contributing conditions: relevant stimulation, and maturational readiness to conduct of neural sensory tissue which is enabling of that particular category of experience. Previously nonconducting neural tissue which is stimulated to conduct by conduction in adjoining tissue will do so only if it is sufficiently advanced in cellular etc. maturation to be able to function.

(3) The organism's having had an experience is recorded permanently or semipermanently in the nervous system in some way, such as a neocortical cell-assembly, as postulated by Hebb. (There are other observed or proposed permanent or semipermanent physiological evidences of learning which will not be itemized here.)

The foregoing formulation provides for this further postulation: Where the neural evidence indicates continued functional immaturity of neural tissue known or believed to be enabling of a particular category of behavior which has not yet emerged at the age observed, then *it is tenable to assume that continuing maturation of such tissue is prerequisite to the eventual emergence of that behavior.* This postulation is important for my purposes because it provides for heuristic speculation beyond the as yet scanty neurogenic data — speculation believed to be warrantable within the context of a theoretical discussion.

OVERVIEW OF NEUROGENIC DATA AND TRENDS

Conel's meticulous histological studies of the postnatal human cerebral cortex, already briefly referred to, are being extensively drawn upon in this section. His work now comprises seven volumes, as follows (38) :

Volume No.	Date of Publication	Brains of Children Who Died At:	Number of Brains Studied
1	1939	birth	6
2	1941	1 month	5
3	1947	3 months	6
4	1951	6 months	7
5	1955	15 months	3
6	1959	2 years	6
7	1963	4 years	8

The varied staining techniques of the professional pathologist was the basic investigative method. Brains removed from children deceased of non-neural causes or complications comprise the bases of the data at each age level; additional preparations of ages in between were also examined on an exploratory basis.

Conel utilizes nine maturative criteria, and on the basis of these criteria, finds these nine maturative trends to be histologically consistent throughout the developmental period so far studied by him:

(1) The width or thickness of the entire cortex and of each cortical layer increases with age.

(2) The number of nerve-cells per study-unit decreases with age because

(3) the size of nerve-cells increases.

(4) There is a progressive change in the condition of the

chromophil substance of the nerve cells, from small granules (immature state), to clumpings of granules, to Nissl bodies (mature state).

(5) Nerve fibrils emerge within neurons (from random granules, to rows of granules, to solid strands, to nerve fibrils) and increase in number with age.

(6) The caliber, length and compactness of nerve-processes (axons and dendrites) increase with age.

(7) Pedunculated bulbs on the dendrites increase in each cell and show up in more cells with increasing age.

(8) Both the quantity and size of exogenous fibers increase with age.

(9) Myelination of nerve cells and nerve processes spreads with age.

Wide individual differences obtained on all these criteria at all ages studied. Possible sex differences were not investigated, unfortunately.

On the basis of the various maturative criteria listed above, Conel's data show that the cells of the human cerebral cortex manifest these simultaneous *or* overlapping growth-gradients:

Topologically or horizontally:

(1) Beginning first and proceeding fastest: the primary-motor and primary-sensory areas; the central-fissure area develops earliest and fastest of all.

(2) Beginning second and proceeding at a slower pace than the first gradient: areas directly adjacent to the primary areas which have a primary-area-modifying function; and a few old cortex areas.

(3) Beginning third and proceeding at a slower pace than the first two gradients: secondary areas in the frontal lobe and old cortex; and the posterior, T-O-P, association area (the outer edges of it — i.e., the areas closest to the sensory-receptive areas — become functional first and the most central area last).

(4) Beginning last, the prefrontal (PF) association area, which lags well behind the posterior association area in onset and in pace of maturation.

Vertically:

(5) Growth proceeds from the inner or bottom neocortical layers up to the outer or upper layers; the top layer, number 1, is the possible single exception to this trend.

Conel's data on the postnatal development of the old cortex is puzzling in light of embryological and phylogenetic growth patterns: they show that the cells of the hippocampus and limbic lobe lag behind those of the primary sensorimotor, central-fissure area. Whether human ontogenesis does indeed *not* recapitulate phylogenesis in this instance, or whether methodological factors yielded incomplete data — for example, unmyelinated fibers may be important in old cortex functioning but were not identified — or some other, entirely overlooked possibility, is not known at this time.

For behavioral-deduction purposes, the design of Conel's research has certain limitations. Nothing is known of the experiences, or of the behavioral status at time of death, of any of the children whose brains were studied. Nor is it possible to know from Conel's data alone (with the possible exception of Trend 9) at precisely what maturative point conduction in a particular cell or a particular area or a particular layer actually begins: there is need for a series of investigations here!

Conel himself has recourse in his first few volumes to data of developmental psychologists such as Carmichael, McGraw, Gesell, to deduce functional status. Also, the possibility of consistent sex differences in development, which the behavioral and the EEG data clearly indicate exist, were not checked on by Conel. In spite of these limitations however, his reports seem to be the only systematic and thorough studies in the literature of the structural changes with development of at least a part of the postnatal nervous system and have therefore been indispensable to this inquiry.

Other, earlier, sources (8 and 102) echo Conel's myelination trend. The myelination pattern of the various neocortical areas, much like that of the interconnecting nerve-tracts, already referred to in Chapter IV, follows their respective phylogenetic and ontogenetic histories: the oldest (primary-somatoviscerosensory and primary-motor) are myelinated earliest, the modifying and secondary areas are myelinated next, and the newest (concentrated associational) areas last.

Turner's cortical studies of gross-structural characteristics show that the cortex as a whole continues to grow after birth both in free surface-area and in fissuration. This growth is especially rapid — fourfold — between birth and six years, with minor or localized changes thereafter (181, 182). As for lobe subpatterns of growth, the following chart of relative rates of growth of each of the four lobes is derived from Turner's discussion:

TABLE V
RELATIVE GROWTH RATES OF NEOCORTICAL LOBES[1]

	Parietal Lobe		*Occipital Lobe*		*Temporal Lobe*		*Frontal Lobe*	
Age Period	*Surface Area*	*Fissuration*	*Surface Area*	*Fissuration*	*Surface Area*	*Fissuration*	*Surface Area*	*Fissuration*
0-2 years	most rapid	rapid	same as the over-all pat-tern (see text)	same as the parietal lobe	moder-ate	rapid in auditory portion.	rapid	moder-ate
2-6	same as overall pattern (see text)	moder-ate			very rapid	rapid in temporal pole.	moder-ate and even un-til near-max-imum	rapid
6 and after	practic-ally none; total at 24 years.	moder-ate, to a sub-max-imum at 10.	none		none	none	imum at 10 (total at 20 years)	moder-ate, to sub-max-imum at 10.

[1]Based on 181, 182.

The rapid rate of growth for the two-to-six-year period in both the temporal and frontal lobes is especially noteworthy.

Biochemical aspects and accompaniments of postnatal neuro-genesis are not being systematically included in this survey. Nevertheless, this question needs to be interjected: why is it that cortical cells begin to function immediately after viable birth and not before, when cells immediately subjacent to the cortex are apparently functioning prior to birth? The answer appears to be: because of the "oxygen barrier," which prevents the presence of function-essential oxygen in the blood supply of the cortex until after birth (12). Only with the inspiration of the birth-cry and subsequent onset of aerobic respiration can subcortical electrical conduction at last trigger cortical-cell conduction. Thereafter, three, rather than the earlier postulated two, factors seem to be operative in the spread of cortical functioning:

(1) shift from anaerobic to aerobic respiration in a particular cortical area and layer;

(2) a sufficient degree (equals??) of cellular maturation in the same area or layer, and

(3) presence of stimulative conduction in adjacent or subjacent neural tissue.

Impulse conduction appears to serve not merely an "enabling" function, but also a growth-promoting function, causing an increase in blood oxygen in adjacent cortical tissue and consequent acceleration of cellular maturation. It is this intervening physiological process which seems to underlie the maturation-promoting influence of individual experience that has frequently been pointed to.

Developmental trends in cortical electrical activity, summarized in Table VI below, are derived from studies to be individually cited in subsequent chapters in this section; this summary assumes that the reader is familiar with the material in Orientation Supplement 6. EEG studies of changes in neocortical electrical activity with age reveal that these parameters of the EEG record show developmental changes:

(1) continuity and regularity-stability;
(2) (a) frequency, and (b) proportions, of each type of frequency: delta, theta, alpha, beta;
(3) voltage or amplitude;
(4) state-of-consciousness differentiation;
(5) patterns characteristic of the various stages of sleep;
(6) transition from a sleep-pattern to a waking record upon arousal;
(7) asynchrony versus synchrony;
(8) asymmetry versus symmetry;
(9) area differentiation *or* degree of organization.

Girls' EEG records are more mature than boys' at every age studied. Also, wide ranges of individual variation in rate and pattern on every EEG index are typical. Clinical use of the EEG

TABLE VI
POSTNATAL DEVELOPMENTAL TRENDS IN THE EEG

EEG Parameter	*Overall Trend*
Continuity and stability-regularity.	(1) The young infant's EEG is labile and diffuse in patterning, with periods of total lack of activity. Continuity of activity and stability-regularity of activity and of overall patterning steadily increase up to neurological maturity. Also, a child's EEG is more affected by overbreathing than an adult's.
Frequency; and proportion of each type of frequency. Voltage or amplitude.	(2) Frequency tends to increase with age, while (3) Amplitude tends to decrease. Delta activity (up to 1½-3 cps) is the most typical wave-band up to one year; theta (4-7 cps) is the dominant activity from 2 to 5 years, theta and alpha (8-13 cps) are about equally frequent at 5-6 years, and alpha is increasingly the most common frequency after 6 years. Beta waves (14 cps and higher) increase variably with age; fast records become increasingly common between 15 and 60 years.
State of consciousness differentiation. Patterns characteristic of the various stages of sleep.	(4) Initially, the EEG record shows no difference between waking and sleeping; by maturity, it shows consistent differences not only between sleeping and waking but between seven stages of sleep: drowsiness, very light sleep, light sleep, moderately deep sleep, deep sleep, early-morning sleep, arousal. Most of the activity in the waking record comes from lower-than-vertex and posterior areas; during sleep, most activity is at the veretex and from the frontal areas (151). (5) The electrical activity associated with the various stages of sleep show characteristic developmental-level patterns.
Transition from a deep-sleep record to a waking record upon arousal.	(6) In children, there is an intermediate phase, electrically, between the sleeping and the aroused-waking record. Beyond the midteens, arousal is usually abrupt, without this intermediate phase.
Asynchrony vs. synchrony.	(7) Asynchrony of the wave-forms from analogous areas is typical of the infant's record. Synchrony increases steadily during the first several years.
Asymmetry versus symmetry.	(8) Asymmetry — activity in only one hemisphere — is frequent during infancy and early childhood. With increasing age, matched activity from corresponding areas in both hemispheres becomes typical.
Area differentiation or degree of organization.	(9) Electrical activity is originally diffusely and unpredictably distributed over the neocortex. With age, activity becomes increasingly organized and delimited according to cortical areas, and there is also a developmental progression in intra-area activity and in acquisition of mature patterning: the parietal area shows regular activity first, the primary-motor and occipital lobe (visual) areas are next, with the occipital areas shortly overtaking the parietal lobe in proportion and regularity of activity. The activity of the prefrontal

EEG Parameter	Overall Trend
	regions differentiates last and takes the longest to attain a fully adult pattern. In general, according to Monnier (132), electrical activitty becomes more monomorphic, localized, systematized and structured, with definite irreversibility: once a more mature pattern is acquired, it will not regress to the previous stage, unless disease occurs.

shows that whether a particular EEG pattern is considered normal or abnormal is frequently a function of the patient's age. Persistence of patterns which are typical of — and therefore normal for — the young child into adolescence and adulthood are almost invariably associated with at least some categories of behavior disorder, especially of "acting out" and psychopathic categories.

The data in Table VI suggest that regularly repeated early EEGs may at last provide an index of infantile mental functioning which will later correlate respectably with later tested IQ. Do children who later test out bright (1) manifest certain EEG patterns younger, and (2) go through each phase in the developmental patterning of waves, etc. at an earlier age, than do children who later test out as average or slow?

Another question deserving of investigative checking is: Which parameters of the EEG record are entirely maturational and which are affected by the individual's life experiences? And another: Is the gradual emergence of EEG patterns associated with various stages of sleep related to the onset of function in the succeeding lower to upper layers of the cortex?

A consistent theme of the behavioral data, the developmental retardation of the male organism in comparison with the female, appears to rest on a neural base: the male human nervous system is less advanced in maturational status at birth, and this lag is maintained throughout the entire growth-to-maturity sequence. This culturally touchy datum is being neither ignored nor minimized in the ensuing presentation, not only because it exists and there is therefore an obligation to report it. The possibility that this apparently biologically determined circumstance is of major theoretical, individual *and social* import constitutes an additional reason for its careful documentation.

Chapter IX

FROM BIRTH TO TWO YEARS

FROM BIRTH TO ONE MONTH

F<small>ROM THE MATERIAL</small> included in Table IV, *The Human Neonate,* in Chapter IV, the following are key *behavioral characteristics* of this period:

(1) Basic mammalian reflexes — feeding, protective, foot, hand — are present. In Piaget's schema (148), the first month is the first, "exercise of innate sensorimotor schemata" phase of the "sensorimotor period," the first stage in the development of intelligence.

(2) The oral drives are dominant; the mouth also acts as an orientation device to the babe's immediate external world.

(3) There is only gross emotional reactivity, chiefly in response to inner needs: the frequent vocalization shows different cries for hunger, pain, discomfort. Only two attitudes towards an external stimulus have been observed: accepting or rejecting.

(4) Vowel sounds are five times as frequent as consonants.

(5) Physiological homeostasis is not yet established; the basic vegetative processes are unstable.

(6) Motor and sensorimotor coordination and control is lacking.

(7) Thermal sensitivity is present at birth and shows a foot-to-head sensitivity gradient. Pressure, then pain, sensitivities emerge shortly after birth, showing a head-to-foot sensitivity gradient. There is only gross sensitivity to light; the pupillary reflex, a thalamic reaction, is present — it emerges during the first week; girls are more visually sensitive than boys. There are only gross reactions to auditory stimuli; girls react faster than boys. Taste and olfactory sensitivities are rudimentary.

(8) Awareness of and response to the external environment is minimal.

Still from the material included in Table IV, the following are key *neural characteristics* of the neonatal period:

(1) The only cortical areas showing some degree of cellular development are, in decreasing order: the central-fissure (primary sensorimotor) area, the primary-visual area, a hippocampal area, a limbic area, the primary-auditory area. Electrical activity has been recorded only from the central-fissure area during the first month; at birth, from only the primary-somatoviscerosensory section of the parietal lobe.

(2) Myelin is present on vertical exogenous fibers (from subcortical centers) only in the lowest cortical layer.

(3) In both the primary-motor and the primary-somatosensory area, the cells of the subarea for trunk and shoulders are somewhat more developed, those of the hand and the leg subareas are next in degree of development, and those of the head subarea are least developed. All cells showing some degree of development are in layers 6 and 5, with a very few in layer 4 in the most advanced areas.

(4) Anaerobic metabolism is probably still present in layers above layer 5 in all but the primary-sensorimotor area; the instability of cortical electrical functioning, evident in the EEG items, seems to be a reflection of this basic metabolic immaturity.

(5) Only the two bottom neocortical layers show a fair degree of cellular development and presence of exogenous fibers, but are not yet conducting impulses beyond the central-fissure area; the dominance of slow, delta, electrical activity seems to be directly related to this lack of neocortical functioning — i.e., subcortical functioning is being recorded. (Or are delta waves a reflection of the functioning of layers 6 and 5 in at least the central-fissure area?)

During the *first month* of postnatal life, these *relationships between neural and behavioral events* appear to obtain:

The EEG records brain-wave activity only in the primary somatoviscerosensory area of the neocortex, although cells in the primary-motor and other primary-sensory areas also show some degree of development. This sole evidence of neocortical functioning, as well as the infant's reactivity almost entirely to stimuli impinging directly on the body-surface, imply that (1) internal visceral and physiological processes, and sensations transmitted by the skin-senses (including the mouth) provide the entirety of the neonate's experience; that is, the neonate is essentially internally oriented; and (2) cortical mediating mechanisms are as yet almost or entirely nonexistent, thus putting the neonate at the mercy of immediate stimulation. However, the lack of responsive awareness of the external world, due to minimal exteroceptive conduction, blocks out most potentially traumatic external stimulation — except that received by the body senses. The instability of homeostatic functioning during the first month further suggests that internal physiological processes are frequently a major source of discomfort to the babe, especially when caretakers do not intervene immediately to satisfy basic vegetative and motility needs.

The presence of the basic-mammalian reflexes, the lack of motor coordination and control, and the nonfunctional status of most of the primary and modifying neocortical motor areas, together indicate the continuing dominance of subcortical motor centers.

The "short circuit" of the Intraorganismic subsystem appears to be functioning, albeit imperfectly, by the end of the first month. The accepting or rejecting attitudes towards stimulation suggest that the thalamic component of the "long circuit" may also have begun to enter into the functioning of the Intraorganismic subsystem.

The sensory aspect of the short circuit of the Transactional subsystem, only, appears to be functioning. Whatever integrative interaction exists between the two subsystems probably occurs in the bulbar and mid-brain sections of the reticular formation and possibly also in the thalamus.

AT ONE MONTH

Continuing with the data given in Table IV, additional *behaviors* evident at one month include the following:

(1) Some degree of homeostatic control has emerged.

(2) There is some evidence of the beginnings of motor coordination and control: the babe can lift his head when prone, and also shows passive leg extension and active kneel. In Piaget's schema, a shift has occurred from the innate sensorimotor sche-

mata's passive release by stimulation, to active groping on the part of the infant.

(3) Some visual abilities are evident: can now fixate on a light and "pay attention" visually.

(4) There is still gross emotional reactivity, directly related to inner needs; but there are now active signs of pleasure and displeasure in response to the immediate external world.

Additional *neural* characteristics at one month are:

(1) Langworthy's data (Table III) indicate some degree of functioning of: the pyramidal (voluntary-motor) tract, cerebellum-centered tracts, the tract connecting the two cerebral hemispheres, subcortical components of the "limbic system."

(2) The primary-sensorimotor area has advanced in development since birth, more so in the primary-motor section; the hand motor subarea has advanced most.

(3) Cortical areas related to vision have advanced: the primary-visual area and the frontal-motor area which mediates contralateral eyeball movements. Also, visual and auditory tracts from the thalamus have acquired myelin.

(4) The six-layered cingulum of the limbic lobe shows cellular development in the two bottom layers.

(5) The cells of the two bottom layers in the central-fissure area are now conducting; the differentiation of the waking EEG record from the deep-sleep record may be related to this circumstance.

At one month, the distance-exteroceptive modality of vision has begun to play some role in the infant's experience, audition less so. Tract myelination, EEG, and behavioral data together show that in addition to earlier functioning thalamic—somatovisocerosensory cortex circuits, thalamic—primary-motor, -visual, -auditory cortex, as well as thalamic—hypothalamic and cerebellar circuits have begun to function.

Rudimentary awareness of and reactivity to the external world is evident at one month; these evidences of consciousness seem to be related to the onset of functioning in at least the bottom neocortical layer in several areas. One can guess at the subjective concomitants of this level of neural functioning: the neonate seems to be immersed in inner feelings as in a boundless and timeless sea, with few referrents beyond feeling *per se*. Reactive signs of pleasure and displeasure to external stimulation give evidence of increasing thalamic dominance.

These various events imply that the Transactional subsystem has begun to play some role in the infant's experience at one month, although he is still strongly internally oriented. Hippocampal—thalamic—hypothalamic sections of the limbic circuit may have begun to conduct impulses, adding a strong affective dimension to the functioning of the Intraorganismic subsystem.

The lesser degree of development of the male neonatal nervous system implies that (1) physiological instability is greater and more prolonged among boy babies than among girl babies, and (2) cortical mediating mechanisms begin to develop later and take longer to develop among boy babies; this delay implies that boys are dependent upon, vulnerable to, immediate skin-contact stimulation for a longer period during infancy than are girls.

FROM ONE MONTH TO THREE MONTHS

Behavioral characteristics of this period include:

(1) Many homeostatic mechanisms are established by three months.

(2) There is further growth in motor coordination and control: during the third month, infant lifts chest, can lift head up to 90°, shows symmetrical leg-extension, draws up one knee by flexion, flexes arms slightly forward, and shows alternate leg extensor-kick at three months.

(3) The various types of eye-movements emerge in sequence: horizontal (at four-and-one-half weeks), then vertical (at nine weeks), then circular (at ten weeks).

(4) Other sensory modalities improve: the sense of smell, poor during the first month, begins to function at four-and-one-half weeks; there are wide individual differences in auditory sensitivity now and later; kinesthesis is still undeveloped.

(5) Various sensorimotor coordinations emerge: hearing and phonation; a CR to a puff of air using auditory and visual CSs can be established during the second month; sucking and grasping,

and position and grasping (at two months) ; a natural CR, crying for food, is established during the third month; visual comparison, hearing and sight, first attempts at eye-hand coordination (reaches for object and misses) — all at three months. In Piaget's schema, items 5 and 6 (following) together comprise the earlier part of the sensorimotor-stage phase of "primary-circular reactions" in the development of intelligence. As during the first month, the complementary adaptive processes of accommodation and assimilation are not separated.

(6) Begins to play with own arms, feet, fingers, at three months.

(7) The vowel-consonant ratio is 4:1 during the second month; front vowels make up 72 per cent of vowels uttered at two months; coos, babbles, vocalizes one syllable during the third month — that is, the raw material for later verbalization is beginning to emerge.

(8) There are growing evidences of social awareness and responsiveness: at two months, responds to persons in line of vision, is not disturbed when handled by strangers; at three months, stops crying when attending adult comes, give heed to another's voice, turns gaze at a person, whimpers and cries when person leaves, gives a responsive, "social" smile to other's gaze or smile, "knows" his-her mother (first clear sign of memory) , reacts positively to the human voice, reacts to changes in the adult's voice, shows signs of pleasure at sight of a familiar face and of displeasure at an unfamiliar one (compare with two months) .

(9) Emotional reactions begin to show some selectivity: first evidences of delight at two months; at three months, there are clearer evidences of delight, reacts emotionally to external situations only if their disturbing or satisfying qualities can be discriminated, shows signs of pleasure at sight of a familiar face and displeasure at an unfamiliar one. But other emotional behavior reveals the continuing dominance of subcortical centers: tumescence of the penis at least once daily (from three to twenty weeks) ; global physical reactions during emotional episodes from one to four months (crying, screaming, struggling, starting, restlessness) ; facial expressions associated with emotion (which are apparently innate, since they also occur in infants born blind) .

Table VII summarizes neural structural and EEG data covering the one to three month period.

TABLE VII
NEURAL DEVELOPMENTAL INDICES: ONE TO THREE MONTHS

A. Myelination of Neuraxis at Two Months (102)

　　1) Pyramidal-tract fibers are myelinated down through the medulla oblongata and lightly down through the upper and middle cord; there is practically no myelin in the caudal portions of the spinal cord.
　　2) The myelination pattern of the Rubrospinal tract is much the same as #1.
　　3) Spinocerebellar fibers are heavily myelinated.
　　4) Myelination of the cerebellar hemispheres has advanced markedly.
　　5) The tract from the cerebellar peduncles to the ruber nucleus (in midbrain) is heavily myelinated; the upper continuation of this tract is myelinated to the ventral n. of the thalamus.
　　6) The olivocerebellar tract shows myelin for the first time.
　　7) The tract from the globus pallidus (a basal ganglion) to the ruber n. is myelinated.
　　8) The thalamo-olivary (pons) tract shows myelin for the first time.
　　9) Tectobulbar and tectospinal fibers from the subthalamic region are beginning to show myelin.
　　10) Optic nerves, chiasma and tracts (Cranial II) are almost completely myelinated (are now more advanced than the acoustic, even though the latter began to show myelin in the sixth fetal month).
　　11) There is no myelin in the fornix and only a little around the mammillary bodies of the hypothalamus and on the mammillothalamic tract.
　　12) These thalamic nuclei show myelin: ventral centrum medianum, semilunaris, the geniculates. The anterior, medial-lateral and pulvinar nuclei still do not.
　　13) Fibers from the geniculate nuclei of the thalamus show myelin up into the internal capsule of the cerebral medulla, as do projection fibers from the ventral n. There is much myelin on the sensory section of the posterior limb of the internal capsule (auditory, optic and somesthetic fibers); there is less myelin on the motor section.
　　14) Olfactory (?) tracts show first signs of myelin. The hippocampus has scattered and lightly myelinated fibers, as do the olfactory (?) tracts in the septum pellicidum and surface of the corpus callosum. The stria medullaris and stria semicircularis are fairly well myelinated.
　　15) Temporo-pontine fibers are lightly myelinated, fronto-pontine fibers not at all.
　　16) Few fibers of any type to the frontal lobe anterior to the primary-motor areas are myelinated.

B. Neocortical Cellular Changes Between One and Three Months (38).

　　1. The layer pattern:
　　　　— in order of degree of growth since one month: layers 1, 6, 3, 2, 5, 4.
　　　　— functioning cells are almost all in layers 6 and 5; there are also a few in layer 4 and in the lower section of layer 3. At 3 months, the cells in the upper sections of layer 3 and in layers 2 and 1 are too poorly developed to be functioning.
　　　　— the axon-mesh is dense in layer 4 in most sections of the old cortex.

　　2) The area pattern:
　　　　— in order of the extent of growth since one month: primary-motor area (upper trunk and arm subareas have advanced most), primary somesthetic area (trunk and arm, and hand, subareas have advanced most), primary-visual, primary-auditory.
　　　　— myelin has increased rapidly in the nonauditory parts of the temporal

TABLE VII
NEURAL DEVELOPMENTAL INDICES: ONE TO THREE MONTHS (con't.)

lobe and in the part of the frontal lobe directly anterior to the primary-motor area, with wide individual differences in the degree of increase. Myelin has increased since one month in the old cortex.

3) Fiber pattern:
— the greatest increase in horizontal exogenous fibers and in subcortical association fibers is in layer 6.
— there are more vertical exogenous fibers in the limbic lobe than in the hippocampus.

C. Electrical Activity From One to Three Months.
1) Low-voltage, arhythmic activitty is characteristic of this period, with slightly higher amplitude and slower dominant frequency in the posterior regions. Prior to 3 months in the occipital region there are only slow and irregular potential changes; rhythmic activity is present here only in the 3-4 cps range. As the infant goes to sleep, there is a dampening of activity, along with overall slowing and increase in amplitude. At 3 months, for the first time photic stimulation produces a clear arousal response from the occipital region (151).
2) After one month, steady high-voltage slow waves (2-4 cps) appear during drowsiness (up to 6 months). After the second month, bursts of 14 cps activity in central areas in both hemispheres are typical during light sleep. Also, after 2 months, in half of the records examined, high voltage slow waves appear continuously during arousal. At 3 months, waves of 4-5 cps (theta) are present in all areas (64).
3) From one to 3 months, the sleep delta from the posterior areas becomes continuous. A diffuse pattern of activity appears on top of the earlier waking pattern. There is also a slowing of frequency and an increase in regularity of rhythm and in amplitude. At 3 months, a "second important stage in the maturation of the waking EEG" emerges: a definite topographic organization appears for the first time, along with occipital predominance. Preciseness of reactivity is shown by blockage of the occipital rhythms by all sensory and psychic stimulation. Diffuse waking activity increases proportionately. Synchronous and asynchronous spindles of 12-13 cps emerge in the primary-sensorimotor region. The earlier brief lack of activity periods drop out permanently (42).

The following listing of *neural characteristics* is based on Table VII:

(1) At three months, the cells of the primary-motor area have advanced most of all other areas in development since one month, and within it, the subareas of upper trunk and arm show the greatest amount of development. At two months, cerebellar-associated tracts to both lower and higher centers show myelin. But the pyramidal tract, originating in the primary-motor cortex is still not entirely myelinated — down through the medulla oblongata and only lightly in the upper cord, with practically no myelin in the caudal sections of the cord.

(2) The cells of the primary-sensory areas have also advanced in development since one month, in this subarea order: primary-somatovisceral, primary-visual, primary-auditory. In addition, a primary-area-modifying area in each of the four lobes shows, at three months, definite advances in cellular and fiber development since one month.

(3) The limbic and hippocampal sections also show an advance in development; and some subcortical tracts associated with the old cortex show their first signs of myelin.

(4) Advancing development in the occipital lobe is accompanied by myelination of vision-related subcortical centers and tracts: optic nerves, chiasma and tracts, geniculate nuclei of the thalamus, and associated incoming and outgoing (to higher levels) tracts. Prior to three months, the only rhythmic electrical activity present in the occipital region is in the theta range, and changes in potential are slow and irregular. At three months, photic stimulation produces a clear arousal response from the occipital region for the first time. Also at three months, occipital predominance, along with a definite topographical organization, appears for the first time on the EEG. There is also more precise occipital-area reactivity: all sensory and psychic stimulation now blocks the occipital rhythms.

(5) Is the emergence of a continuous sleep delta and the increase in regularity of rhythm related to the continuing spread of function in neocortical layers 6 and 5? Is the differentiation of a light-sleep pattern, of an arousal pattern, of a diffuse pattern of activity on top of the earlier waking pattern, and emergence of a definite topographical organization of electrical activity, related to the beginnings of conduction in layer 4 and lower-layer 3 in the more advanced sections?

At three months, the following *relationships between neural and behavioral events* appear to obtain:

The increased stability of physiological functioning implies that hypothalamic and autonomic subforebrain connections have been established and are functioning — i.e., the Intraorganismic short circuit has been established.

The sense of smell emerges at the same time that the neocortical areas mediating smell have advanced in functioning: *more needs to be known about the role of smell in early experience!* Underlying the marked improvement in visual functions is the onset of functioning in precentral-fissure areas controlling the muscles of the eyeball, as well as in association areas adjacent to the visual cortex which provide for visual recognition and discrimination. Occipital lobe EEG reactivity implies that thalamic—visual cortex lemniscal connections and circuits are now functioning. Near vision now provides a major source of experience for the infant. Is the emergence of cooing and babbling related to the onset of functioning in layer 4 in the speech areas?

Increase in motor coordination and control appears to be related to the circumstance that the neocerebellum has established spinal connections and that the first neocortical—basal gangliar—cerebellar circuits have been established. These developments also appear to underlie the babe's beginning to play with own arms, feet, fingers; this activity adds the gnostic senses of the hand to the infant's sources of external-world experience (beginning with one's own body!). Lack of development of relevant neocortical association areas implies that only isolated, uncoordinated sensations are as yet available through the hands.

Increased evidences of responsive consciousness appear to be related to the establishment of the BSRF-centered ascending reticular activating system, together with the functional addition of layer 4, and possibly lower 3, to that of layers 6 and 5.

These various sensory, motor and association area advances imply that at three months, distance-exteroceptive components of the Transactional subsystem are approaching its interoceptive and somatosensory components *and* the subcortical parts of the Intraorganismic subsystem in importance as a source of experience for the infant. The circumstance that the basic facial expressions associated with emotional expression are apparently innate suggest that *control* of the facial musculature is associated with the development and functioning of the long circuit of the Intraorganismic subsystem. Some integration of the two systems is probably occurring, but at the brain-stem and diencephalic (thalamic) levels only, as yet.

FROM THREE TO SIX MONTHS

Behavioral trends during this period include the following:

(1) Hearing improves: pitch discrimination shows improvement at four months; sound localization begins at five months.

(2) Motor coordination and control continue to advance:

(a) At four months: the adult startle pattern replaces the Moro reflex; babe sits with support; swimming movements when placed on tummy. Low creep at five months. At six months: sits in high chair; "frogging" (symmetrical extension of arms and legs) ; advanced unilateral knee-thrust.

(b) There is rapid progress in control of the hand and in eye-hand coordination: looks, grasps, brings to mouth, by end of third month; intentional but awkward grasping from four to five months; at six months, the involuntary hand-grasp reflex drops out, child grasps dangling object with flexion of fingers, retains transient hold of a cube in each hand.

(c) Active but still awkward exploration of the immediate physical world is typical from four to six months. In Piaget's schema, three to six months straddles the latter half of the sensorimotor-stage phase of "primary circular reactions" and the earlier part of the "secondary circular reactions" phase.

(d) From four to six months, extends earlier self-play with arms, feet, fingers, to exploration of body.

(3) Sounds basic to speech increase in variety; vocalization is highly responsive to social stimulation:

(a) Coos and vocalizes two syllables between three and four months; self-initiated sound-play and back vowels begin to emerge from four to five months; the beginning of the babbling period, between five and six months, coincides with sitting up.

(b) Low throaty sounds to social stimulation at three to four months; turns head at sound of another's voice and responds to another's voice by making sounds, at four to five months.

(c) Children reared from birth in an orphanage made

fewer and less varied sounds from one to six months than children reared in their own homes.

(4) Although emotional responses show increasing adaptiveness, as well as reactivity to the immediate social world, they continue to be spontaneous and uncontrolled:

(a) Under one year, expressions of anger are global and explosive. Emotional episodes from one to eight months occur most frequently as reaction to thwarting (involving physical discomfort) and to cessation of adult attention. Beginning at five months, the hungry infant shows anger if feeding is delayed after the bottle has been seen. The negative emotions of fear, disgust, anger, emerge between five and six months. At six months, crying unaccompanied by gross body movements may appear; also signs of "hurt feelings."

(b) Quieted by touching at three-and-one-half months; at four months: active signs of delight in social situations — loud laughter, responsive smiling, efforts to raise oneself toward attentive person; "sobers" at strangers; during negative emotional episodes holds out arms, refuses and resists, cries and calls, throws things.

(c) Vocalization reflects inner feelings and is highly responsive to social stimulation.

(5) There are many signs of active social awareness, discrimination, adience:

(a) At three-and-one-half months, "sobers" at strangers; at four-and-one-half months, discriminates between mother and persons seen less frequently, turns head at sound of another's voice and is more discriminative of another's tones and expressions; the first signs of timidity and shyness appear during the fourth and fifth months.

(b) Smiles at another child, is more active in reaching out towards others (vocalizes, attempts to grasp and to touch), begins to imitate another's behavior in order to get something wanted — all during the fifth month. Develops a strong attachment to mother by six months; between five and seven months begins to push away strangers and to make stronger claims on the mother's presence.

(6)   In general, the normal four to six months infant shows a strong adient approach to her immediate external physical and social world.

Table VIII summarizes neural structural and EEG data covering the three to fifteen month period.

TABLE VIII
NEURAL DEVELOPMENTAL INDICES: THREE TO TWELVE MONTHS

A. Gross-Structural (181-2).

    1) There is an increase in the surface-area of the neocortex between birth and 2 years; the parietal lobe increases most.

    2) There is a rapid increase in the fissuration of the parietal and occipital lobes until 2 years, also of the auditory sections of the temporal lobe. Frontal lobe fissuration increases moderately.

    3) The corticospinal (pyramidal) motor tract is rapidly myelinated during the latter part of the first year and the early part of the second year (144).

B. Neocortical Changes Between Three and Six Months (38).

    1) Layer pattern:
       — bottom part of layer 3 has advanced throughout the cortex, especially in growth of neurofibrils and of large pyramidal cells. The chromophil substance in layer 3 in the frontal lobe is more advanced than in any other layer in that lobe.
       — nerve processes continue to be densest in layer 4.
       — layers 6 and 5 have increased most in width in the hippocampal areas.

    2) Area pattern:
       — in the primary-motor area, the subarea of the hand is now as developed as the trunk and arm subareas.
       — limbic areas are about as developed as secondary frontal lobe areas.
       — myelination has advanced in all hippocampal areas;
       — secondary areas in all lobes have continued to advance.

    3) Fiber pattern:
       — subcortical association fibers are most numerous in areas where development has been most active: primary-motor, primary-somesthetic, primary-visual, primary-auditory.
       — there are practically no myelinated fibers above the bottom section of layer 3 at 6 months.

C. Electrical Activity From Three to Twelve Months.

    1) Delta is the dominant rhythm up to one year; is usually diffuse and asymmetrical (151).

    2) At 3 months, occipital-wave-frequency ranges from 3.3 to 7 cps, with a mean amplitude of 37 microvolts (108). These waves are highly variable until 5 months (170). By 6 months, activity in the occipital area is the most developed of all other neocortical areas (64).

    3) Slow, high-voltage waves of drowsiness are between 2–4 cps from 3 to 6 months (64).

    4) At 5 months, occipital electrical activity acquires a rhythmic, sinusoidal character much like the adult alpha rhythm in its purity and stability, although its frequency is 4-6 cps (theta) at this stage (42).

TABLE VIII
NEURAL DEVELOPMENTAL INDICES: THREE TO TWELVE MONTHS
(continued)

5) There is a rapid rise in occipital frequency, from 3-4 cps at the end of 3 months to 7 cps at 15 months. There is much overlap in wave-frequency from the sensorimotor and occipital areas (170). At 6 months, the occipital rhythm ranges from 4.0 to 4.8 cps, with a mean amplitude of 42 mv.; at 12 months, it ranges from 5.5 to 7.0 cps. (108).

6) At 6 months, the diffuse waking activity noted at 3 months continues to increase in proportion, and a hypersynchrony emerges and gradually increases up to at least 3 years. At 7 to 8 months, going-to-sleep becomes characterized by a slow, diffuse hypersynchrony of 3-4 cps, usually a bit slower in the occipital regions, attaining an amplitude of 100-150 mv. Between 8 months and 2 years, this activity has an occasional paroxysmal character. At 9 months, the continuous sleep delta drops out and diphasic spikes emerge in the primary-motor area (42).

7) Between 6 and 12 months, biparietal "humps" appear during very light sleep — high voltage, spike-like waves, usually diphasic, and with a duration of 1/3 to 1/8 of a second; are of highest voltage in the parietal areas. Are also associated with lower-voltage disturbances in the frontal and occipital areas and with waves that appear independently in the left and the right temporal areas. About 20 per cent of children between 6 months and 6 years have bursts of low-amplitude fast activity (20-30) cps) interspersed between these biparietal humps (64).

8) Asynchrony and asymmetry are normal until 6 months while awake; by one year these become abnormal characteristics. Drowsiness is accompanied by general slowing, plus increase in voltage, most marked in the parietal leads. The difference between drowsiness and light sleep is not clear until after 6 months. Sleep spindles show up toward the latter part of the age-period: 13-15 cps, clearest in the parietal leads, least clear in the frontal areas; the basic pattern is: irregular 3-6 cps waves with superimposed low-voltage fast activity. Some children show 18-22 cps activity while awake and at all times except during deep sleep. Deep sleep is accompanied by further slowing and irregular high waves without humps and spindles. An arousal pattern becomes differentiated between 4 and 12 months: paroxysmal, synchronous slowing, with high-voltage sinusoidal 2-4 cps waves appear in all leads. Some persisting occipital slowing is frequent after arousal (53).

9) There is a steady increase from birth to 2 years in the voltages in the theta band; they decline thereafter (64).

10) The A-wave of the electro-retinogram shows up at 12 months, for the first time; this represents the achievement of the adult ERG pattern (197).

D. Neocortical Changes Between Six and Fifteen Months (38).

   1) Layer pattern:
      — layers 2, 6, 1, 3, 4, 5 have grown, in order of the number of areas that have increased in width since 6 months.
      — myelination of exogenous fibers is very scant above the bottom section of layer 3.
      — the cells of layers 4 and 2 have increased in size in all neocortical areas. In the hippocampus, only pyramidal cells in layers 6 and 3 have increased in size. In all frontal lobe areas, the greatest development has been in the pyramidal cells in layer 3. In most of the cortex, cell development in the upper parts of layer 3 has almost caught up with that of the lower part.

   2) Area pattern:
      — the large cells in layers 3 and 5 are especially large in the motor eye-field and Broca's area for coordinated speech (both in the frontal lobe). The anterior portions of the frontal lobe are still minimally developed.

— the order of degree of development of subareas in both the primary-motor and primary-somesthetic areas is: hand, upper extremity, head, lower extremity. The primary-auditory area continues to be less advanced than the primary-visual.

— limbic areas are more advanced in growth; are now in about the same state as secondary areas in the frontal lobe forward of the basic motor areas. Hippocampal areas have also advanced.

— growth in the primary, "leading" areas in each lobe seems to slow down between 6 and 15 months, while development in the secondary areas increases in rate — so that although the primary areas are still ahead of the other areas, the gap between the primary and the secondary areas is not as great at 15 months as it was at 6 months.

3) Fiber pattern:
— exogenous fibers make no direct contact with the dendrites and axons of cortical neurons; there are no branches on any of these fibers.

— many nerve-processes originating in layers 6 and 5 extend tangentially into layer 1; the tangential fibers in layer 1 are as developed as the horizontal fibers in layer 5a.

— the mesh formed by axons on Golgi type II cells is present in all layers in all areas of the cortex; it is thickest in the primary-afferent areas and thinnest in the primary-motor areas.

— dendrites and axons of all neurons in all parts of the cortex have increased in size, length and compactness.

— horizontal exogenous fibers are still very little developed in layer 2. Subcortical association fibers are more numerous than horizontal fibers in layer 6 in all areas.

— very few vertical exogenous fibers go higher than layer 4 (which occurs only in the primary-visual area) at 15 months; they are more numerous than subcortical association fibers in all neocortical areas.

— fiber myelination lags behind cortical fiber formation.

E. The cerebellum, the major subcortical motor center, attains 80 per cent of its adult weight by 2 years (82) .

The following listing of *neural developments* from three to six months is derived from Table VIII:

(1) The primary-motor and primary-sensory areas of the six-month infant have all advanced in development since three months; subcortical association fibers are most numerous in these areas. In the primary-motor area, the subarea of the hand is now as developed as the trunk and arm subarea.

(2) Modifying neocortical as well as old cortex areas have continued to advance in development; limbic areas are about as developed as secondary areas of the frontal lobe; myelin has advanced in all hippocampal areas.

(3) The bottom part of layer 3 has advanced in development throughout the cortex, with myelin evident through this layer

in several sections at six months. Nerve processes are densest in layer 4. Is the emergence of the adult wave-form in the occipital area at five months related to the stabilization of functioning of layer 4 together with the onset of functioning in lower-layer 3?

From three to six months, these *relationships between neural and behavioral events* appear to obtain:

The improvement in auditory discrimination reflects the advance in development of the cells in the primary-auditory area of the temporal lobe.

The replacement of the Moro reflex with the startle pattern indicates the emergence of neocortical control over some subcortical reflex centers; developmental advances in primary-motor area 4 and modifying-motor area 6 immediately anterior to it would appear to underlie both this change and the increase in voluntary motor control. The advance in eye-hand coordination implies that some sections of the posterior association cortex have begun to participate in the neocortical—basal gangliar—cerebellar circuits — i.e., in the functioning of the Transactional short circuit. The active gnostic exploration of own body, which emerges between four and six months, appears to be related to these neural events, and would seem to provide the initial basis for the eventual formation of a coherent body-image.

The infant's high degree of awareness and responsiveness in social situations at six months is clearly evident in deliberate imitation of a "close" other's behavior, increasing appropriateness of emotional reactions to external events including evidences of "hurt feelings," more frequent vocalizations which reflect inner feelings with increasingly greater accuracy. All suggest, at the least, marked advance in visual acuity and discrimination, which is in turn directly related to the developmental advance in both the primary and modifying visual areas — i.e., in Transactional subsystem functioning. These social behaviors also suggest that some degree of awareness of self as a center of action, some "future orientation" at the ANS level at least, some memory capacity, *and* a basically adient orientation toward one's immediate environment are now present; the first and last behaviors are believed to be mediated by the Intraorganismic long circuit, implying that at least the lower layers (6, 5, 4) of the gyrus cinguli are functioning. These developments also imply that nonauditory portions of the temporal lobe are beginning to enter into the circuits integrating the Intraorganismic and Transactional sub-systems by six months.

The continuing dominance of the delta EEG rhythm and the uncontrolled character of emotional reactions at six months may be related. Note that the strongest emotional reactions are negative in tone at this period, in our culture at least, expressing resistance to the external world's intrusion upon the organism's inner balance.

Vocalization is coming to reflect inner feeling with greater accuracy, at the same time that the infant's growing awareness of and responsiveness to his immediate social world is providing speech-models to imitate. There would seem to be some significance for speech and auditory development, at least, and probably also for personality development, in the circumstance that the infant begins to exteriorize his inner world at about the same time that he is becoming actively responsive to and imitative of the speech patterns of those physically and emotionally close to him. If during the first several months of life, the infant's immediate social world is not positively responsive to his first attempts at speech, or is markedly inarticulate (which is not unusual among culturally deprived groups), or there is a fundamental split between close-adults' feelings and their verbalizations, or some combination of these possibilities, basic and pervasive distortions in the infant's auditory discrimination and/or in his desire and ability to express his inner feelings may occur.

In Piaget's terminology, the inter-related adaptive processes of accommodation and assimilation begin to be differentiated from each other by six months, the former expressing itself in imitation of others' movements and speech, the latter process in playful verbal and coordinated-motor repetitions.

FROM SIX TO TWELVE MONTHS

Behavioral trends during this period include the following:

(1) There is a marked advance in voluntary motor coordination and control: upright posture and locomotion is achieved,

and refined manipulative activities emerge during this period, as follows:

Age (in weeks)	Posture and Locomotion	Directed Manipulation
28	Sits alone. Has more refined control of arms and legs.	Prefers radial grasp and manipulation from here on.
30	Does a low creep.	
31	Does backward crawl.	Seizes cube with paw-like movement, all fingers together.
32	Stands with help.	Thumb opposition.
34	Crawls.	
35	Does a high creep.	
36	Does backward creep.	Uses only tips of fingers and thumb in grasping.
37	Creep-crawls.	
40	Stands, holding to furniture. Creeps.	Extends index finger.
40-50	Walks when led.	Grasps more delicately and precisely.
52-60	Stands alone, then walks alone.	Right-handedness emerges in the majority, in our culture.

(2) The previous active exploration of own body is extended to the immediate physical environment, using the mouth and hands.

(3) Only bright colors (red and yellow) are responded to from six to twelve months. Receptor activity in the rods and cones does not begin until twelve months; the adult retinal receptor pattern (ERG) emerges shortly thereafter. The taste buds are still concentrated mostly around the tip of the tongue.

(4) Development of the speech rhythms and sound patterns of one's (sub-) culture *and* accommodation to adult verbal communications emerge during the second half of the first year.

(a) Between seven and eight months: adopts two-syllable words in which the second syllable is a repetition of the first (e.g., mama, dada); back consonants begin to appear. Between eight and nine months: attends to familiar words, imitates intonations of another's voice, repeats a word or sentence, imitating sound-groups without understanding their meaning. Most children utter their first clearly intelligible word (of one syllable) between ten and thirteen months — this development usually coincides with standing alone. After eleven months, a moderate-positive correlation between speech development and fine motor coordination emerges.

(b) Between six and seven months, is able to distinguish between friendly and angry talking. Between eight and nine months, understands another's gestures and adjusts to sounds. From nine to twelve months, responds to gestures and to "bye-bye." At twelve months, waves bye-bye and often says it. Responds to commands of various sorts from ten to thirteen months.

(5) Emotional reactions show increasing appropriateness of response; vocal expressions of inner feeling-states are frequent.

(a) Gives strong negative reactions to confinement at about seven months; from eight to nine months, may show pleased anticipation in the same situation which prompted anger earlier (delay of feeding after seeing bottle) ; from eight to twelve months, shows resistant behavior during emotional episodes, as well as attempts to adapt; at ten months, being handled by strangers is disturbing; also, judges can identify child's emotional state correctly from facial photographs; at twelve months, is likely to form a strong attachment to a real or toy animal and is no longer disturbed by strangers.

(b) Between six and seven months: vocalizes pleasure with crowing and cooing, tends to use low throaty sounds, may coo to music. Between seven and eight months: vocalizes recognition to another and satisfaction on attaining a desired object; emits singing tones. Between eight and nine months: vocalizes an interjection. Towards end of first year (and up to three years), rhythmic vocal accompaniment to physical activity is typical.

(6) With a positive relationship with the mother already established, the normally developing infant starts at about seven months to reach out actively beyond her and relate to others in the immediate environment, using vocal and physical means to establish social contact. In turn, is influenced by others' verbal communications beginning about ten months.

(7) The first evidences of ideational activity (intention, mem-

ory, rudimentary imagery, reasoning) emerge during the latter half of the first year.

(a) Frequent silent observation of people and objects, beginning at six or seven months; looks in order to act, and deliberately repeats manipulations as if trying to understand effect of own actions on immediate environment, beginning about eight months.

(b) Memory is shown after a delay of one minute at ten to eleven months; towards end of first year, memory is aroused only by sensory stimulation; can recall events other than own actions, at the end of first year.

(c) True problem-solving reasoning was shown during the twelfth month: drew in a toy by its attached string, turned a lever to bring a ball within grasping distance.

(d) Most items on Bayley's First Year Test which proved to have some correlation with later IQ scores were in the six to twelve months section. A definite shift in the nature of this test's items at the nine-month level from sensorimotor functions to adaptive ones has been pointed to by Werner (192).

(e) Eight or nine months to eleven or twelve months covers Piaget's fourth sensorimotor-stage phase, that of "coordination of sensory schemata"; this complex phase is composed of these overlapping-successive adaptive developments: behavior (especially manipulative) evidencing recognition of the difference between means and ends emerges; the child foresees an event independent of own action; the child searches for vanished objects, indicating initial discovery of a universe independent of self (which eventually leads to discrimination between "me" and "not-me") ; appreciation of causality extends to recognition that things happen independently of one's own activity; an elementary appreciation of a temporal sequence emerges, along with the first evidences of memory for a sequence in which the child was not actively involved; genuine, deliberate imitation of another's activity (which the child is already capable of performing) occurs, together with evident interest in the novel; inner development of images — that is, of central processes representing concrete actions — appears.

(8) The first clear evidences of self-awareness emerge during the last quarter of the first year: overt expressions of emotion indicate ability to adapt selectively to external events; and the child discovers she can have an influence on her physical and social environment through resistance, vocalizing, purposeful movements and manipulations.

(9) Unequivocal signs of the earliest diagnosed serious behavior disorder, early infantile autism, become evident between nine and twelve months; they are extreme "alone-ness" (i.e., a complete lack of social responsiveness) and obsessive insistence on sameness. (Although this disorder is now being attributed to a CNS dysfunction which is present from birth — *viz.* B. Rimland, *Infantile Autism,* 1964 — a certain diagnosis is difficult before the fourth quarter of the first year, apparently because it is not until then that the deviance of the autistic child's behavior from that of the normally developing child becomes unmistakable.)

Table VIII includes material, chiefly EEG data, on the six to twelve month period. Conel's findings on the fifteen-month cortex, also given in Table VIII, have been utilized as well in the following listing of *neural developments*:

(1) From the fissure-development pattern of the parietal, occipital and frontal lobes, and Conel's fifteen-months data, it is evident that secondary areas of these lobes begin to advance markedly in their development at about six months. Specific frontal areas mentioned by Conel as advancing in their development include the area for coordinated speech and the motor eye-field. But the prefrontal areas are still minimally developed.

(2) The subarea order of development in both the primary-motor and primary-somesthetic area is: hand, upper extremity, head, lower extremity.

(3) Limbic and hippocampal areas have made definite advances in development.

(4) The upper section of layer 3 has advanced in development between six and fifteen months; the lower section appears to be functional.

(5) Nerve fibers and nerve processes have markedly increased throughout the cortex.

(6) There is a rapid rise in occipital area wave-frequencies, with a 5.5 to 7.0 range at twelve months.

(7) The voltages of waves of the theta band increase up to two years.

(8) Synchrony and symmetry of electrical activity develop between six and twelve months; after one year, asynchrony and asymmetry are usually considered abnormal.

(9) EEG patterns differentiating various states of consciousness emerge between four and twelve months: an arousal pattern shows up between four and twelve months, a going-to-sleep (drowsiness) pattern emerges at seven to eight months, the deep-sleep pattern changes at nine months.

From six to twelve months, the following *relationships between neural and behavioral events* appear to obtain:

Achievement of upright posture and locomotion is dependent upon the advancing development in both the neocortical primary and modifying motor and somatoviscerosensory areas and upon the establishment of feedback circuits between the neocerebellum and spinal cord and motor cortex, as well as between the basal ganglia and neocerebellum. Directed, precise manipulation, entailing eye-hand coordination, depends also upon continuing advances in posterior, T-O-P, association cortex functioning.

Responsiveness to colors in addition to the brightest ones begins at about one year; this development is related to retinal rod and cone and related visual cortex receptivity. The rapid rise in occipital frequency between four and fifteen months appears to be related to the maturation of retinal and visual cortex functioning; probably also to the emergence to functioning of layers 4 and all of 3 in the visual cortex (primary and modifying areas).

The infant's extension of gnostic exploration of own body to the immediate physical world, in combination with the increasing acuteness and discriminative capacity of the distance receptors, provides the experiential basis for formation of inner representations of the immediately tangible physical world (*viz.* Hebb's cell-assembly construct) in the T-O-P association area. It also leads, very probably, to an initial, vague awareness of a distinction between one's own sentient body and nonsentient objects external to that body. Continuing functional development of the posterior association cortex would appear to be prerequisite to such perceptual developments.

There seems to be a mutually facilitating interaction between vocalization and motor activity during this period. Is this circumstance related to the spatial contiguity, or even overlapping, of the motor-speech area and centers for other coordinated movements?

Social development and speech development appear to be mutually reinforcing. Earlier identification of another human being as a source of both primary-needs satisfaction and responsive sensory stimulation provides the motivational foundation for the strong social adience typical of the normally developing seven to twelve months old. Such social interaction in turn provides speech models for the infant: speech rhythms and intonations are imitatively practiced during this period, and the first clearly intelligible, one-syllable word is spoken towards the end of the first year (for most children). In turn, the child's use of speech promotes more and richer social interaction. Continuing development of motor-speech areas, of circuits between the speech areas and the T-O-P association area, and of continuing integration of the Transactional and Intraorganismic systems would appear to be prerequisite to this reciprocal relationship.

If the six to twelve months period is as crucial for speech development as the data suggest it is, then the following subcultural comparison study should be undertaken. Systematically observe mother-child interaction longitudinally from three to twelve months, with emphasis on the mother's quality and use of speech during such interaction, in (1) a sample of culturally deprived, lower lower-class families, and (2) a sample of culturally privileged, middle-class families, *keeping sex and ethnic and "racial" factors constant.* The developmental status of all the infants included in the study, as determined by a good infant scale and by patterning on the EEG, should be closely similar initially. On the basis both of the speech-status findings at twelve months and the home's levels of speech and of emotional acceptance of the child, predictions should be made as to probable relative speech status at two, four and six years of (a) each social group, and (b) each child, and longitudinal follow-up done subsequently to check on the accuracy of the respective predictions. A similarly designed study to check on Inhelder and Piaget's proposition that early play with, manipulation of, objects in the child's immediate physical world is the first stage in the development of "logical thinking" (88) should also be undertaken, holding sex constant.

Appropriateness of emotional response to external events continues to increase from six to twelve months and may be assumed to be related to broadening cortical participation in the Intraorganismic subsystem, as well as, during the last quarter, to advancing integration of the Intraorganismic and Transactional subsystems.

EEG patterns characteristic of five different states of consciousness gradually emerge between four and twelve months. Is this increasing differentiation in cortical electrical activity related to the spread of functioning in layers 4 and lower and upper 3 during the same period? Is the onset of functioning in upper layer 3 also related to the first clear signs of self-awareness and ideational-adaptive behavior?

A shift from sheerly sensorimotor reactions to the world to the beginnings of ideational and adaptive behavior, the first clear evidence of awareness of self, unmistakable signs of the first serious behavior disorder — all occur during the last quarter of the first year: may there be a common basis for all three of these apparently disparate occurrences?

Since nine months seems to mark a major transition-point in development, the key behavioral developments of the six weeks to nine months period (approximately) will be reviewed as a preliminary step to answering this question.

Most homeostatic coordinations have been established by six months. The exteroceptive sense-modalities emerge and become discriminative; visual abilities emerge first and refine the fastest. Voluntary motor control of the upper half of the body is achieved, basic sensorimotor coordinations emerge, rapid progress in control of the hand and in eye-hand coordination occurs, crawling and creeping locomotion is achieved by nine months. Evidence of affectivity towards the environment begins with active but undifferentiated signs of displeasure and pleasure at one month, proceeding to more discriminating and differentiated emotional reactions to persons and situations at nine months; the infant is strongly reactive to social stimulation by six months. Vocalization expressive of organismic needs, only, occurs until three months, together with lack of responsive awareness of others' speech rhythms and sounds until about four months, when high vocal responsiveness to social stimulation emerges. The raw material of later verbalization begins at three months with cooing and babbling; by nine months, the infant's vocalization shows: assimilation of the speech sounds and rhythms of the family, awareness of the emotional undercurrents in adult speech, awareness of own vocalization as a means of social control, and more differentiated use of vocalization to express inner feelings. The first signs of memory (of events directly affecting own physical welfare) show up at three months; memory continues to be non-ideational through the first year. The first evidences of ideational activity appear about six to seven months in silent, concentrated observation of persons and objects and own manipulative activity. The diagnosis of autism can be made with certainty at about nine months, when clear signs of self-awareness and a shift from sheerly sensorimotor abilities to adaptive functions on the Bayley First Year Test have begun to occur in the normally developing child.

Neurally, during the second half of the first year, there is a marked increase in intra-cortical nerve-fibers and nerve-processes and a major maturational advance in modifying-sensory, modifying-motor, and the T-O-P association areas; and synchrony and symmetry of cortical electrical activity emerge. There is undoubtedly also a proliferation of cell-assemblies during this period. Concerning the three neural systems postulated in Chapter VII, it is hypothesized that the following occurs:

(1) One to six months: first stage in the development of the Transactional sub-system — the primary-motor and primary-sensory cortical areas begin to function, and branches 1 and 2 of the CI circuits (see page 159) parallel these motor and sensory tracts.

(2) Two to nine months: incorporation of the lower layers

of the cingulate gyrus into the Intraorganismic subsystem, and branch 3 of the CI circuits parallels these tracts.

(3) Six to nine months: beginning of functioning of the peripheral sections of the T-O-P association area, and branch 4 of the CI circuits (see page 159) parallels these sections' thalamic connections.

(4) Eight to nine months: beginning of *coordinated* functioning of branches 1 to 4 of the CI circuits; and as this occurs,

(5) the first sensory-modifying cortical-in-origin motor tracts become functional — i.e., the first stages of the Transactional long circuit begin.

In answer to the question raised a page or two ago, the emergence of neural processes 4 and 5 above is believed to constitute the "common factor" behind the varied behavioral developments which occur during the last quarter of the first year.

Process 4 represents the first, intrathalamic, stage in the development of the forebrain integrative circuits which knit together the two neural sub-systems and which make possible normal personality and cognitive development and functioning. However, both *processes 4 and 5 are dependent upon the prior undistorted occurrence of processes 1, 2, 3.* If this first integrative stage fails to develop because of major gaps in processes 1, 2, 3, then the ability to cope with reality adaptively does not emerge — and earlier evident signs of autism become unmistakable. It is hypothesized that processes 1, 2, 3 are not entirely innately determined, sheerly maturational processes. Whether they occur without distortion appears to be at least partially dependent upon a responsively enabling human environment — that is, one which provides neither of two extremes: marked responsive, sensory, and/or basic needs deprivation, *nor* overstimulating bombardment of the as yet highly vulnerable, unstable infant nervous system with invasive or contradictory stimulation. Since a particular organism's threshold of resistance to the effects of deprivation or of overstimulation is an innately determined matter, individual constitutional factors very definitely enter into the situation.

Less extreme gaps in neural processes 1, 2, 3 may result in less extreme psychological impairment than autism. Various defects in sensory and perceptual discrimination, especially those involving hearing and language abilities, probably also have their origins in the imperfect establishment of early CI circuits and Transactional long circuit functioning.

It is interesting to note that the initial symptomatology of Heller's disease, a degenerative neural disorder caused by brain-damage, is closely similar to that of the functional disorder of early infantile autism; this disease involves severe degeneration of cortical nerve cells, with eventual atrophy of the brain, espe cially of the frontal lobe (16) .

FROM ONE TO TWO YEARS

Behavioral trends during this period include:

(1) Voluntary motor coordination and control continues to advance and now includes some basic vegetative processes:

(a) Bowel control emerges between fifteen and twenty-four months; daytime urinary control is achieved between twenty and thirty-six months; girls are ahead of boys on both. The Babinski reflex drops out at two years.

(b) Manipulative activities and competencies increase:
— at thirteen months, spontaneously puts crayon to paper;
— between eighteen and twenty-one months, lifts cup to mouth, drinks well, hands cup back;
— at two years, holds glass in one hand and drinks from it, can insert spoon in mouth in proper position, can button and unbutton if allowed plenty of time, can make vertical scribbles with pencil.

(c) Locomotor abilities advance: at twelve to thirteen months, stands alone and climbs stair steps while hanging on to banister; walks alone during the thirteenth month; can jump from a higher to a lower level at two years.

(d) Rhythmic responses are common: at eighteen months, may start to respond rhythmically to music; up to three years, rhythmic vocal accompaniment to music is typical. At two years, laughs most often in response to own and other's movements (and to socially unacceptable situations) .

(2) With the ability to walk, active exploration of the environment is extended to a broader physical area.

(3) Practice of rhythms of the mother tongue, comprehensibility of speech, vocabulary, understanding of words, use of language to communicate — all increase from one to two years.

(a) Expressive jargon is common from thirteen to seventeen months. Consonants appear in great variety after one year.

(b) For children between one and two years of age, twelve to eighteen months is the period of greatest incomprehensibility. Boys are more incomprehensible than girls throughout the early speech period.

(c) Vocabulary increases slowly between thirteen months (three or four words) to eighteen months (five to twenty-two words), but jumps markedly between eighteen and twenty-one months to an average of 118 words.

(d) The early-sentence stage is from thirteen to twenty-seven months, with a preponderance of pronouns.

(e) Much of the child's speech is emotionally toned during this period. There is a peak in speech problems at twenty-one months. (A discussion of the relationship between speech development and development of the self is included in the two to six year period.)

(4) Among normal-range children, there is a strong desire to establish social contact with "important" persons, both adults and peers:

— from twelve to twenty-five months, emotional episodes occur most frequently in connection with thwarting of social approach;

— at eighteen months, the "social" emotions of jealousy and of affection emerge;

— from nineteen to twenty-five months, the child initiates much social contact and overt friendliness towards partner, uses play materials as a means of establishing and maintaining social contact, accommodates play behavior to partner's reactions.

(5) The second year is a highly emotional period, with strong negative reactions to thwarting of social and environmental explorations typical (in the middle class American setting, at least) :

— from twelve to sixteen months, struggling and running away are added responses during emotional episodes;
— at eighteen months, the social emotions of jealousy and affection emerge;
— eighteen to twenty-three months is a peak period for resistant behavior in girls (boys' peak comes later) ;
— from eighteen to thirty months, a large percentage of all vocalizations are emotionally toned: commands, requests, threats, desires;
— at two years, anger episodes are chiefly prompted by authority figures' pressures, demands, expectations; laughs most often in response to socially unacceptable situations (and to own and others' movements) .

(6) As reported by mothers, frequent behavior-problems at twenty-one months were enuresis, speech problems, temper-tantrums, thumbsucking — i.e., body-centered reactions reflecting failure to adapt to training routines:

— Girls more than boys were food-finicky, sucked their thumbs, had specific fears, demanded attention excessively.
— Boys more than girls had enuresis, were excessively irritable and emotionally dependent, had restless sleep.

(7) Memory improves rapidly and markedly between one and two years, showing greater reliance on imagery towards the end of the period.

(a) At thirteen months, there is recall after delay of one minute; at twenty-one to twenty-four months, there is recall after delay of seventeen minutes.

(b) The memory-span for words begins to increase at eighteen months.

(c) Memory is better for persons and/or objects than for situations during the first two years. By the end of the second year, memory has shifted to a more ideational basis — sensory stimulation is no longer necessary.

(8) Perceptual discrimination develops steadily, but is still physiognomic at this stage.

(a) Between fifteen and twenty-four months, simple forms (triangle, circle, etc.) and three-dimensional objects were discriminated; slower children learned faster when they traced the objects with their fingers. At two years, more complex forms (such as a small cross in the center of a figure) can be discriminated; a triangle regardless of its size or position or background can be discriminated; one and one-half familiar pictures placed among strange ones are recognized.

(b) Color is still not used as a discrimination cue over form and position during this period.

(9) Mental and motor behaviors become relatively independent of each other at eighteen months (r drops from .50 to .20), but it is impossible to predict the later IQ of any one child from a prior-to-two years scale.

(a) In the development of understanding of conceptual hierarchies, the first verbalized discriminations occur at eighteen months.

(b) In Piaget's schema, from eleven or twelve months to between eighteen and twenty-four months is the fifth sensorimotor-stage phase of "tertiary circular reactions"; this phase comprises these six successive developments: observation of one's own efficacious activity; beginnings of curiosity as a result of interest in novelty; discovery of new means of acting on the environment through active experimentation; systematic verbal and motor imitation of new models and development of new activities through such imitation; increasing grasp of object permanence and appreciation of an object (and its characteristics) on its own merits; grasp of objective causal, temporal, and spatial sequences.

(c) Continuing with Piaget's schema, from eighteen to twenty-four months is the sixth and last sensorimotor-stage phase in the development of intelligence, that of "internalization of sensorimotor schemata," during which genuine intelligence first emerges. This phase comprises these six successive developments: invention through mental combinations of new means of relating to the environment; orientation to one's immediate objective spatial field (can now keep track of where the various objects and persons in one's physical life space are located); ability to construct through mental operations the cause of an event from only its effects; occurrence of delayed imitation; emergence of genuine playful make-believe (assimilative) activities; beginning of thought "reversibility": can now reach a given mental goal by various reasoning routes.

(10) There are increasing evidences of perception of self as a separate entity during the second year:

— from sixteen to twenty months, hiding face, crying and saying *no* occur during emotional episodes;

— resistant behavior reaches a peak between one-and-one-half and three years (eighteen to twenty-three months among girls and thirty to thirty-five months among boys) ;

— a very high proportion of the child's speech is emotionally toned between eighteen and twenty-three months;

— Russell says the child is likely to have some grasp of self as a physical entity at two years (161) ;

— further discussion of self-development during this period is included in the two to six year period.

(11) The peak in incidence of infantile autism occurs during the second year. Symptoms of childhood schizophrenia begin to show up between one-and-one-half and two-and-one-half years.

Table IX summarizes both histological and EEG data covering the one to two year period. Data on cortical status at fifteen months, already given in Table VIII, are also being utilized.

The following listing of *neural developments* is derived from both Tables VIII and IX:

(1) At fifteen months, the hand subarea continues to be the most advanced subarea in the primary-motor and primary-somesthetic areas.

(2) Some secondary areas in all lobes have apparently begun to function at fifteen months, as have a few sections of the old cortex. Two frontal secondary areas, those for coordinated speech and the motor eye-field, appear to be functioning at fifteen months.

(3) Most of layer 3 seems to have become functional in all primary areas and in several secondary areas at fifteen months.

(4) Nerve processes and exogenous fibers have increased markedly throughout the cortex, but vertical exogenous fibers

TABLE IX
NEURAL DEVELOPMENTAL INDICES: ONE TO TWO YEARS

A. Cortical Changes Between Fifteen and Twenty-four months (38).

1) The frontal lobe has grown more between 15 and 24 months than any other section of the cortex, especially in its middle and anterior sections. But the PF association area is still little developed. The difference in degree of development between the primary-motor area and the rest of the frontal lobe is not as great as at 15 months. The area directly in front of the primary-motor area now seems to be exerting control over it. Myelinated vertical exogenous fibers have increased in only two frontal areas: the subarea of the head in the primary-motor area and Broca's speech center. What little development has gone on in the prefrontal section has occurred mostly in layer 3.

2) Layer pattern:
   — order of increase in layer-width since 15 months is 6, 4, 5, 1 and 3, 2.
   — the axon-mesh is densest in layers 4 and 3c; it has more elaborate branching than at 15 months (at 24 months, this mesh is thickest in the primary-afferent areas and thinnest in the frontal lobe).
   — layer 1's tangential fibers are more developed in its outer than its inner half.
   — there are still very few horizontal exogenous fibers in layers 3 and 2. Layer 6 has more, and more developed, subcortical association fibers than horizontal exogenous fibers.

3) Area pattern:
   — the primary-somesthetic and primary-motor areas are equally developed on most of the growth criteria.
   — secondary areas in the parietal, occipital and temporal lobes have all developed since 15 months; the primary-auditory area is still not as developed as the primary-visual.
   — limbic areas have advanced in all growth criteria; their status is like midfrontal secondary areas. Hippocampal areas have also advanced in growth; the large pyramidal cells in its deepest layer are as advanced as in layer 6 of the neocortex.
   — there is some evidence of handedness at 24 months: the hemisphere of the dominant hand is slightly more developed than the other.

4) Fiber pattern:
   — the vertical exogenous fibers (v-e-fs) are the earliest cortical fibers to develop, then the subcortical association fibers (s-a-fs), then the tangential fibers in layer 1, then the horizontal exogenous fibers (h-e-fs). The ascending v-e-fs lie at right angles to the s-a-fs and h-e-fs in all areas of the cortex. In the earliest stages of development, these v-e-fs end in layers 6 and 5, and in later stages in layers 4 and 3c. (Conel speculates that the v-e-fs are afferent and efferent fibers connecting the cortex with subcortical neurons, while the other three types of fibers are all intracortical.)
   — in the sub-areas for the head and the lower extremity of the primary-motor area, the tangential, horizontal and s-a fibers are equally numerous, but v-e-fs are less numerous in the lower extremity sub-area. More v-e-fs end, and go higher up, in the primary-somesthetic area than in any other cortical area. Myelinated v-e-fs go higher in the temporal lobe than at 15 months, but none goes higher than layer 3b. The v-e, h-e, and s-a fibers are all larger in the primary somesthetic area than in the primary-motor area, at 24 months. Myelinated tangential fibers in layer 1 are more numerous in the primary-somesthetic area than in any other parietal lobe area.
   — there are more, and more heavily myelinated, fibers of all types in the old cortex than at 15 months. V-e-fs end higher and have more myelin in the gyrus cinguli than they did at 15 months.

TABLE IX
NEURAL DEVELOPMENTAL INDICES: ONE TO TWO YEARS (continued)

B. Electrical Activity From One to Two Years.

1) At 12 months, occipital frequencies range from 5.5 to 7.0 cps, with mean amplitude of 52 mv; such high-voltage slow waves are common at one year (108).

2) At 15 months, occipital frequency goes up to 7 cps. The rate of increase slows down beginning about 15 months (170).

3) The steady high-voltage slow-waves during drowsiness, which showed up after one month, still appear in the majority of one year old subjects, and are 4-6 cps (theta) at one year. They have a very high voltage and occupy long stretches of drowsy-state records. During the second year, they break up into short runs or paroxysmal discharges, looking much like the high-voltage slow waves of petit-mal epilepsy (64).

4) Sleep spindles of 12-15 cps are synchronous and are most marked in the parietal leads, but are also seen in occipital and frontal areas (64).

5) There is a steady increase from birth to 2 years in the voltages in the 4-6 cps (theta) band; they decline thereafter. At 2 years, a hump develops in the 9 cps range (64).

6) At 2 years, the occipital frequency ranges from 5.0 to 9.6 cps, with a mean amplitude of 49 mv (108).

7) At 2 years, the hypersynchrony, diphasic-spike pattern, sensorimotor area spindles, and diffuse electrical activity cited at the previous age period all reach the highest proportions of the period studied (fifth fetal month through 2 years). From 5 to 18 months, there is very little change in the EEG (42).

8) Up to 2 to 3 years, theta frequencies are augmented by emotional episodes (crying, hunger, laughing) and by closing the eyes. The occipital alpha is rarely responsive to visual stimuli before 3 years (but is frequently so after 3 years) (151).

9) The electrical discharge of the infant's and young child's brain is ten times as great as that of the adult brain (108).

(sub-cortical connection functions) go no higher than layer 4 except in the primary-visual area at fifteen months. Nerve processes originating in layers 6 and 5 extend tangentially into layer 1, and these layer 1 fibers are as developed as the horizontal exogenous fibers in layer 5. Note that many fibers in layer 5 originate in the cingulum, which plays a major role in man's affective life.

(5) Voltages of waves in the theta band increase steadily from birth to two years, and decline thereafter. Up to about three years, theta frequencies are augmented by emotional episodes and by closing the eyes. The slow waves of drowsiness reach the theta range at one year and are of very high voltage.

(6) The occipital frequency reaches the mature, alpha, frequency-range at two years in a few children. The occipital alpha is not readily responsive to visual stimuli until after three years. The rate of increase in occipital frequency slows down beginning at fifteen months. Are the nearly mature pattern of occipital fre-

quency *and* the domination of the theta-band waves after one year both related to (a) ongoing integration *within* the thalamus, and (b) onset of functioning in all of layer 3 in the visual area?

(7) The EEG shows evidences of continuing instability during the second year.

(8) Between fifteen months and two years, there is marked growth in all of the frontal lobe *except* the PF association section. The head sub-area of the primary-motor area and Broca's speech area both have more myelinated vertical exogenous fibers at two years. The premotor area has begun to exert control over the primary-motor area. Vertical exogenous fibers are less numerous than other fibers in the lower-extremity subarea of the primary-motor area.

(9) Secondary-area development in all lobes and old cortex development both advance between fifteen months and two years. Thalamic connections with the gyrus cinguli seem to be functionally established.

(10) Layers 4 and 3c have many more nerve processes at two years than at fifteen months; most are in the primary-sensory areas. Layers 3 and 2 still have very few fibers from other cortical areas.

(11) Myelinated vertical exogenous fibers go higher in the temporal lobe than at fifteen months, but none goes higher than temporal layer 3b at two years.

(12) There is a change in the EEG pattern during moderately deep sleep and deep sleep at two years.

From one to two years, these *relationships between neural and behavioral events* appear to obtain:

Voluntary motor coordination and control now encompasses the entire body: upright locomotion is achieved, as well as the beginning of more complex skills dependent on it; manipulative activities and skills increase. The emergence of bowel control (and also urinary control in girls) is the first evidence of voluntary — i.e., cortical — control over some autonomic functions: is the gyrus cinguli involved in this development? Continuing functional development of frontal and parietal and posterior-association areas and their incorporation into the Transactional short circuit, as well as further development of the CI circuits and extension of the Transactional long circuit would seem to under-lie this period of sensorimotor consolidation.

Walking makes available a broader physical area of exploration. There are many attempts to establish social contacts, especially with peers. This is a period of strong reactivity to the environment, both physical and social.

The first intelligible word, of one syllable, is spoken at twelve to thirteen months on the average. Speech then emerges slowly and with poor articulation until eighteen months; thereafter there is a rapid increase in the size of vocabulary, much improvement in articulation, and a strong tendency to use language as a tool of interpersonal communication, beyond its earlier use as primarily a vehicle of emotional expression. This sudden spurt in speech abilities coincides with the emergence to function of nearly all of layer 3 in most of the cortex: is there a functional relationship between these two events or are they merely coincidental? Since speech is believed to be subserved by the Transactional subsystem, this development is evidence of continuing advances in this subsystem's functioning.

There is much resistive emotional expression. Normal-range behavior-problems are body-centered reactions reflecting failure to adapt to culturally imposed "training" routines. Mothers also report a peak in speech problems at twenty-one months. The speech and behavior problems typical of the second year in our culture, especially among boys, would seem to be expressive of psychological stress — stress arising because the yet immature and unstable nervous system is unable to function in the coordinated and controlled manner expected or even demanded by adult caretaker(s). The possibility is well worth investigating that these pressures, converging with as yet highly unstable nervous system functioning (*viz.,* the EEG data), may precipitate the first attack of epilepsy in genetically vulnerable individuals.[1]

---

[1]This suggestion is buttressed by material from Brazier (25) already cited under section D of Orientation Supplement 6, and here repeated in paraphrased form: "The spike discharges from cortical dendrites which are characteristic of infancy and of the excessive discharge of epilepsy are absent in the normal brain, due to the presence of certain inhibitory-in-function interneurons, as well as to sub-cortical influences." Do these interneurons not develop *or* not become functional in epileptics? If not, why don't they? Are the reasons primarily of an imprinting-experiential

The marked lability of emotional reactions during the second year is associated with theta rhythm dominance on the EEG, which is in turn associated with the dominant role of the thalamus in forebrain functioning during this period. The appearance of theta waves during drowsiness suggests that cortical control diminishes as the child goes to sleep — a circumstance borne out by young children's tendency to relax and share withheld concerns freely at such times.

If rhythmic responses are a function of the Intraorganismic subsystem, which I believe they are, then such controlled-rhythmic activities as singing, creative dance and playing of musical instruments represent an integrative tie between the Intraorganismic and Transactional subsystems. Also the circumstance that at two years, laughter is most frequent in response to unacceptable social stituations suggests that laughter, a uniquely human reaction, serves a stress-relieving — that is, integrative — function.

Memory improves markedly from ten months to two years, with much greater reliance on imagery at the end of the period. Simple perceptual and verbal discriminations, reasoning utilizing mental imagery, beginnings of perception of self as a separate entity — all emerge during the latter half of the second year. There is a progression from deliberate and closely observed repetition of manipulative activities at eight months, to the first evidences of true problem-solving at twelve months, to the first verbalized discrimination of conceptual hierarchies at eighteen months, to evidences of real thinking from eighteen months to two years. Mental and motor abilities separate out at eighteen months. The emergence to function of most of layer 3 between one-and-one-half and two-and-one-half years, the marked advance in nerve fibers and nerve processes throughout the cortex between six months and two years, further T-O-P area development, and the apparent advances in the CI circuits appear to underlie these progressive mental developments. In Hebb's terms, phase-sequences based on earlier-formed cell-assemblies are also developing rapidly.

---

character, or is hereditary defect responsible — or is there a convergence of both factors?

The physiognomic character of perception (i.e., fusion of its feeling and discriminative aspects) typical of this period and for some years following, is probably due to the continuing dominance of the thalamus in forebrain functioning; although the peripheral sections of the T-O-P association area appear to be functioning by this time, its more advanced perceptual role is still not established during early childhood.

The peak in the incidence of autism occurs during the second year. The relationship between this early psychological disorder and abnormal neural development has already been referred to in the discussion of the previous age period, and will be further gone into under the two to six year period, following. Defective sensory and perceptual discriminations stemming from gaps in earlier-period development of the long Transactional circuit and first Integrative circuits begin to show up during the second year.

Chapter X

FROM TWO TO SIX YEARS

BEHAVIORAL AND NEURAL EVENTS

B*ehavioral developments* during this period include the following:

(1) Refinement of locomotor and manipulative control and coordination increases; all the basic locomotor and manipulative skills are apparently acquirable by six years.

    (a) The plantar reflex replaces the Babinski after two years.

    (b) Susceptibility to conditioning reaches its maximum at four years, after which it drops off.

(2) Speech articulation, verbalization, sentence-length, grammatical correctness, all increase markedly; girls are ahead of boys in all phases of speech and language development during this period:

— a marked increase in accuracy of articulation occurs between two and three years;

— the largest increase in verbalization (number of words spoken per time-period) occurs between two-and-one-half and three years;

— between two and three years, there is a period of several weeks when the child tends to repeat words and syllables;

— complete sentences emerge at four years.

(3) Language becomes simultaneously a tool for relating more adequately to one's physical and social environment *and* a means of self-regulation:

— from three to five years, 10 to 15 per cent of all conversation is questions;

— physical means of aggression decline from two to four years among girls, while verbal means increase; this change occurs later among boys;

— from three to four years, the child regulates his behavior with overt self-instructive speech; such speech becomes

215

internal between four-and-one-half and five-and-one-half years (112).

(4) This is a period of high emotionality:

— until about five years, emotional reactions are tied directly to immediate, concrete events and interactions;

— fear reactions are prompted by the unexpected and the unfamiliar and have the greatest personal impact (along with joy);

— anger reactions become less labile, more adaptive and have longer-lasting physical and psychological after-effects after four years;

— the more complex "social" emotions of envy, shame, hope, disappointment, affection for adults emerge at around five years;

— emotional factors have a strong influence on the tested IQ during nursery-school years.

(5) American middle-class values concerning sociability, sexual modesty, interpersonal rivalry, relative status of the sexes and of adults *vis à vis* children are gradually internalized from three to six years — but at a good deal of emotional cost:

— crying is more often due to psychological hurt than to physical hurt after three years;

— boys show twice as many anger-outbursts as girls between two and five years; thirty to thirty-five months is the peak period for resistant behavior among boys (girls' was from eighteen to twenty-three months);

— self-stimulation of the genitals is a common self-comfort activity at three years; imaginary companions are common from two-and-one-half to four-and-one-half years — they tend to have virtues, powers, privileges which the child lacks and he may excuse or defend his "companion's" conduct; at three years, laughs most at socially unacceptable situations;

— emotional factors have a strong influence on the tested IQ during the nursery-school years.

(6) As reported by mothers, behavior problems show a progression between twenty-one months and five years from overt, body-centered reactions reflecting failure to adapt to imposed

training routines, to more internal-type reactions reflecting self-depreciation and/or indirect expressions of hostility against others. Boys make this shift later than girls or do not make it at all.

(a) Problems having an early peak (before three years) for both sexes, with decreasing incidence thereafter, were (in order of incidence) : soiling and enuresis, thumb-sucking, destructiveness, temper-tantrums, overactivity, speech problems.

(b) Typical behavior problems from three to five years:

Age (yrs.)	Behaviors Expressed By 1/3 or More of Ss At, or an Age-peak For Age:	Behaviors More Common Among Boys	Behaviors More Common Among Girls
3	Food-finickiness, overactivity, temper-tantrums, specific fears, disturbing dreams, stealing.	Food-finickiness (girls' peak was at twenty-one months) .	Thumb-sucking, destructiveness; specific fears, excessive modesty.
3½	Lying, overactivity, oversensitiveness, specific fears, tempers.	Negativism, specific fears, irritability.	Food-finickiness, physical timidity, jealousy, excessive modesty.
4	Same as at three and one-half, plus: insufficient appetite (four to six years) .	Emotional dependence, excessive demands for attention	Irritability, lying (four to six yrs.), negativism, oversensitivity (and thereafter) , thumbsucking.
5	Overactivity, oversensitiveness, jealousy, excessive reserve, specific fears, tempers.	Somberness, negativism, excessively modest, lying (five to six years) , destructiveness, jealousy, temper-tantrums.	Physical timidity, jealousy, thumbsucking.

(c) Sex-differences in age of incidence of problem-behaviors:

Earlier Peaks for Boys in:
Excessive dependence, food-finickiness, poor appetite, somberness, negativism, speech retardation, thumbsucking, physical timidity.

Earlier Peaks for Girls in:
Jealousy, excessive modesty, lying, oversensitiveness, attention-demanding, destructiveness, stealing.

(7) Memory becomes increasingly more ideational in basis and the time-span of sustained attention and of delayed recall lengthens. Together with the increase in language abilities, these developments result in more, and more complex, situations and materials being remembered, and in greater detail. Also, memory is better for emotionally vivid and/or personally related events.

(8) Especially visual discriminations improve (auditory also), but until six years perceptual errors are frequent. Two-point body tactual discrimination is poor under six years. Increasingly detailed and complex perceptual discriminations emerge as memory improves and cues from several sensory sources are utilized simultaneously.

(9) The development of mental processes shows several concurrent trends:

(a) Imaginative, esthetic, artistic, creative activities show a trend from whole-body involvement at the beginning of the period to a more motorically differentiated and ideational approach.

(b) Reasoning related to problem-solving also shifts from an initial "body" approach to a more ideational one, between three and six years.

(c) The earlier tendency to perseverate within one perceptual or memory system when attempting to solve problems begins to give way to the ability to shift to other perceptual and memory systems (i.e., greater perceptual flexibility emerges) beginning about five years. (Also see number 8 above).

(d) Development of time concepts shows three concurrent trends: from immediate to distant, from subjective to objective, from concrete to abstract.

(e) Other concepts (number, quantity, causality, genus-species relationships, etc.) show two successive developmental trends: (1) from global to differentiated (i.e., from lack of differentiation from the "surround" to abstraction from surround), (2) thence to hierarchic integration.

(f) Ability to generalize others' feelings and reactions sufficiently to recognize them in pictures emerges between two and four years.

(g) The correlation of mental functioning with what IQ tests later test increases steadily from two to six years; intellectual functioning begins to approximate at five years what IQ tests later test.

(h) In Piaget's schema, two to four years comprises the first, "preconceptual," phase of the "concrete operations" stage, the second one in the development of intelligence. This phase consists of three successive-overlapping developments: construction of mental symbols or images which represent oft-repeated action-schemata; capacity to distinguish between the name for an object and the object itself as a result of imitation (accommodation) and imaginative play (assimilation); projection of already developed symbolic schemata onto new objects and situations and beginnings of a tendency to identify self, or parts of own body, with others and with things; beginnings of genuine communicative language; acquisition of a mental picture of topological space, although imagery still lags behind a physically direct, sensorimotor, approach to the external world at this period.

(i) Continuing with Piaget's schema, four to seven or eight years comprises the second, "intuitive," phase of the concrete operations stage. During this phase, further extension of the child's "action images" occurs, along with correction of an as yet intuitive picture of reality, through continuing environmental manipulation, and also through social communication "feedback" towards the latter part of the period.

(10) Trends bearing on the self include the following:

(a) The child's psychological world is centered in self throughout this period, although

(b) there is a gradually growing awareness of "others present" separate from self. But at five years, even "important others" are still perceived in a diffuse, undifferentiated manner:

— From twenty-four to twenty-nine months, *I, me, my,* were the most frequently used pronouns, with *it* next. From thirty to thirty-five months, *you* became third most frequent.

— Piaget says 55 per cent of speech is egocentric at three to four years. From three to five years, nursery-school conversations revolve around self and self-interests in a sort of monologue.
— At four to five years, physical appearance of mother is still not clear: she is seen primarily in terms of her relationship with child. In drawing and in answers to questions, very few children aged four years distinguished father from mother overtly.
— Five-year-olds start to use *my* mother to distinguish her from others' mothers.

(c) Subcultural values (as transmitted by family members) are assimilated unconsciously and begin to affect perception of others and of self; language plays a key role in the assimilation process:
— Imaginary companions, frequent from two-and-one-half to four-and-one-half years, tend to have powers, privileges, virtues, which the child lacks, and child may excuse or defend the "companion's" conduct.
— From thirty-three to sixty-four months, children tended to see the opposite sex as larger than themselves, girls more so than boys; mother and father are seen as larger than self, and father as larger than mother.
— Awareness of sexual identification emerges between three and four years, along with knowledge of sexual taboos.
— Overt, self-instructive speech shifts to internal speech between four-and-one-half and five-and-one-half years.
— By six years, child understands meaning of competition; many are sensitive to ridicule and failure.

(d) The two-year-old's global perception of self as a center of activity is succeeded by the three- and four-year-old's (still global) perception of self as a center of reactive feelings, which is in turn succeeded by the five- to six-year-old's highly vulnerable psychological self or ego:
— at two years, is likely to have some grasp of self as a physical unity;
— from three to five years, conversations revolve around self and own interests in a sort of monologue;

— from three to six years, crying occurs more in response to being thwarted or psychologically hurt and less in response to cuts and bruises;

— from four to six years, the emotional after-effects of anger are almost twice as frequent and prolonged as under four years;

— emotions of envy, shame, disappointment, hope, emerge at five years; by six years, many are sensitive to ridicule and failure.

(11) Types of childhood schizophrenia begin to show up after two years, more frequently among boys than among girls.

Table X summarizes neural changes between two and six years.

The following listing of *neural developments* is derived from these data.

(1) Between two and four years, the width of layer 6 has increased most in the temporal lobe, and that of layer 3 has increased most in the frontal and limbic lobes. The cells of layer 3 have increased most in size of all neocortical neurons. Layer 2 is still very little developed throughout the cortex at four years.

(2) The PF association section is still very little developed at four years. Nor has any cortical area and layer reached full maturity at four years.

(3) Wave-frequency continues to rise after two years but wave amplitude drops sharply between two and four years.

(4) A steady 7-8 cps occipital rhythm is typical by the fourth year and the occipital frequency reaches a pre-adolescent maximum of 9 cps at eight years.

(5) There is a change in the light-sleep EEG pattern at three years, another change after four years, and a change in the arousal pattern (shown in the parietal area) around five to six years.

(6) Theta waves: constitute the major rhythm from two to five years and are more prominent in the dominant hemisphere, are polyrhythmic up to about five years and monorhythmic thereafter, are diffusely distributed up to about five years but are more delimited to the temporal lobe thereafter.

(7) The posterior part of the temporal lobe (auditory functions) increases its surface-area and its fissuration rapidly between

TABLE X
NEURAL DEVELOPMENTAL INDICES: TWO TO SIX YEARS

A. Gross Structural Changes (181-2).

   (1) The increase in the surface-area of the parietal and occipital lobes continues at a rapid pace up to 6 years, while their fissuration continues at a moderate pace between 2 and 6 years. The rate of increase in the surface-area of the temporal lobe is at its most rapid between 2 and 6 years. The temporal pole fissurates rapidly between 2 and 5 years and then stops. The increase in the surface-area of the frontal lobe continues at a moderate and even rate from 2 to 10 years. Its rate of fissuration is most rapid between 2 and 6 years.

   (2) The brain is 80 per cent of its adult weight at 4 years and 90 per cent at 6 years (82).

   (3) Myelination of the pyramidal tract (voluntary-motor) is well advanced during this period (102).

B. Cortical Changes Between Two and Four Years (38).

   (1) Layer pattern:
        — layer 3 has increased most in width in the frontal and limbic lobes. Layer 6 has increased most in width in the temporal lobe (while layers 3 and 2 have increased least).
        — the cells in layer 3c have increased most in size in all parts of the new and old cortex; those in layers 3b and 3a have also increased a good deal in most sections.
        — the nerve cells and fibers in layers 6 and 5 in the primary-motor area are equally developed in the head and lower extremity subareas, but those in layers 4, 3, 2 are more advanced in development in the head subarea than in the lower extremity subarea. (All layers are equally advanced in the other subareas of hand and upper extremity, which are more advanced than are the head and lower extremity).

   (2) Area pattern:
        — in the frontal lobe, the primary-motor area continues to be the most advanced area in development on all criteria, and the gradient of development decreases from the back to the front of the lobe on all criteria; the PF area is still little developed.
        — the primary sensory areas in the parietal, occipital and temporal lobes continue to be the most developed area in each lobe, with the secondary areas in each lobe decreasing in development in proportion to their distance from the primary-reception area.
        — cell processes have increased appreciably in all areas except the insula and the gyrus cinguli.

   (3) Fiber pattern:
        — no vertical exogenous fibers end higher than layer 3b except in the primary-motor and primary-somesthetic areas, where a few end in layer 3a and a very few end in layers 2 and 1. They are larger in all sections of the frontal lobe except in the subarea for the lower extremity in the primary-motor area.
        — the horizontal exogenous fibers have increased most in layers 4, 3c, 3b in the frontal lobe and are most numerous in the subarea for the lower extremity in the primary-motor area. They have also increased in primary and secondary areas in the other lobes.
        — all types of fibers have advanced in development in most of the old cortex areas.

TABLE X
NEURAL DEVELOPMENTAL INDICES: TWO TO SIX YEARS (continued)

— all myelinated fibers have more myelin at 4 years than they did at 24 months. Except for the PF section of the frontal lobe, there are more myelinated fibers in every layer in every area of the cortex; in the frontal pole and anterior part of the three frontal gyri, there are no myelinated fibers in layers 3a and 2. (There were wide individual differences in the amount of myelin in each area and on the other criteria of development, in all brains studied.)

— since birth the order of development of nerve cells and fibers in the cortex is (1) v-e-fs in the cores of the gyri; (2) the s-a-fs; (3) the neurons and h-e and v-e fibers in layers 6 and 5, and tangential fibers in layer 1 (which originate in layer 5). (4) (5) (6) (7) neurons and exogenous fibers in layer 4, 3c, 3b, 3a. (8) neurons in layers 2 and 1, and exogenous fibers in layer 2 (after 4 years). The tangential fibers appear to originate in the cingulum, which extends the entire length of the corpus callosum.

(4) No area and no layer has reached full maturity on the nine growth criteria at 4 years.

C. Electrical Activity From Two to Six Years.

(1) After 2 years, the frequency continues to rise, while the amplitude begins to decrease. From 5 months to 3 years, the amplitude decreases from 75-110 mv. to about 50 mv; it continues to decrease thereafter to adulthood. Most of the decrease occurs between 2 and 3 years (cf. Lindsley's data, #4, below) (42).

(2) From 15 months, there is a tapering off in the rate of increase in the occipital frequency, to a preadolescent maximum of 9 cps at 8 years (170).

(3) The delta rhythm declines steadily between one and 6 years; after 6 years, it appears normally only in sleep records. Theta is the dominant rhythm from 2 to 5 years; theta and alpha are about equal at 5 to 6 years. Theta waves are more prominent in the dominant hemisphere; are diffusely distributed up to about 5 years, and are more delimited to the temporal lobe among older children; are polyrhythmic in younger children and monorhythmic (4-6 cps) in later childhood (151).

(4) Frequency and amplitude pattern of occipital rhythms from 2 to 6 years (108):

Age	Frequency Range	Mean Amplitude
2 years	5.0— 9.6 cps	49 mv
3	4.3— 8.5	51
4	6.0— 9.2	27
5	7.3— 9.4	31
6	7.3—10.3	27

(5) Two years: 14 cps spindles disappear during moderately deep sleep; deep sleep is now marked by irregular slow waves of 1½-3 cps, with intermittent 4-8 cps waves mixed in.

Three years: biparietal humps which showed up during light sleep between 6 and 12 months are still very evident from 3 to 9 years. Ten to 40% of all Ss over 3 years have 10 cps spindles diffusely distributed during moderately deep sleep.

Four years: a steady 7-8 cps occipital frequency is typical by the fourth year. After 4, 12 cps spindles occur during light sleep, usually in only one hemisphere, and have their highest voltages in the frontal areas.

Five years: 25% of 5 year olds had records like that of normal 10 year olds. From 5 to 6 years, high voltage 4-8 cps waves appear continuously in the parietal areas during arousal (64).

birth and six years. Fissuration of the temporal pole, where stream-of-consciousness memories have been located, increases markedly between two and five years — and then stops.

(8) Delta rhythms decline steadily between one and six years and appear normally after six years only in sleep records. Theta and alpha waves are about equal in proportion at five and six years; alpha dominates thereafter.

(9) The frontal lobe fissurates rapidly between two and six years. The width of layer 3 increases most in the frontal and limbic lobes between two and four years. The 12 cps spindles, which occur during light sleep after four years, have their highest voltages in the frontal areas; is this circumstance related to these structural changes?

From two to six years, the following *relationships between neural and behavioral events* appear to obtain:

The maturation of voluntary motor abilities by six years is based on: continued development of primary-motor and modifying-motor cortical areas; full sensory control over voluntary motor activity; smooth functioning of cortical-striatal-cerebellar-cortical feed-back circuits — i.e., on establishment of the Transactional short circuit and advancing development of the long circuit, and on emergence to functioning of all layer 3 in the sensorimotor and related association areas.

The improvement in the motor aspects of speech appears to be related to the functional emergence of all of layer 3 in the speech areas — as well as to opportunities to imitate good speech models. The growth in the symbolizing and communication aspects of language is related to the speech areas' incorporation into the Transactional subsystem, bringing the perceptual functions of the T-O-P area and speech into close functional collaboration. Eighteen months to three years appears to be a period of stress in relation to speech — or better, it is a period of overall stress because of cultural pressures, and the stress affects speech development since it is at this stage a newly developing, and therefore an as yet unstable, ability.

Our culture's expectations of child behavior at this age continue to be too demanding for many children's perceptual, understanding and control capacities. Less mature children, mostly boys, express the resulting stress in anger outbursts and other "acting out" behaviors. More mature children, mostly girls, are sensitive to parental disappointment in their "shortcomings" and internalize it in the form of self-depreciation.

The increasingly ideational nature of memory and the longer time-span of attention and delayed recall appear to be related to advancing mid-frontal and temporal lobe development, and possibly, also, to emergence of all of layer 3 to functioning.

More accurate visual discrimination stems from the functioning of modifying-visual areas and vision-related sections of the posterior (T-O-P) association area. The increasing accuracy of children's drawings throughout this period also reflects broadening T-O-P association area functioning. The perceptual errors common during this period seem to be related to the "in-process," incomplete character of the mediating circuits.

The shift from body involvement to a more exclusively ideational approach in imaginative and reasoning activities is believed to be related primarily to the functional emergence of cortical layer 3 *and* to appropriate prior direct physical contact with objects in one's immediate environment. Greater perceptual flexibility and the advances in various basic concepts are related to the functioning of layer 3, to continuing development in the T-O-P association area, and to growth in self-integration — which is in turn related to advancing CI circuits functioning, a proposition which will be elaborated upon shortly. Greater stability and differentiation of electrical activity accompany these various developments.

In light of the nonauditory temporal lobe's adult function as a memory-repository of emotionally charged experiences, there would seem to be a good deal of significance in the circumstance that its gross *and* fine growth is most rapid during a period when much of the child's experience is of a highly emotional, stressful nature. As to the question on page 118 concerning the relationship between extent of layer functioning and degree of consciousness, the postnatal data to this point indicate this answer: the unconscious level of experience is mediated by cortical layers

6—5—4, variable or borderline consciousness by the lower sections of layer 3 (3c, 3b), and alert, conscious awareness by upper-layer 3 and above.

After four years, a number of behavioral and neural events converge. The child's emotional and social behaviors become increasingly tied to the self, and as this focusing occurs, emotional reactivity becomes more stable, there is a sharp drop in the amplitude of the cortex's electrical activity, and after five years of age, theta rhythms — which are associated with emotional reactivity and which are the dominant EEG rhythm from two to five years — become more delimited to the temporal lobe. Three to five years appears to be the period when temporal-pole centers are incorporated into the CI circuits.

INITIAL STAGES IN THE DEVELOPMENT OF THE SELF

Psychologically, the most significant development of the many important developments of the two to six years period is the emergence of the psychological self, a process which I believe to be anchored in specific neural developments. A review of the epigenetic nature of the growth in self-awareness in the normally developing child serves as an introduction to the attempt to document this proposition.

At six months there is a vague awareness of self as a center of action. At twelve months there is some awareness of self as a center of efficacious action. By two years, there is some awareness of self as a physical unity in which efficacious action is centered. From two to four years, there is a qualitative change. The heretofore uniperspective, "external" awareness of self acquires another dimension: at the same time that one is coming to perceive oneself as an entity distinct from other animate and inanimate entities in one's psychological life-space, one is also becoming aware that this separate entity is a center of overpoweringly *strong reactive feelings*. These "outer" and "inner" dimensions of self are initially quite unintegrated, certainly between two and four years, because the neural mechanisms mediating each dimension are minimally integrated. Thereafter, two processes have to happen for normal personality and intellectual-cognitive development to continue, the second process dependent upon the occurrence of the first: (1) the inner and the outer dimensions of self have to become integrated, and (2) some degree of what Arieti calls the "abstract attitude" towards oneself (9) has to be acquired: one has to come to see oneself as one appears to others — i.e., from a vantage-point external to oneself. Whether or not — and to what degree — these two processes actually do occur is not determined sheerly by innate-maturational, biological factors. The child's experiences prior to and during this pivotal age-period play a crucial role.

A rather lengthy digression is necessary at this point to present the neural and psychological rationale underlying the foregoing, five-pronged proposition that (1) an "outer" dimension of self analogous to Cooley's "looking-glass self" (39) develops first; and that (2) an "inner" dimension emerges independent of the outer dimension between two and four years; and that (3) these two dimensions are initially quite unintegrated neurologically and therefore subjectively; and that (4) the child's experiences play a major role in the manner in which the integration of the two dimensions of self proceeds, and that (5) subsequent continued normal personality and mental development is dependent upon the integration of these two dimensions of experience.

The polarization of "subject" (the knower) and "object" (the known) within the T-O-P association area, a process basic to perception (already referred to in Chapter VI), underlies the emergence of the "outer" component of self. That is, one comes to see oneself as an entity distinct from other animate and inanimate entities in one's life-space — an entity which, as it takes shape, inevitably includes those cumulative reactions to, and evaluations of, it by "important others" that the infant has heretofore absorbed.

As for the emergence of the "inner" dimension of self, "overpoweringly strong" emotional reactions have been occurring within the child for some time, ever since the spinal ANS, the hypothalamus, the hippocampus, and probably the lower layers of the gyrus cinguli also, have been functioning together as a coherent circuit: what, then, is new now? The incorporation into the heretofore incomplete Intraorganismic subsystem of its subfrontal component, (layer 3 of) area 24, the gyrus cinguli, an area on which is projected a re-representation of the ANS, and, possibly also, incorporation of the lower layers of the PF association area — *that's* "what's new!" With this-these functional addition (s) , one becomes *aware* of one's reactivity to one's ongoing experience.

The child is now aware not only of his separate identity and of others' reactions to him, but also that he is the focal center of strong needs and reactive feelings towards others, towards that entity — his perceived physical self — which is in process of differentiation from other entities in his perceptual field, *and* towards his ongoing experience. It is this awareness of and reaction to one's ongoing experience and reactions which is the basis for the reaction-formations which play so large a role in personality formation.

Since the thalamic nuclei related to the Transactional subsystem and the thalamic nuclei related to the Intraorganismic subsystem have not established firm intrathalamic connections at this early, two to four years period (*viz.,* Romer's "there has been in higher vertebrates a welding together of somatic and visceral structures and function, but their union is still far from perfect or complete") , these neurologically separately mediated experiences of self are initially unintegrated psychologically also. With the functional emergence of the Intraorganismic long circuit in addition to the already established Transactional long circuit, branches 1, 2, 3 and 4 of the CI circuits, all of which converge in the thalamus, can now — and in the normally developing child do — begin to function as a single coherent neural system. The life-long process of integration of the outer aspects of self (which are undergoing constant change) and the inner aspects of self (which are also undergoing change) , is thereby initiated.

The emergence of this cortical-participative integrative process signals the shift from dominance of the "mammalian principle" in human development to dominance of the "human principle": it has already been pointed out that our species' genetic inheritance endows us with both principles at birth, the former as actuality, and the latter as potentiality.

However, this important initial integrative process does not occur — nor proceed — as a result of sheerly maturational, innate-biological factors: it is much affected by both the level of anxiety which the child's experiences have heretofore generated *and* by the amount of anxiety which the child's current experiences are generating.

The anxiety which is being generated by the ongoing process of outer-self differentiation can, if it is high and converges with a high level of anxiety already associated with inner, physiological, functioning, markedly hinder and/or distort the "welding together" process to which Romer refers. In such individual instances, the integrative process *in and of itself* generates strong feelings of anxiety.

The next few pages consist of excerpts from a paper of the author's, "A Species Theory of Anxiety," presented at an international conference in 1957 but not published until 1963 (129). Relatively minor modifications necessitated by later knowledge have been incorporated.

I have termed my analysis a *species* hypothesis because it is based explicitly on aspects of development which are characteristic only of the human being and which stem directly from the unique nature of the human CNS. *The implication is that anxiety is indigenous to the human species.*

The aspects of human development just referred to are (1) the postnatal pattern of development of the CNS (it is explicitly acknowledged that the *early phases* of this pattern are shared with other higher mammals); (2) the limits of development of the human cerebral cortex, which allow the neurologically mature adult to acquire a broader, more varied and more complex range of reality awarenesses than can the adult of any subhuman species; (3) the extent to which the behavior of the human adult is a product of his socially induced learning experiences during the period of growth from birth to neurological maturity and after — again, to a far greater degree than for any subhuman species.

By anxiety, I mean a stirred-up state of the organism with two essential components: first, physiological reactions governed by the autonomic nervous system, with sympathetic action dominant — like Cannon's "fight or flight" reaction, but usually less intense and more diffuse, pervasive and prolonged; and second, the cortically mediated awareness of these inner reactions, an awareness with highly unpleasant, even painful, feeling concomitants. Low-level anxiety is experienced by the individual as mildly distracting and uncomfortable. Acute anxiety has an organismic effect similar to a strong fear reaction: the functioning of the lower, life-mediating centers of the neuraxis become so active, the cortex's activity is depressed because of diversion of oxygen to the lower centers, and the action of the lower centers is as a result partially released from cortical domination. The subjective effect for the individual is that coherent, organized intellectual activity ceases, the organism is "taken over" by the viscera, and the unpleasant feeling-tone accompanying these inner events is well connoted by the word "dread."

I hypothesize two basic types of anxiety as indigenous to the human being, the latter type divisible into two phases. These two types are differentiated *not* on the basis of the physiological manifestations which constitute the sensory foundations of anxiety — these manifestations are common to both types — but are differentiated, rather, on the basis of (1) the *sources of the stimuli* which elicit these physiological reactions, and of (2) the *cortical level* which first mediates these stimuli. These differing sources and levels are a direct outcome of the unfolding stages of postnatal development of the human CNS.

"Existence" anxiety, the first type, I see as indigenous to the period of infancy, beginning shortly after birth — possibly shortly before. It is initiated by stimuli from the infant's internal world and skin-surface which reach the immature neuraxis through the interoceptors and skin receptors (which enter the CNS through the already functioning spinal cord), and which are mediated by the phylogenetically older parts of the cortex. [In the terminology of this monograph, existence anxiety is mediated entirely by the Intraorganismic subsystem].

"Transactional" anxiety, the second type, I divide into two phases, *identity* and *cosmic* anxiety. Identity anxiety emerges two to three years earlier than cosmic anxiety. Both phases of transactional anxiety are initiated by stimuli from the physical and social world external to the individual, stimuli which are ordinarily transmitted to the more-advanced-in-functioning CNS through the distance receptors (vision and hearing), and which are perceived and interpreted by phylogenetically newer

parts of the cortex. [Transactional anxiety is partially mediated, that is, by the Transactional subsystem.] . . .

The presence of specific pain and pleasure foci in the mammalian neuraxis (142) and their close association with the basic life processes suggest that nature has here provided a potent mechanism for ensuring the continuing existence and growth of the individual and of the human race: activities which are essential to that existence (intake and digestion of food, warmth, sexual activity, new experience) are normally experienced as pleasurable and therefore to be actively sought, while a *lack* of these experiences (that is, continuing unsatisfied basic needs) — which is as threatening to life and the species as are directly life-threatening experiences which induce reactions of fear — is, like fear, experienced as painful or highly unpleasant.

The degree of painfulness or unpleasantness experienced is a function partly of the actual extent of deprivation, i.e., of acuteness of threat, and partly of the individual infant's genetically as well as congenitally determined constitutional make-up. There is probably, for a particular infant and child, a "safe" time-range of deprivation, psychologically: it is only after its continuance beyond a certain length of time that an unpleasant feeling-tone becomes permanently associated with basic autonomic reaction-patterns and that a proneness for exaggerated physiological response to similar experiences beyond infancy is established.

The implications of these several characteristics of the early-infantile CNS for the very early experience of the infant would seem to be these:

(1) The infant's major sources of sensation are his own internal functioning and those aspects of his external environment which impinge directly on his body surface.

(2) Since his organism is physiologically unstable at this early stage, his inner world is, even with the most responsive care, frequently and unavoidably a source of painful sensation — hunger pangs, cold, chafing, digestive upsets.

(3) *He is entirely dependent upon agents outside himself for everything which makes his body a source of pleasurable sensation to him* (or at least, not a source of painful sensation):

food, warmth, changes in position, bubbling, gentle physical handling, body-contact with another warm, nonrejecting being, variation in experience. The fundamental association of food with love becomes understandable in this context, as does the older infant's and young child's reluctance to go to sleep or do anything that represents renunciation of pleasurable sensations.

(4) Basic associations of unpleasantness (leading to avoidance behavior) and of pleasure (leading to adient behavior) become attached to the basic life processes during the first very few months of life, *while the infant is still an almost entirely noncognitive being.* If these basic life activities are preceded or accompanied by a great deal of painful experience, such as habitual prolonged hunger or being fed or handled by a rejecting person, a dual feeling-tone may develop which will be even more unpleasant and disturbing than a simple uncomplicated painful concomitant: very fundamental and pervasive emotional and self-perception problems may accrue from the development of such a dual painful-pleasurable association.

(5) These experiences are registered in the lower layers of the six-layered cortex, the only neo- and meso- cortical layers functioning at this early period.

Without the intervention of outside agents, then, the infant's basic organismic processes inevitably become a source of painful sensation to him. The organism reacts to an *absence* of life-sustaining sensations, that is, to continuing strong physiological tension, much the same as it reacts to stimuli from the external world perceived as directly life-threatening. Here is the physical foundation of infantile existence anxiety. These unconscious, ANS-associated anxiety reactions are thereafter an integral part of the Intraorganismic system and are activated whenever it is. *The circumstance that girls are born with a more mature nervous system than are boys suggests that boys are inherently prone to higher levels of existence anxiety than are girls.*

To the extent that early care is not geared to the unstable nature of the young infant's organismic functioning, to that extent is existence anxiety maximized. Positive and responsive care can minimize it, but if and until we invent and use widely, gadgets so sensitive they signal the babe's internal discomfort even before it becomes discomfort to him, existence anxiety cannot be entirely eliminated.

Infantile anxiety is not confined to only the human species. Because of early CNS developmental-pattern commonalities, the newborn of the other higher mammals show reactions to attentive care and to neglect similar to those of the human infant. Rather, *it is in the nature of the adult caretaker of the infant that the distinctively human element enters in* to my postulation of existence anxiety. The subhuman mother is governed in her reactions to her young by hormonal patterns which, unless she is killed, impel her to give the sustenance and constant physical care required by her young. *Human* maternal care is so largely a function of socially-induced learning on the one hand, and a reflection of the total personality of the individual woman (which is also a product of culturally-derived experience) on the other hand, that the chances the human infant during its long period of total dependency will be given care inappropriate to a greater or lesser degree to his stage of development is very great, particularly in complex societies.

As an interpolation, it would seem that psychiatrists and applied psychologists have been misplacing their emphasis rather badly in stressing in a disembodied way the psychological importance of good infant care. It is the biological inappropriateness of cultural patterns of child-rearing, and the individual woman's "gut-level" acceptance of, and ease in, her maternal role — also strongly affected by cultural values and practices — which we must become concerned about if we hope to improve the physical and psychological health of each new generation.

Unlike cosmic anxiety, the effect of existence anxiety on organismic functioning and on subsequent development and learning is negative. In later years, attacks of existence anxiety are invariably disorganizing to cognitive functioning.

"Identity" and "cosmic" anxiety are grouped together because I see them as two phases of essentially the same order of reactions: the individual's reactions to his perception of himself - as - an - entity - separate - from - other - entities - within -

an - ever - expanding - physical - and - social - environment. This perception broadens quantitatively and qualitatively with age and greater experience, and identity anxiety, the initial reaction to this perception, merges into cosmic anxiety, a later development.

Identity anxiety emerges sometime during the second or third year of life for most children, shortly after the neocortical sensory and related association areas have matured enough for the child to be aware of his identity as a being separate from the other beings and objects in his immediate environment, and to become aware that events can and do occur outside his body and that these events — as he gradually discovers throughout later infancy and early childhood — are not subject to his control. Lack of feelings of "mastery," due to earlier limited opportunity for active, unpunished, sensorimotor experimentation with objects in the physical environment, serves to heighten identity anxiety. These awarenesses constitute the first stages of development of the self or ego, and *identity anxiety is an unavoidable concomitant of this development.*

Neurological data indicate that the sensory and perceptual processes which make these two sets of awareness possible are initially a good deal more advanced in development than the neural processes which allow the child to comprehend and to control his world — that is, to reason, and to perceive and solve problems. (Particularly the latter processes are far more developed and complex in the human being than in any subhuman species.) *It is this discrepancy in the pattern of cortical development which makes inevitable feelings of threat and the resulting generation of anxiety.* (The postulated functional sequence is: a perception of discrepancy originating in neocortical centers and initiated by external stimuli activates the anxiety-inducing centers in the thalamus? old cortex?. These centers act on the hypothalamus, which initiates visceral and somatic reactions, the stimuli from which feed back into the neuraxis and are experienced as anxiety.)

And because this discrepancy is a function of the uniquely advanced nature of the human cerebral cortex, it would seem to make transactional anxiety uniquely indigenous to our species.

If, as has already been intimated, both identity and existence anxiety are high, the beginning phases of integration of the self generate still more anxiety. This situation sets up a vicious circle: the physiological components of this by-product of the integrative process are fed back into the anterior thalamic nuclei by the hypothalamus, which in turn transmit the stimuli to the old cortex where they are reinterpreted as anxiety. If the anxiety induced is acute and the sources of anxiety-inducement are chronic, the functioning of the T-O-P association area, which is the source of the disturbing outer-self data, and the functioning of the gyrus cinguli, which is the source of disturbing inner awarenesses, may both be depressed — and childhood schizophrenia results.

Why is T-O-P area and gyrus cinguli, and possibly also the beginning phases of PF area, functioning depressed as the result of prolonged anxiety? As postulated earlier, acute anxiety has an organismic effect similar to that of a strong fear reaction: the functioning of the lower, life-mediating centers of the neuraxis become so active — and therefore so oxygen-consuming — the cortex is deprived of sufficient oxygen for *its* optimal functioning, and its activity is depressed. The first parts of the cortex to be affected are those last to develop: the association areas and the higher cortical layers. If the anxiety continues to be both acute and chronic, the cortical oxygen deprivation and consequent depressed functioning is also chronic — and degenerative changes in both the posterior association cortex and frontal lobe eventually occur. If schizophrenia occurs in early childhood, before the PF association area has begun to function, and there is no remission, the PF area either does not become functional at all, or only minimally so — and the highest human behaviors do not emerge.

Less severe amounts of identity anxiety — and existence anxiety also — result in variable or "gappy" T-O-P area and gyrus cinguli functioning and hence gaps or distortions in the data picked up by the related CI circuits (e.g., especially painful aspects of the outer-self picture may be completely blocked out, perceptually), and the tenuous coordination of the outer and inner aspects of self which results leaves the individual vulnerable to later stress experiences provoked by perceived outer-world events, and schizophrenia, or merely (!) severe anxiety states, may develop in preadolescent, adolescent, or early-adult years. A significant item of information in this context is that "barbiturates have a markedly depressant effect on thalamic transmission" (3).

The circumstance that the Transactional long circuit (which includes the sensory-modifying motor tracts) is strongly influenced by the ongoing outcomes of the integration-of-self process accounts for its key role in perception: selective or biased or gappy perception has its bases here.

In our culture, it is the coincidence of culturally imposed toilet-training (from about eight months to eighteen months) with the period when a keen awareness of the external aspects of self is emerging that makes how this training is handled so important, for good or for ill, for the developing personality: it is this convergence rather than the training *per se* that is psychologically significant.

A similar situation holds for speech development. Although vocalization is shared by both the Intraorganismic and Transactional subsystems, verbalization (and the various stages in between early vocalization and later verbalization) is Transactionally mediated. If first attempts at verbalization (also from about ten to eighteen months) are met with disinterest or ridicule or demands for levels of articulation that are beyond the child's capacities, the newly developing verbalizing process will be fraught with anxiety, just at the time when the child is becoming aware of his independent existence. As a result of the poor initial integration of self in such instances, speech may not be adequately related to the inner aspects of self and the later symbolizing and communication roles of speech and language may continue to show dissociation from the inner aspects of self.

The interesting phenomenon of glossolalia or speaking in "tongues" and its recent revival among some Protestant church-groups becomes understandable within this context. A news item in the *New York Times* of July 25, 1964, referred to the award of a research grant for a psychological and linguistic study of glossolalia and then stated:

The glossolalist speaks fluently in what sounds like a foreign language but he does not know the meaning of what he says. . . . "From a psychological point of view," Dr. Kildahl said, "the common denominator of the experience seems to be *a lessening of conflict and anxiety.*" (Italics EM's.)

Glossolalia may thus be interpreted as a regression experience for the individual practicing it; that is, *dis*integration and regression to one of the less anxious, preverbal stages in speech development: young children quite frequently indulge in the equivalent of glossolalia. The difficulty in blending words auditorily, discovered to be common among retarded readers (122), may also have its roots in this early period of speech *and* self development.

Corroborative evidence for the foregoing self-integration and related anxiety formulation would seem to be provided by Levy and Kennard's finding that the EEG abnormality characteristic of the schizophrenic patients of their study was "a high percentage of fast [i.e., beta] activity in the frontal poles" (106). Recall Walter's description of the beta rhythm as "common in tension, whether acute or in the form of chronic anxiety states" (184, p. 153).

Arieti's postulation of the role — and effects — of anxiety in (adolescent and adult) schizophrenia, summarized in the two excerpts following, provides further corroborative evidence for the foregoing formulation of identity anxiety.

> Schizophrenia is a special reaction to an extreme state of anxiety, originating in childhood, and reactivated later in life by psychological factors. The specific reaction consists of the adoption of archaic mental mechanisms, which belong to lower levels of integration. Inasmuch as the result is a regression to, but not an integration at, lower levels, a disequilibrium is engendered which causes further regression, at times to levels even lower than the one in which certain perceptions are possible (9, p. 384).

> In [the earlier stages of] schizophrenia, there is a gradual return from the abstract to the concrete, from highly specialized symbols to paleosymbols, from high conceptual constructions to sensorial perceptions, and finally from perceptions to

sensations. In other words, there is a reluctance to use the most central parts of the T-O-P area. . . . It seems as if some of the sensory stimuli are not even perceived or recognized, although they are experienced as sensations. . . . Finally, when the illness progresses, there is a tendency to abolish almost entirely the functions of the T-O-P area and to use only the residual parts of the temporal, parietal and occipital lobes. . . .

I feel that the psychological conditions of the patient compel him to avoid[1] those high symbolic functions which perpetuate or increase his anxiety and to descend, in a protective way[2], to less elevated functions which do not arouse so much anxiety (p. 417).

And further evidence from another source, surgery as a means of alleviating some schizophrenic symptoms (67), is pertinent:

Surgery is conceived as producing its effects by creating a defect-state. Reverberating circuits, or 'long-circuiting' in Fulton's sense, is cut down. The mechanism for prolongation [of neural activity] in time is impaired (p. 404).

K. Livingston, following his experiences . . . with bi-medial operations, operated on a series of cases in which he merely separated the anterior cingulate gyrus from the rest of the frontal brain. . . . The effects of this limited operation, which apparently involves 50% less cutting than the bimedial operation, rivaled, according to Livingston, the results obtained with bimedial surgery (p. 411).

Upon the nature and extent of the coordination of the two aspects of self depends whether or not, and to what degree, the young person is thereafter able to acquire the "abstract attitude" — that is, to "take the role of the other towards himself," an acquisition which is the prerequisite, as George Mead so cogently reasoned, for the emergence of the higher mental capacities and processes (120). How many lines of evidence and of theory converge here!

[1,2]If the physiological effects of acute anxiety, referred to earlier in this chapter, are taken into account, the questionable implication of conscious motivation in such phrases as "compel him to avoid" and "in a protective way" can be dispensed with: a regression to lower levels of functioning is virtually automatic.

Ironically, it is Piaget's great contribution — his consistent attention from birth onward to the cognitive aspects and implications of human development and especially of early experience — which appears to be at the same time the source of the core weakness in his conceptual system. Perhaps because his professional experience and experimentation has been (apparently) only with the psychologically normal-range products of the stable family-life of the Swiss middle-class — which provides for the growing infant and child a very particular kind of early mothering, a particular quality and range of social relationships and opportunities for environmental contact, and later, a particular kind of school curriculum — Piaget, apparently lacking an anthropological perspective, has *taken for granted what is actually the prerequisite* for his post sensorimotor-stage picture of the "development of intelligence": *the impact on the child's early personality development of his/her first social relationships and experiences with the immediate world.* That is, experience is even more important in the development of intelligence than Piaget (or Hunt, 86) conceives it to be, but a *much wider range of experience than he has taken into account.* In essence, Piaget has described the course of development of "intelligence" (which is itself a culturally defined concept) in a particular western European cultural setting — a setting which has sufficient similarity to today's American upper middle-class subculture in its goals and values to make his picture particularly meaningful to members of that sub-culture.

Before proceeding to the next developmental period, it is important to emphasize that at four years, the oldest cortex so far reported on by Conel, these structural aspects remain minimally or completely undeveloped: the pre-frontal association area, and layer 2 throughout the cortex. Nor has any cortical area or layer attained full histological maturity at four years. Also, at six years, electrical activity has not reached a mature state in any part of the cortex.

Chapter XI

FROM SIX YEARS TO NEURAL MATURITY

FROM SIX TO ELEVEN YEARS

Beyond four years, the lack of exact area and layer developmental data, so usefully provided by Conel's studies, handicaps continuing attempts to posit relationships between the neural and the behavioral orders of development. However, neural trends and relationships have emerged sufficiently clearly by four years to warrant predictive extrapolation. Gross structural and pertinent EEG materials continue to be available.

Behavioral trends during this period include the following:

(1) With opportunities provided for practice of already matured voluntary motor abilities, there is increasing smoothness and efficiency of the major locomotor and manipulative skills. With appropriate training, most complex motor skills can be learned by the end of the period. There appears to be a relationship between degree of motor competence and level of speech development.

(a) Extraneous movements disappear, speed and coordination increase, basic skills become more automatic and are applied to new situations.

(b) A group of speech-defectives aged nine to eighteen were found to be also inferior as a group on three sets of motor ability tasks.

(2) The various exteroceptive modalities and related abilities mature variably:

(a) visually based perception reaches its maturational peak at about six years;

(b) auditory acuity reaches its maturational peak at about ten years;

(c) orientation to one's own body and to physical space improves in a directly parallel manner throughout (and beyond) this period (see also #5) ;

240

(d) kinesthesis improves, but is still incompletely developed by eleven years (it matures about midadolescence) .

(3) The focus of speech and language development shifts still further from acquisition of basic skills (clear articulation, vocabulary, word-usage) to making it an increasingly accurate and effective means for communicating with others.

(a) By six-and-one-half years, 91 per cent of speech sounds are articulated correctly; there is very little increase thereafter.

(b) In the early grade-school years, children have a concrete approach to defining words on the Stanford-Binet (gave use, descriptive, demonstration types of definition) ; an abstract or conceptual approach occurs later.

(c) Sentences begin to be longer and more complex at nine years (in grade four) .

(d) Up to nine-and-one-half years, girls are better than boys in articulation, word-usage, length and complexity and grammatical correctness of sentences. They are also more fluent verbally throughout grade and high school.

(4) As the basic social attitudes and values of the child's sub-culture are internalized, awareness of the world in relation to self (the "abstract attitude") emerges.

(5) Perceived social space gradually expands from the immediate circle of family and friends to persons more removed in space and time. (See also third point under #2.)

(6) Sex differences in practiced social relationships and preferred activities emerge during this period in the American middle-class subculture:

(a) Boys are small-group oriented; girls have one or two close friends. There is voluntary sex-segregation from seven to eleven years in the American culture. The essential characteristics of boys' activities may be summarized as follows:

Age	Boys' Group Organization	Boys' Group Play Activities
6	A mere aggregate.	Are of a gross-motor character.
7–9 or 10	Leaderless coherence of five to eight boys around a common interest.	A peak in the variety of these gross-motor activities is reached at 9 years.
9 or 10 to 12 years.	Members are likely to act as an organized unit under a common leader.	Basic motor activities become a means to more complex ends, such as highly organized games.

(b) Girls see human relationships as more wanted, rewarding, liked. Boys are more activity and skills oriented.

(c) Girls initially conform more readily to adult values and pressures than do boys.

(7) Socially based experiences increasingly influence the content of emotional reactions during this period:

(a) Anger and humor both begin to have a strong anti-adult aspect towards the end of middle childhood.

(b) Concrete and imaginative fears are most, and about equally, frequent from five to twelve years.

(c) Girls are more secure than boys during middle-childhood, but the reverse situation begins to emerge in the pre-adolescent period (beginning about eleven years).

(d) Girls achieve dependable emotional control by the end of this period while boys have yet to do so.

(8) Behavior problems reported by mothers reveal consistent sex differences, both in their bases and in the child's manner of reacting thereto:

(a) Throughout the age-period, boys have strong feelings of hostility against controlling and "pressuring" elders, and express these feelings in acting-out behaviors; beginning about ten years, feelings of insecurity and self-depreciation also emerge and are reacted to in both attacking and withdrawing behaviors; there are some evidences of "internalization" among boys towards the end of the period.

(b) At around six years, girls end an earlier period of hostility against external pressures, expressed in covertly negative behaviors; throughout the middle-childhood period, they have feelings of insecurity and self-depreciation, reacting to them primarily with evidences of "internalization" and withdrawal.

(9) Memory-span for digits, for length of sentence recalled, for letters, for reversed digits, increases, as does logical and rote memory and ability to sustain attention. Boys are not as good as girls of the same age in memorizing ability throughout pre-school and school years.

(10) There is a shift from a physiognomic and a global perceptual approach at the beginning of the period to (an initially

unsure) differentiation of the stimulus on its own merits beginning at nine years.

(11) Cognitively, the shift from a global to a differentiated approach is accompanied by "externalization" of that which is perceived, by awareness that there are realities outside one's immediate experience, by a trend to accommodate to external reality (after the earlier trend to assimilate it — as per Piaget). Ideationally, there is a shift from concrete, bodily manipulations-operations to mental manipulations-operations, and the ability to symbolize consciously — i.e., to grasp that a word or a number stands for an entity or concept — develops.

(a) Basic arithmetic skills and mathematical reasoning increase during this period; boys are consistently more competent than girls in this area.

(b) The approach to time shifts from the immediate and concrete to the distant and conceptual-abstract.

(c) Problem-solving reasoning shows three parallel developments during this period:
— an initial tendency for concrete, body-movement trial and error shifts to mental trial and error (i.e., to ideation) ;
— there is increasing ability to "get outside" the problem, to remove oneself from it, to "objectify" it, to perceive it on its own merits;
— there is increasing ability to differentiate the relevant subparts of the problem and to grasp their inter-relationships.

(d) The ability to conceptualize — to form generalizations from specific instances, increases markedly from six to eleven years, when it apparently reaches a subadult level.

(e) Beginning at nine-and-one-half years, there is a marked falling-off in the proportion of questions in conversation; it would seem that the "abstract attitude" is well developed by this age.

(f) In Piaget's schema, seven or eight years to eleven or twelve years is the third and final phase of the "concrete operations" stage in the development of intelligence. The lag between the child's immediate perceptions and his grasp of their meaning becomes evident to *him* and results in active efforts to reconcile the two; as a result, thought becomes detached from immediate perception and action, classifying and ordering emerge, and a relatively sudden transition to a new intellectual level occurs about eleven years: can now grasp conservation of quantities and numbers, construct adult conceptions of space and time and shift from part-part to part-whole relationships. These abilities are dependent upon social interaction and the circumstance that the child is now able to appreciate the point of view taken by another individual.

(12) Trends bearing on the self include the following:

(a) Progressive differentiation of the parts of own body parallels the progressive expansion and differentiation of one's psychological life-space:

— development of right-left discrimination begins about five years, grows rapidly to six to seven years, decreases in growth-rate between seven and nine years, and is achieved about eleven to twelve years;

— finger-localization begins at six years and is achieved at eleven to twelve years;

— of topics contributed to class discussion in grades two to six, seven to eight year olds contributed "personal activities" — 61 per cent, and "current happenings in world at large" — 18 per cent; while eleven- to twelve-year-olds contributed "personal activities" — 18 per cent, and "current happenings in world" — 60 per cent;

— see also third subpoint under #2, and #5.

(b) Emergence of the tendency to judge self and work with critical objectivity precedes the emergence of differentiated perception of others as sentient beings with feelings, rights, concerns, like one's own.

(c) Culturally derived learnings contribute to sex differences in opinion of own and other sex and to cultural differences in conscience development (to cite only two areas in which research on cultural differences has been done).

(13) Six to ten years is the second "critical period" in the incidence of childhood schizophrenia. It is a period when the child's immediate social world — family, school, friends — increases its demands on and expectations of the individual. More boys than girls succumb during this period.

TABLE XI

NEURAL DEVELOPMENTAL INDICES: SIX YEARS TO THE THIRTIES

A. Gross Structural Changes.

   (1) Although the increase in the surface-area of the parietal and occipital lobes stops at 6 years, fissuration continues at a moderate pace to a submaximum at 10 years. The increase in the surface-area of the frontal lobe continues at a moderate pace to its near-maximum at 10 years; the fissuration pattern is similar (181-2).

   (2) The cerebellum achieves its full adult weight at 13 years, but the entire brain does not achieve its full weight and volume until "during the third decade" (82).

   (3) Between 6 years and mid-adolescence, the dark pigment of the substantia nigra (in the upper mid-brain), which is associated with finely controlled movement (also kinesthesis?) develops rapidly (144).

B. Electrical Activity.

   (1) From 6 to 10 years, theta rhythm declines in proportion; the EEG record vacillates between theta and alpha rhythms. The adult pattern of alpha dominance emerges clearly about 10 years, although it began to emerge after 6 years, and is stabilized at about 12 years. Alpha rhythms are more prominent on the right side from 6 to 8 years and from 10 years on; at 9 years, they are nearly symmetrical in distribution (151).

   (2) After the sixth year, the low amplitude fast activity found in 20 per cent of the 6 to 12 months records disappears; it is not present in normal adults (64).

   (3) Occipital-alpha range and amplitude from 6 to 16 years (108):

Age	Range	Mean Amplitude	Age	Range	Mean Amplitude
6	7.3-10.3 cps	27 mv	12	8.0-12.0 cps	20 mv
8	7.3-10.3	21	14	8.7-12.2	18
10	8.0-11.6	19	16	9.0-11.0	13

   (4) Individual and sex differences from 5 to 17 years (77):

     — There is considerable individual variability in the age when the occipital alpha becomes stabilized at the adult level.

     — Individuality of pattern is consistent: a child with an initially fast alpha tended to remain on the fast side as he/she grew older; similarly for a child with an initially slow alpha.

     — Girls showed faster mean-alpha frequencies than boys throughout the period studied; also a low-voltage, fast type of record was more common among girls; both are maturer characteristics.

     — Girls had significantly: faster delta activity from the occipital area at 8 years, faster delta activity from the central areas at 10 years; more delta activity from the motor area at 10 years.

   (5) Developmental patterns between 8 and 15 years for three brothers (132):

     — The alpha rhythm becomes more monorhythmic and monomorphic; it becomes more localized in the occipital region and better organized into harmonious spindles.

     — In the temporal area, percent-time delta decreases, and the theta frequency-band becomes narrower and decreases in voltage (from 12 to 15 years, theta disappears altogether during the resting state, emerging thereafter only during emotional states). Thus, "the activity of the temporal region also becomes less polyrhythmic and polymorphic."

     — In general, electrical activity becomes more monomorphic, localized, systematized and structured — i.e., shows growing equilibrium, with definite irreversibility: once a more mature pattern is acquired, it will not regress to the previous stage, unless disease occurs.

TABLE XI
NEURAL DEVELOPMENTAL INDICES: SIX YEARS TO THE THIRTIES
(continued)

(6) Patterns during various states of consciousness (53):

Eight to 10 years: — humps are always present in light sleep, but of lower voltage than earlier; very frequent from parietal leads;
— in deeper sleep, there are 14 cps spindles of lower voltage from the parietals, with occasional 12 cps spindles from frontal areas.

Eleven to 14 years: — occipital alpha is flattened by eye-opening and during states of relaxation;
— 8-10 cps frequencies are typical during waking, plus some 13-14 cps activity;
— during drowsiness, there is lowered amplitude, with sinusoidal 5-7 cps waves of medium voltage in the frontal areas;
— in light sleep, humps of moderately high amplitude from parietal leads occur regularly;
— in deeper sleep, 12 cps spindles occur, most clearly in the frontal areas;
— the transition from sleep to waking is usually rather sudden; marked slowing is usually absent during arousal; when paroxysmal slowing occurs, it is in the frontal area and usually 5-7 cps.

(7) Area patterns (64):
— During the ninth year, the record from the occipital area is very much like that of an adult, but there is more slow and 7-9 cps activity in the parietal and frontal areas than is common among adults.
— In the tenth year, 9 and 10 cps activity reaches its maximum.
— From 10 to 19 years, 12 cps spindles during light sleep are most evident.
— Twelve to 17 years are characterized by the commonness of short runs of 5-7 cps waves during drowsiness in the frontal and parietal areas.

(8) From 14 to 30 years (64):
— All types of adult records are obtained, but many adult records have childish characteristics.
— The low-voltage fast activity in the occipital areas found in 20 per cent of adult records hardly ever occurs before age 14; slow activity in the form of a shifting base-line diminishes after 14 years.
— The adult arousal response consists of a quick return of the normal waking pattern without transition through a stage of high-voltage fast activity, typical of children
— Paroxysmal slow waves, first seen during the second year, are rare after 15 years.
— Five to 7 cps (theta) waves in the frontal area are a normal EEG feature from 15 to 20 years; the frequency is faster thereafter.
— The highest voltage of the 14 cps light-sleep spindles is reached between 15 and 20 years; they are entirely absent in 20 per cent of adults over 60 years.
— Except for the prefrontal section, most persons have normal-adult records after 19 years.
— The voltage of frequencies from 1-3 cps (delta) declines up to at least 29 years; frequencies between 11 and 19 cps increase gradually until at least 29.
— Biparietal humps during light sleep are typical of 20 to 50 year records.
— Between 15 and 60 years, fast records are increasingly common, while

TABLE XI
NEURAL DEVELOPMENTAL INDICES: SIX YEARS TO THE THIRTIES
(continued)

---

slow records become increasingly atypical; after 60 years, more slow records emerge.

(9) From the thirties on (64) :
— The adult drowsiness pattern (flattening and some slowing) is found in almost all Ss during their thirties and forties; this pattern does not become common until the tenth year. Positive spike-like patterns are also common during light sleep during the thirties and forties.
— Isolated 6-8 cps waves appear in the temporal lobes after 40 years, and in other areas such slowing appears after 60 years [are the temporal areas more vulnerable to aging?—EM].
— During the fifties and sixties, large slow delta (1½-3 cps) waves in both frontal areas during drowsiness become common.

(10) A fully adult pattern from all parts of the brain including the PF area emerges between 25 and 35 years (184) .

(11) EEG patterns associated with various psychological disorders from 5 to 55 years (106) :
— Aggressive, paroxysmal rage pattern *or* a low frustration threshold is related to focal theta activity in the temporal region; psychomotor seizures show the same relationship. The percentage of abnormal records among the behavior-problems sample was at its highest point between 5 and 12 years.
— Schizophrenics show a high percentage of fast activity in the frontal poles. The percentage of abnormal records among the schizophrenic sample was at its highest point between five and eleven years.
— The psychopaths had a significant relationship between high alpha index and theta activity.

Table XI summarizes the findings of studies on neural electrical activity after six years as well as studies on gross structural changes.

The following listing of *neural changes* from six to eleven years is derived from these data:

(1) At six years, alpha and theta waves are about equal in proportion. From six to ten years, theta waves decline in proportion and the record vacillates between dominance of alpha and theta rhythms, with alpha gaining an increasing edge.

(2) The alpha waves assume adult: percentages (dominant), form (monomorphic), area-patterning (occipital localization) and right side dominance, between ten and twelve years.

(3) Changes in the patterns distinctive of light sleep and of deeper sleep occur between eight and ten years.

(4) Temporal-lobe activity becomes more stable between six

and twelve years; the proportion of delta rhythms decreases, while the theta rhythms decrease in voltage and contract in frequency.

(5) Girls' records show more mature characteristics than boys' at each age between five and seventeen years.

(6) Schizophrenics show a high percentage of fast activity in the frontal poles; the percentage of abnormal records among the schizophrenic sample was at its highest point prior to the mid-forties between five and eleven years.

(7) The sex psychopaths had a significant relationship between high alpha index and theta activity. Levy and Kennard quote Denis Hill as saying that "delayed maturation underlies behavior disorders of adolescents, delinquents, psychopaths."

(8) The percentage of abnormal records among the behavior-problems sample was at its highest point between five and twelve years. Focal theta activity in the temporal region was associated with psychomotor seizures, with a low frustration level, and with aggressive, paroxysmal rage patterns.

From six to eleven years, these *relationships between neural and behavioral events* appear to obtain:

Continuing auditory and kinesthetic development implies continuing maturation of related neural mechanisms.

The maturation of the motor speech areas appears to be completed near the beginning of this period. Thereafter, opportunity to imitate good models is the crucial factor in continuing growth in clear articulation. Increase in the accuracy and effectiveness of language as a tool for social communication appears to depend on the amount and the emotional quality of social-interaction experiences prior to and during this period — which is in turn related to perceptual factors. Arieti has pointed out that:

> In all probability, impulses reverberate continuously in the language centers and T-O-P area, and the increase in symbolization and socialization necessitates the contemporary development of both (9, p. 417).

The parallel manner in which orientation to one's body and orientation to physical and social space and time proceeds appears to confirm Herrick's conception of perception as a process of gradual polarization — and differentiation — of the "knower" and the "known." An investigation to answer this question would seem to be useful: If a child has been prevented from free tactual exploration of his body during infancy and early childhood, does his exploration and discrimination of near physical space during late-infancy and early childhood *and* his subsequent conceptualization of far space and time proceed normally or not?

The expansion of perceived physical and social space and time (i.e., of the psychological life-space), which begins towards the end of this period and continues through adolescence, is believed to be immediately dependent upon both a well-advanced level of self-integration and continuing neural maturation, probably in the PF association area. The beginnings of the ego-ideal component of the superego (to use Freudian terminology) stem from this expansion.

As the (sub-)culture stresses — and imposes — behaviors considered to be sex-role appropriate, sex differences in values, interests, social behaviors, self-evaluations, emotional reactions, behavior problems, emerge. The continuing sex-group discrepancy in neural maturity appears also to contribute to these differences. Boys' greater manipulative interests and skills and mathematical competence may be conceived as expressing a reaction-formation against their greater vulnerability to external reality — these activities, that is, reflect a strong reactive drive for mastery of the external world. Girls, on the other hand, more typically show self-differentiation and integration, and the ability to identify with and internalize adult emphases on control and foresight earlier: they develop the conscience aspect of the superego by the end of this period while boys have yet to do so. They also show a stronger drive to understand and come to terms with the immediate human relationships in which they are involved than do boys.

Sex-group differences in emotional reactions and behavior problems, especially, appear to be influenced by the relative neural maturity of boys and girls. Behavior problems which emerge during this period are classifiable into three categories, according to the data:

(1) active resistance against an external social world perceived as excessively demanding (more typical among boys);

(2) self-referrent internalization of the negative judgments of one's immediate social world (more typical among girls) ;

(3) total withdrawal from an external social reality which is too threatening psychologically to be coped with (six to ten years is the "second critical period" in the incidence of childhood schizophrenia, to which boys are more prone than girls) .

These reactions seem to be a function of the interaction of three factors: the degree of differentiation and integration of self, the degree of maturation of cortical emotional-control mechanisms (in the PF association area or in the gyrus cinguli?), and the degree of social pressure on the child for expression of behaviors he is insufficiently advanced in development to express. The circumstance that there are sex differences in the first two, neurally related, factors, at least, appears to contribute to the sex differences in style of reaction. For example, at age eleven among normal-range youngsters, girls begin to show the early-adolescent regression to body-focused symptoms (probably related to the shake-up in the body-image in the T-O-P association area) while boys do not yet do so.

Levy and Kennard's study (cited in Table XI) indicates that five to twelve years was the period of highest incidence both of schizophrenia and of behavior problems in their hospitalized groups. It would appear from the EEG data that for children having immaturities carried over from infancy, the strong pressures from cultural agents, typical of this period, precipitate severe emotional disorders.

The increase in memory-span and in sustained attention reflects continuing frontal lobe maturation. The increase in logical and rote memory is probably related to continuing neural integration.

Cognitive development is intimately inter-related with self-development during this period, and both are dependent upon the nature and extent of socially based experiences prior to and during the six to twelve year period, as well as upon continuing neural maturation. The perceptual and cognitive trends of this period — gradual differentiation of the parts of one's body; expansion and differentiation of one's psychological life-space; perceptual discrimination proceeding from global to differentiated, near to further away, concrete to abstract; domination of what is perceived by inner needs to domination by the object being perceived; and a shift from physical manipulation of reality to its mental manipulation — all proceeding in parallel, reflect the perceptual outcomes of: the continuing "polarization of the perceiving subject against the things perceived" in the T-O-P electrodynamic field, the emergence to functioning of cortical layer 2 throughout most of the cortex (a projection beyond the available data), and increasingly coordinated functioning of the CI circuits.

Not only the external aspects of self become differentiated as a result of the perceptual polarization process, then, but also "that of which the self is conscious" — i.e., external reality. This simultaneous process means that at the same time that the child is beginning to integrate the outer and the inner aspects of self, he is also trying to understand and come to terms with the external physical and other-people world that is opening up around him. But the neural processes which have begun to integrate the Transactional and Intraorganismic subsystems are the same ones which will eventually enable him to comprehend himself and his world — and these integrative neural processes are not nearly as advanced in development around five to eight years of age as are the neural mechanisms which serve to inform him that events can and do occur outside his body and that these events are not subject to his physical or mental control. As a result of this developmental discrepancy, the child frequently feels threatened and helpless, unavoidably so, and what has elsewhere been termed "cosmic" anxiety is generated (129; also see previous age-period). Because this developmental discrepancy is especially characteristic of the advanced human brain, it would seem to make cosmic anxiety also indigenous to our species.

Unlike existence anxiety, cosmic anxiety can and does have constructive life uses. It seems to be the primary motivation for formal learning: the only way the individual can lessen his cosmic anxiety is to "encompass" his world and himself through increasing his knowledge, skills, understanding, ability to solve problems. Intrinsic, dependable motivation for formal, society-sponsored learning is established if and when the child discovers that such learning helps him to develop a broadening, effective understanding of his environment and of himself — and therefore contributes to a diminution in his anxiety level, even if such diminution is only occasional and temporary (129, p.234).

Much as the young child enjoys trying to "make sense" of the world all by himself — his early imaginative, "magical" explanations represent the best he can do with the degree of knowledge and neural integration available to him at this developmental period, he becomes even more receptive to the knowledge of his elders when he comes to realize he cannot do so all by himself: from four to eight years, 10 to 20 per cent of all conversational remarks are questions! He is receptive, that is, *if* the important adults in his world have come to represent an emotionally positive area of experience, to *some* extent at least, and *if* the outer and inner integration of self is proceeding without generating too much anxiety.

With these conditions met, the advancing development of the more central parts (and upper layers) of the T-O-P association area and of the PF area, and their respective incorporation into the CI circuits, results in the development of the "attitude of the other" towards reality and towards oneself. Assuming the abstract attitude leads to the removal of oneself from the perceived outer world — that is, to its externalization or objectification, or, as Piaget terms this process, "decentering"; and externalization in turn contributes to the emergence of the higher thought processes of classifying, generalizing, abstracting, conceptualizing, and so on. It is the convergence of an appropriate background of social experiences with the functional emergence of relevant cortical mechanisms that lies behind the relatively sudden shift to a new and higher level of intellectual functioning that Piaget and other investigators have observed: neither factor in itself can bring about this shift. Again, that is, *both* neural maturation and relevant experience are necessary.

Apparently, all is not lost if the attitude of the other is not acquired by preadolescence. Many biographies and autobiographies indicate that persons who later turned out to be very bright indeed were not able to develop this capacity during childhood because of unfortunate family situations and/or social isolation. Not until their avid reading had brought them into emotional contact with "others" distant in time and space did they develop the abstract attitude and a whole new world of the intellect was opened to them. It is possible that the lack of early pressure for advanced intellectual performance and the more adequate "others" so identified with may actually have contributed to such persons' eventual intellectual superiority.

The youngster's self and social development also begins to show the effects of acquisition of the abstract attitude towards the end of this period. She becomes able to judge her work — and herself — with some degree of objectivity. The evaluation that others make, and the picture they have of her have increasingly greater influence and she begins to accept and to measure self against this picture and its explicit or implied cultural evaluations. The motivational and aspirational basis for the later, adolescent-period, remaking of self is so laid down. Having acquired a more objective picture of self, she can now start to see others more roundedly and on their own unique merits, not solely from her own previously biased, physiognomic, perspective.

FROM TWELVE YEARS TO THE THIRD DECADE

Behavioral developments during this period include the following:

(1) Accurate discrimination of all parts of own body emerges around mid adolescence, parallel with the development of accurate perceptual assessment of physical space and objects. Boys' assessments of space are more correct than girls'.

(2) Adult levels of comprehension of distant time emerge beginning in mid-adolescence.

(3) Verbal mediation (to use Mussen's term, 136) continues to increase markedly during adolescence and early adulthood:

Age in Years	Recognition Vocabulary	Use Vocabulary	
10	24,000 words	5,000 words	(These figures are
15	40,000	10,000	believed to be too low for the present
20	62,000	12,000	generation.)

(4) Ideational memory increases up to at least the mid-twenties. Beginning about age nine, visual memory appears to be better than auditory memory.

(5) Mental (cognitive and ideational) processes reach mature levels at middle-to-late adolescence.

(a) In Piaget's schema, eleven or twelve years to fifteen or sixteen years is the "formal operations" period, the last stage in the development of intelligence. The youngster now systematizes his classifications, serial orderings, etc. (i.e., his concrete operations) and then goes on to express such operations in verbal propositions. Increasing neural maturation permits him to consider the sum total of possibilities rather than those provided by the immediate situation — and the final stages in "reversibility" (ability to approach the problem from many perspectives, including mutually opposite ones) are attained. The adult level of ability to do logical thinking emerges at about fifteen years: he can now operate with the *form* of an argument while disregarding its actual content. With the acquisition of the hypothesizing and deductive methods of science, he sees that there are many other ways to do things than are being done and he assumes the roles of critic and social reformer.

(b) Whatever mental abilities IQ tests test, they continue to increase steeply on a group-testing basis until seventeen to eighteen years. The rate of increase decelerates markedly thereafter, but growth continues until at least fifty years (15).

(6) Social behavior in the American middle-class subculture reflects (a) internalization of culturally based concepts and evaluations of sex-roles, and (b) a strong drive for self-discovery and self-identity, which in adult-dominated situations is expressed by a thrust for autonomy and in peer situations by role-experimentation and reliance on peer evaluations. Individual value-systems begin to emerge in early adolescence along sex differentiated lines.

(7) Emotional problems in our culture during this period reflect conflict between the desire for self-identity and autonomy on the one hand, and sensitivity to obstacles to its attainment in one's social world on the other hand. The drive for autonomy is

as yet not as strong among girls as it is among most boys and so the conflict is not as intense nor as prolonged among girls. Boys do not achieve dependable emotional control on the average until mid-adolescence, and for many of them, the basic obstacles-to-identity conflict persists well into the college years (among those in the middle classes). (In all probability, in today's confused world, more high school and college failures and drop-outs are due to this conflict than to basic lack of intellectual ability.)

(a) Over fourteen years, boys become more emotionally secure than girls: girls' fear dreams increase, while boys' decrease.

(b) Sex differences continue to be consistent in behavior problems reported by mothers: hostilities and inner tensions are high among both sexes, but boys continue their earlier tendency to act them out, while girls turn them inward against themselves — including indications of psychosomatic reaction (poor appetite) at the beginning of the period.

(c) Twelve to fifteen years is the third "critical period" in the incidence of childhood schizophrenia: during this period the youngster has to face up to his/her sex-identification and its culturally determined sex-role concomitants. Again, more boys than girls are affected.

(8) The post-adolescent period is being summarized in the subsequent, "relationships," section.

The following listing of *neural developments* is derived from Table XI, inserted earlier in this chapter:

(1) The voltage of the occipital alpha decreases. The occipital alpha also shows reactivity to eye-opening and relaxation.

(2) Drowsiness, light sleep, deeper sleep, all show characteristic patterns between eleven and fourteen years.

(3) A sudden EEG transition from sleep to waking emerges between eleven and fourteen years; the former transitional stage of high-voltage fast activity usually disappears, although paroxysmal slowing sometimes occurs in the frontal areas.

(4) Theta rhythms in the temporal areas disappear in the resting-state after twelve years, reappearing only during emotional states.

(5) The voltage of delta activity declines after fourteen years; paroxysmal slow waves, first evident at two years of age, are rare after fifteen years.

(6) There are changes in the patterns characteristic of drowsiness and light sleep during middle and late adolescence.

(7) Theta waves are common in the frontal areas between fifteen and twenty years (higher frequencies thereafter). Does this indicate thalamic dominance, together with the functional emergence of layer 3, in the PF area?

(8) Higher frequencies (11 to 19 cps) increase gradually after fourteen years. Fast records are increasingly typical and slow records increasingly atypical between fifteen and sixty years.

(9) The normal-adult patterning of electrical activity emerges shortly after nineteen years in all areas except the prefrontal. A fully mature prefrontal pattern emerges between twenty-five and thirty-five years.
Post-maturity changes:

(1) Light sleep has a typical pattern from twenty to fifty years; the thirties and forties have a distinctive drowsiness pattern.

(2) Isolated 6-8 cps (theta) waves appear in the temporal lobes after forty years and in other areas after sixty years.

(3) During the fifties and sixties, a distinctive drowsiness pattern (large delta waves) emerges in the frontal areas.

From twelve years until the third decade, when neural maturity is apparently reached, the following *relationships between neural and behavioral events* appear to obtain:

In light of the apparent perceptual relationship between discrimination of the "knower" and discrimination of the "known," the circumstance that boys' assessments of space are more accurate than girls' raises these questions: (a) Is boys' bodily discrimination also more accurate than girls'? (b) Do boys tactually explore their bodies more than do girls during infancy and early childhood?

Lacking specific histological and other neural data, the following relationship must be put in the form of a question. Is the appearance of mature levels of intellectual functioning related to emergence to functioning of layers 2 and 1 throughout most of the cortex as well as of the central sections of the T-O-P area, and to the consequent expanded and smoothly coordinated functioning of the CI circuits?

The adult level of comprehension and discrimination of distant space and time begins to manifest itself about mid-adolescence. These abilities are postulated as being related to the individual's earlier, directly-physical experiences with near space and apprehension of immediate time, as well as upon accurate differentiation of one's own body — i.e., they are a function of the polarization of the knower and the known in the T-O-P electrodynamic field. When the CI circuits are completed with the inclusion of the PF association area, the polarized images of the T-O-P area are made available to the PF area; are these images integrated with other transmitted data in the PF area and comprehension of distant space and time made possible as a result?

Dependable emotional control, which emerges about this time, somewhat earlier among girls (eleven to twelve years) and somewhat later among boys (fourteen to sixteen years), seems to be related to the disappearance of theta rhythm in the temporal lobe in the resting-state. The reciprocal participation in the CI circuits of the PF area, the temporal pole and the upper layers of the gyrus cinguli appears to underlie the emergence of emotional control.

Is the typicality of "fast" EEG records after fourteen years a species phenomenon, or is it primarily a function of the high anxiety levels associated with adulthood in complex cultures?

The emotional storms of the adolescent period are frequently considered to be a function of the changing endocrine balance initiated by the pubertal process. The contributive physiological process is in actuality much more complex. Body-image patterns — in Hebb's terms, a complex phase-sequence — have been well established in the T-O-P area by pre-adolescence. The bodily changes initiated by puberty — *and* the reactions to and evaluations of important-others to these changes — lead to the "breaking up" of these well-differentiated patterns: new cell-assemblies, phase sequences and polarizations develop thereafter, resulting in reorganization in the functioning of the Transactional subsystem, especially in the functioning of the Transactional long circuit. At the same time, the changing endocrine balance and other physiological shifts associated with sexual maturation are expressed at the conscious — i.e., Intraorganismic long circuit — level in the form of new psychological needs and new reactivities to the changing external aspects of self. These shake-ups in Intraorganismic and Transactional subsystems' functioning necessitate changes in the thalamic-centered integrational processes as well. In sum, the psychological changes initiated by puberty depart from a neural base: neurologically mediated changes in the external and internal aspects of self, followed by a whole new phase of self-integration.

But not only neural events are influencing social and self development during this period. The late-childhood acquisition of the abstract attitude also affects other aspects of development. In pre- and early- adolescence, one judges oneself through the eyes of peer-group "others," and self-integration proceeds in line with these evaluations. Probably most adults do not go beyond this "immediate-other directed" aspirational picture of self. During adolescence and early adulthood, the aspirational self-picture of the more intellectually able typically acquires an additional, broader, dimension through their indirect contacts with complex others removed in space and time. Such immediate and distant identifications are alike Transactionally mediated, and are frequently incorporated into the external aspects of self. Whether or not the adult "behaving self" eventually reflects the influence of these identifications depends upon the degree of integration of the outer and the inner aspects of self that is achieved during adolescence.

Past adolescence, behavioral developments are summarizable as being primarily, if not entirely, related to the uniquely human, entirely learned behaviors of: values and value-systems, ethics, esthetics, exercise of "intelligent foresight and the inhibition of action in anticipation of more remote prospects" (103), ability to project oneself in time and space at will, penchant for formulation of conceptual — including religious — systems. The large numbers of individuals and peoples who do not come to express these behaviors testify to their being dependent upon opportunities for relevant experience. Optimum personality functioning in adulthood is almost universally considered — in complex cultures, at least — to entail: dependable self-control, basic self-acceptance, personal autonomy, and the ability to subsume oneself within a larger whole — the capacity, that is, to subordinate one's (and one's family's) immediate welfare to broader and future social ends. Because of our technological and status-oriented culture's pattern of reinforcing-rewards, middle-class men do not usually go beyond the adolescent level of esthetic and ethical expression and degree of personality integration during early and middle adulthood: they are so occupied with their attempts to gain mastery over their occupational and social environment, they do not, typically, achieve stable PF area dominance until later life periods.

As for the foregoing post-adolescent behavioral developments, the circumstance that the PF association area is the last cortical area to mature histologically and in brain-wave patterning makes it logical to hypothesize that there is some relationship between individual development beyond adolescence and PF area functioning. My present guess about this relationship is as follows: All CI circuits *except* that to and from the PF area (branch 6) may be considered the integrative "short circuit," which initially becomes a functional unity during the first self-integration stage. If the adolescent individual's experience is conducive to the smooth reestablishment of the integrative short circuit after the body-image and other changes of puberty — a very big "if" indeed! — then the PF area, as its layers 3 and 2 become functional, completes the integrative circuit. It may well be that this results in a representation of the *integrated* self in the upper layers of the PF area. With this emergence of the integrative system's long circuit during late adolescence and early adulthood, the highest, uniquely human behaviors become expressable.

However, it is important to emphasize that beyond adolescence neural factors play a less important role than cultural factors in individual development. Together with the individual's already acquired perceptual selectivity, culturally derived experience is *the* shaping force in further personality development. But since cultural values and practices can serve to foster *or* to hinder neurally subserved personality integration, the circumstance that postpubertal reintegration of self, with the achievement of a mature personality as its goal, has become the complicated and difficult matter that it has in urban, technological societies, *is* neurally related.

Having already devoted major parts of a book to the implied proposition that present American values and practices are hindering rather than fostering personality integration (127), I shall not pursue this particular application of the role of culture in personality integration further at this point. But the concept of an "enabling" environment for optimum species development does seem to be relevant in the context of an inquiry into the relationships between neural and behavioral development, and is therefore being discussed in the final chapter of this monograph.

Chapter XII

DEVELOPING THE HYPOTHESIS, SECOND PHASE: A TENTATIVE ANSWER TO "WHAT HAPPENS DURING THE DEVELOPMENTAL GAP BETWEEN BIRTH AND NEURAL MATURITY?"

OVERVIEW OF NEURAL-BEHAVIORAL DEVELOPMENTAL RELATIONSHIPS

THE ANSWERS to the two questions which introduced section D (*What* neural maturative changes occur between birth and maturity and *when* do they occur? When developmental trends in behavior are matched against indices of neural development, do relationships between the two orders of data become apparent?) have emerged piecemeal throughout the three foregoing chapters. When the entire sweep of what happens between birth and neural maturity is examined as an organized totality, trends of neural change and of neural-behavioral relationship become more clearly evident; such an overview is being undertaken in this chapter. Some of the material in the following summary represents reasonable projections beyond the age-related data available.

At birth, the neural and behavioral status of a member of our species is much like that of any other higher mammal at birth, except that (1) the functioning of the diencephalic centers, both hypothalamus and thalamus, is unstable, and remains so for several weeks at the least, and (2) the cortex is entirely nonfunctional, and subsequent cortical onset of function proceeds at a much slower pace than among other primates. The thalamus is functioning sufficiently at birth to relay the visceral and body senses to the primary-somesthetic cortex and to contribute an affective tone to these sensations. The hypothalamus is functioning sufficiently to mediate the basic vegetative processes, but its homeostatic role, which depends on the stably coordinated functioning of hypothalamic centers having opposing functional effects, is not yet established at birth.

During the first month of life, the external world is experienced through the skin and visceral senses, since only the primary-somesthetic area of the cortex is transmitting impulses. The first clear signs of awareness of and reactivity to the external environment — at around one month — are correlated with the onset of function in at least the bottom cortical layer in the central-fissure and primary-visual areas.

The hypothalamus' functioning becomes increasingly coordinated and stable during the first several weeks to few months of life, and as it does, the basic homeostatic functions become established.

As the central-fissure area becomes functional and joins the subcortical somesthetic and motor circuits, the first evidences of motor control emerge in the upper part of the body. The gradient of emergence of voluntary motor control thereafter follows the order of development of the respective body subareas in the primary-somesthetic and primary-motor areas. This order is a cephalocaudal and a proximodistal one because of the reduplication of the primitive, spinal cord, pattern on both these cortical areas. Beginning about three to four months, the subarea of the hand is sufficiently developed for its gnostic exploration to add to the skin senses and vision a third important source of experience of the external world. The first mammalian reflex, the Moro, is suppressed by the motor cortex at about the same time.

As the primary cortical receiving areas for the distance-receptors emerge to function and establish their respective subcortical connections, vision, smell and hearing begin to provide the infant with sources of experience in addition to those provided by the somatic and visceral senses. Vision is the earliest and fastest developing of the distance receptors, although much more needs to be known about the early (including prenatal) development of the sense of smell and its role in infantile experience. As each modifying-sensory area becomes functional and joins cortical—subcortical sensory circuits, sensory discrimination for that modality becomes increasingly precise.

As the sections of the outer perimeter of the T-O-P, the posterior association, area begin to function, the first sensorimotor coordinations and the first perceptual discriminations emerge. As the lower layers of special-function areas in the frontal lobe — areas for speech, eye-movement, immediate recall — begin to transmit impulses and join in related cortical and sub-cortical circuits, the area-associated behavior emerges in rudimentary form. As the lower layers of the gyrus cinguli become functional and add a cortical component to ANS functioning, expression of self-related feelings emerge (at about six months).

As the three subsections of layer 3 become functional in lower-to-higher order in major sections of the cortex, progressively greater alertness, and awareness, responsiveness and adaptiveness to the external world develops. Much responsive social interaction, beginnings of imitation of others' speech and actions, increasing appropriateness of emotional response, evidences of self-awareness, the first ideational-adaptive responses — all coincide with maturation of layer 3's lower sections, which occurs during the last quarter of the first year.

The progressive changes in neural organization associated with these neural and behavioral events — i.e., the gradual establishment of the Intraorganismic and Transactional subsystems and CI circuits from two to nine months, have already been reviewed in Chapter IX (pages 202-3).

As the modifying-motor area (#6) becomes functional and joins cortical—subcortical motor circuits, coordinated locomotor abilities and refined manipulative activities emerge. The first conscious control of an autonomic function (bowel evacuation) occurs at about the time that the lower parts of layer 3 become functional in the gyrus cinguli. The cortical suppression of another mammalian reflex, the Babinski, begins at about two years.

As layer 3 becomes functional in the sensory areas and in the posterior and medial frontal lobe, thalamic dominance in forebrain functioning, expressed physiologically by preponderance of theta rhythms in the EEG, gradually declines and cortical dominance begins to assert itself. As this process proceeds, speech development, memory capacities, perceptual discriminations, cognitive development, all make major advances, and body-movement involvement in ideational processes gradually declines (providing that the child has had appropriate first-hand experiences with his body and his immediate physical world) .

Greater stability and localization of EEG patterning coincides with the early phases of the hypothesized integration of the inner and the outer aspects of self. Forebrain dominance begins to shift to the neocortex at about the same time, evidenced by the equivalence of alpha (the occipitally centered rhythm) with theta on the EEG from five to six years; after six years, alpha gradually becomes the dominant EEG pattern.

Subsequent middle and later-childhood advances in body-localization, memory and perceptual capacities, cognitive processes *and* cosmic anxiety are closely related to emergence-to-function of: (1) the more central parts and upper layers of the T-O-P association area, (2) additional middle and anterior sections of the frontal lobe, (3) layer 2 in most of the cortex, (4) branches 4 and 5 of the CI circuits (described in Chapter VII) , and their joining their respective neural systems.

Localization of all parts of the body, expansion of perceived space and time to far horizons, development of the "abstract attitude," beginning of dependable emotional control, all seem to depend not only on advances in T-O-P area functioning but also on the early stages of PF area functioning, which apparently occur during later childhood and early adolescence. The somatic and the physiological changes of puberty shake up established neurally based perceptual and affective patterns, necessitating an adolescent period of reintegration of self. This period may — or may not — be succeeded by the emergence of the highest human behaviors. The acquisition of such behaviors — controlled foresight, value systems, esthetic appreciations, personal autonomy, social altruism, formulation of and/or adherence to complex cognitive systems — appears to be made possible by the more advanced stages of functioning of the PF association area and its completion of the CI "long circuit."

DEVELOPMENTAL STAGES

Not only trends in neural-behavioral relationships become apparent when the entire growth-to-maturity sequence of human development is analyzed. Schneirla has stated "The problem of ontogeny is . . one of understanding what changing integrations of development underlie successive functional stages characteristic of the species" (163, p. 86) .

It is here posited not only that (1) there are nine successive, partially overlapping functional stages characteristic probably but not certainly of the entire human species, but also that (2) the "changing integrations of development" underlying each stage are *neural* integrations — i.e., that each developmental stage has as its basis a particular phase of neural organization.

In the following schema, the beginning age of each stage has been deliberately indicated as overlapping with the ending age of the previous stage for three reasons: to provide for individual *and* sex-group differences in developmental timing, and for the developmental tendency to slip back to the earlier period of development during the phase of transition to a higher level of functioning (a tendency that Gesell has termed the "spiral" pattern of development) . The successive neural organizations underlying each functional stage are summarized in Table XII following; the neural mechanisms referred to depart from the discussion in Chapter VII.

In addition to presentation of the key behavioral theme(s) and neural characteristics of each stage, the carryovers of each stage which are believed to be essential to *continuing* optimal human development will be postulated. Since what is "optimal" in human development is not as yet universally agreed upon (nor the data unequivocal) , these postulated carryovers are based on a particular individual value-system as well as on the findings of this inquiry.

Developmental Stage 1 comprises the first several weeks after birth. Getting a firm hold on life is its core characteristic. Neurally, the ANS' functional relationships between the medulla oblongata and the hypothalamus, as yet tenuous at birth, firm up and adjust themselves to the conditions of extrauterine living. This development constitutes the establishment of the Intraorganismic short-circuit, which is as yet unstable in functioning at this stage. All behavior during the first few weeks of life is still subcortically

TABLE XII

SUCCESSIVE NEURAL ORGANIZATIONS UNDERLYING THE POSTULATED NINE STAGES OF HUMAN DEVELOPMENT

Dominant Species Principle	Age-Span	Underlying Neural Organization	Associated Cortical Layers	Associated EEG Pattern
A. Domination by the "mammalian principle."	1) First several weeks after birth.	Stable establishment of the Intraorganismic short circuit.	6 and 5	Delta dominance
	2) 1 to 9 months.	Establishment of: — Phase 1 of the Transactional subsystem: Sensory: thalamus $\longleftrightarrow$ primary and modifying primary sensorimotor cortex. Motor: motor cortex $\rightarrow$ cerebellum $\rightarrow$ motor cortex. — CI branches 1 and 2. — Phase 2 of the Intraorganismic subsystem: thalamus and lower layers of the gyrus cinguli are added to the short circuit.	6, 5, 4, 3c.	Emerging theta dominance.
	3) 8 to 24 months.	Establishment, in succession, of: — Phase 2 of the Transactional subsystem: T-O-P association area begins to function, plus thalamic $\longleftrightarrow$ T-O-P area connections. — CI branches 3 and 4, and coordinated functioning of branches 1, 2, 3, 4. — Phase 3 of the Transactional subsystem: the first sensory-modifying cortical-in-origin motor tracts.	6, 5, 4, 3c, 3b.	Theta dominance.
	4) 1½ to 4 years.	Establishment of: — The Intraorganismic long circuit: emergence of the "limbic system." — CI branches 4 (additional tracts) and 5.	6, 5, 4, all of 3.	Theta dominance.

B. Transition Period.	5) 3 to 6 years.	Establishment of the CI "short circuit": branches 1 to 5 join in an unstable functional unity.	6, 5, 4, 3, 2 in primary areas.	Shift towards alpha dominance begins.
C. Domination by the "human principle."	6) 5 to 12 years.	More central parts of the T-O-P area and further sections of the frontal lobe become functional. Stably coordinated functioning of CI branches 1 to 5 is established.	6, 5, 4, 3, 2 except in PF area.	Emergence of alpha dominance. Development of adult alpha frequency.
	7) 11 to 14 years.	Changes in the T-O-P area; shake-up of the Intraorganismic short and long circuits and in CI circuits functioning. Onset of functioning in lower layers of PF area.	6, 5, 4, 3, 2, 1.	Greater EEG stability and organization. Sudden transition from sleep to waking.
	8) 13 to 17 years (F); 15 to 20 years (M).	Re-stabilization of Transactional, Intraorganismic, and CI circuits functioning. Continuing T-O-P and PF association area development. Initiation of as yet unstable CI "long circuit."	Through 3 in the PF area?	Theta in frontal areas.
	9) 16 to 35 years.	Continuing functional development of the PF area. Stabilization of the CI long circuit and of the entire CNS.	All layers in all parts of the cortex.	Systematized, mature EEG.

mediated; by the end of Stage 1, layers 6 and 5 are functioning in the most advanced cortical areas. Delta dominance on the EEG is associated with this stage. Carryovers conducive to continuing optimum development should be: (1) stable establishment of the basic vegetative processes; (2) arousal of minimal levels of "existence" anxiety, through prompt alleviation of basic vegetative needs and bodily discomfort, and through stable, relaxed and responsive handling of the babe by its caretakers.

Developmental stage 2 covers one to nine months of age, and is characterized by (1) the development of affectively and physically firm ties to one's immediate and social and physical environment, and by (2) a "future" orientation at the gut (i.e., ANS) level: that is, the expectation, developed through conditioning, that basic vegetative and other mammalian tensions will be alleviated because they have been consistently satisfied heretofore. The former development is prerequisite to the first stage of perceptual separation of self from "surround," which normally occurs at the end of this period; the latter "learning-set" may well be fundamental to the later normal development of the PF association area which apparently provides for prudent foresight and plays a key role in eventual personality integration.

The Transactional short circuit makes very rapid advances during this period: primary motor and sensory areas are functioning up into layer 3 and join the subcortical sensory and motor networks. The T-O-P association area has entered into Transactional functioning: first, those parts of it immediately adjacent to the sensory-receiving areas, and then, by nine months, enough of its more central areas are functioning for it to serve as an electrodynamic "perceptual field" and for the first, as yet undifferentiated, polarization of self and of surroundings to occur. It appears that this polarization does not occur in cases of infantile autism — and that the next developmental stage does not, accordingly, emerge among such children. The lower layers of the gyrus cinguli (area 24) are incorporated into the Intraorganismic subsystem beginning at about nine months. The BSRF-centered ARAS appears to be established around three months, and branches 1, 2, 3 of the CI circuits begin to function together in a unified manner at the end of this period in the normally developing child. Cortical layers through 3c are functioning in the most advanced areas at the end of the period. Although delta is still the major EEG rhythm, theta is rapidly becoming the dominant pattern at the end of this stage.

Carryovers of this period conducive to continuing normal development should be a series of strongly adient and/or positive attitudes: towards one's physical environment, towards one's prototypical social environment, towards *one's own existence and reachings-out to establish contact with one's immediate world*. As an example of the last-cited attitudinal area, positive feelings towards one's early vocalizing, which is enjoyable in and of itself to the babe, can and should be established through (1) at the least, its not being suppressed by one's caretaker (s) ; (2) preferably, its reinforcement through responsive, answering verbalizing, and (3) the babe's own discovery that his vocalizations are an effective means of social control.

This very crucial stage is Hebb's "primary learning" and Harlow's "learning sets" period (75, 69) .

Developmental Stage 3 covers eight to twenty-four months, and is characterized by the emergence of keen awareness of self as a separate physical entity (the first of the five neurally mediated phases in the development of self), concomitant with a keen awareness of and reactivity to the immediate external world — a reactivity which shifts from an initial period of sensorimotor consolidation to active mental attempts to "make sense" of one's world (the latter beginning about eighteen months) .

The Transactional short circuit is nearly complete by two years; motor speech centers are now included in it. More central parts of the T-O-P association area are functioning by the end of the period and have established reciprocal connections with the thalamus. CI branches 3 and 4 are established, and branches 1 through 4 are beginning to function as a coordinated unity; the Transactional long circuit begins to function as this coordination occurs (towards the end of this stage) . Cortical layers through 3b are functioning in the more advanced areas, and theta is now the dominant EEG rhythm.

Carryovers from this period conducive to continuing normal development include the following:

(1) Reinforcement of exploratory and curiosity and verbalization drives — i.e., acquisition of a feeling of having physical and psychological potency and "elbow-room."

(2) Arousal of low identity anxiety: perception of others' negative evaluations of self should be minimal, as should feelings of helplessness and threat provoked by persistent failure in attempts to cope with adult-imposed expectations.

(3) Feeling that the world is not only a predictable, supportive and "enabling" place, but also a place where one is protected from one's own as yet uncontrollable (and therefore prone to "run away") feelings: i.e., limits are firmly and consistently set.

Developmental Stage 4 encompasses one-and-one-half to four years, and is characterized by the emergence of the awareness that one harbors an inner world of feelings and reactivity to one's ongoing experience and behavior (the second of the five neurally mediated phases in the development of self). Make-believe play is the key overt activity associated with this development, with high emotionality, egocentrism of speech, oversensitiveness (a frequent complaint of mothers), imaginary companions, and overt, self-instructive speech further evidences of it. The doubling of the attention-span between two and four years is directly related to the emergence of this awareness. It derives from the near-completion, between fifteen and twenty-four months, of the Intraorganismic long circuit by the functional incorporation of the gyrus cinguli through layer 3. Functioning in adjacent anterior-frontal areas and establishment of reverberating frontal-temporal pole connections via the thalamus (Penfield's A-mechanism; branch 5 of the CI circuits) are also associated with it.

The carryovers of this event necessary for continuing normal — let alone optimal! — individual development is *its occurrence!* Autism, which begins to show up at nine months and reaches its peak incidence the latter part of the second year, is an indication it has *not* occurred.

"Existence" anxiety has been postulated as directly associated with the physiological, basic life processes; these processes are coordinated by the hypothalamus, which is a major component of the Intraorganismic subsystem and which plays a key role in emotion. If a very high degree of "gut level" anxiety was generated during one's first very few months of life; if firm, adient ties to one's physical and social environment were not established, and if physical self was not separated perceptually from "surround," the first intimations that one possesses an inner world of feeling and reactivity brings these high levels of existence anxiety to the consciousness of the as yet inner oriented and psychologically completely defenseless infant — and intrathalamic functional integration of nuclei subserving the two neural subsystems is impeded. Not only is further frontal and T-O-P area development arrested as a result, but there is also a functional regression to the lower cortical layers, at the least in the gyrus cinguli. The latter part of the second year is also when the first evidences of childhood schizophrenia appear. In this disorder, high identity anxiety, which begins towards the end of the previous functional stage, is an additional contributive factor to that of high existence anxiety.

Full human consciousness begins with the occurrence of this inner-world awareness: it is *one's conscious awareness of one's own reactivity to one's experience that adds a species-unique dimension to human existence.*

It has already been noted that our species' genetic inheritance endows us with two developmental principles: the mammalian and the human. At birth, the mammalian principle is dominant and the human principle exists only as potential. The beginning of the shift from domination of individual development by the mammalian principle to domination of individual development by the human principle is signaled by emergence of the awareness of one's own reactivity to one's experience. The behavioral disorders of autism and early childhood schizophrenia would appear to demonstrate that *this shift is not maturationally automatic*: it does not occur at all in the autistic child and it occurs variably — i.e., in distorted form — in the childhood schizophrenic.

Developmental Stage 5, from three to six years, is the period when integration of the outer and the inner aspects of self, a life-long process, begins — the initial perceptual differentiation of the external components of self (stage 3) and the awareness of one's inner reactions to one's experience (stage 4) having occurred. Cultural dos and don'ts and explicit rights and wrongs are internalized in the course of this initial phase of self-integration, which is the third of the five neurally mediated phases in the development of self; self-regulative language, a cultural acquisition, plays a major role in this internalization. (Children who are simply ignored, whose behavior is *not* regulated verbally by others, do they *not* develop self-regulative speech and are such children later lacking in emotional self-control and other aspects of superego development?) Thereafter, mental processes become more flexible, ideational and discriminative. If familial requirements are too demanding or too contradictory for the individual child's ability to accommodate to, and if one already has high amounts of existence and identity anxiety, childhood schizophrenia may occur.

Additional pathways join the CI circuits during this period: further, branch 4 reciprocal connections with the thalamus as T-O-P area functioning continues to advance; and also, branch 5, which provides for a reverberatory circuit between the frontal and temporal lobes via the thalamus. The cortex is functional through layer 3 in nearly all of the cortex; at the end of the period, layer 2 is also functional in the more advanced areas (?). These layer advances coincide with an EEG shift towards alpha dominance: at five and six years, the alpha rhythms equal the theta rhythms in proportion on the EEG. After six years, the alpha pattern gradually assumes EEG dominance.

The carryovers of this period important for continuing normal development are a series of "template" feelings about oneself and about one's world:

(1) Inner congruence of saying and feeling, saying and doing, feeling and doing.

(2) A fairly clear and consistent picture of what a "good boy" or what a "good girl" is, and the feeling that it is within one's capacities to become a good girl or a good boy.

(3) A feeling of being comfortable with and within one's body.

(4) A feeling that one is *communicating* when one speaks.

(5) A feeling that everybody loses control once in a while but will be able to "hang on" better the next time.

(6) A feeling that the world is like a big box of unbelievably wonderful toys, just waiting for one to open it.

(7) A feeling that books and people, every kind of people, are important and valuable.

This is a nodal time in human development on two scores: on a species basis, and in the individual life-career. Concerning the former, emergence of the CI short circuit plus the shift towards alpha dominance on the EEG together indicate that the human principle in human development starts to assume dominance over the mammalian principle beginning about six years, so far as the functioning of the normally developing individual nervous system is concerned. Concerning the latter, whether one continues with an open, receptive attitude towards the world and one's experience, *or* with conflicted, ambivalent, uncertain attitudes towards self and world, *or* with a psychopathic split between the outer and the inner aspects of self, is largely "set" by the end of this period.

Developmental Stage 6 covers five to twelve years. With the initial phases of self-integration under way, there is a second major adient movement towards the external world. One's perceived physical and social life-space expands *and* becomes increasingly differentiated, at the same time that bodily differentiation is also proceeding. In turn, as one's social world's perceptions, evaluations and values are internalized, awareness of the world in relation to self emerges.

This stage is divisible into two substages:

Substage 1, five to nine years: the adient movement towards one's social world yields the realization that others are perceiving and feeling beings like oneself — and the ability to "take the attitude of the other" towards reality and towards oneself, i.e., the "abstract attitude," is acquired.

Substage 2, eight to twelve years: with the acquisition of the "attitude of the other," one's perceptions of reality and of oneself begin to be "externalized." The multiple perceptual perspectives this objectification process affords permit more rounded and therefore more accurate perception of self and reality — and the experiential foundation for emergence of the higher mental processes and social values is laid down.

Further medial and anterior sections of the frontal lobe (perhaps the lower layers of the PF area also) and more central portions of the T-O-P area become functional during this period, as does layer 2 throughout most of the cortex. The functioning of branches 1 to 5 of the CI circuits becomes stably coordinated. Alpha becomes the dominant EEG rhythm and its frequency reaches adult levels between ten and twelve years among most children.

Carryovers conducive to further optimal development should be as follows:

(1) a steadily decreasing level of existence anxiety;

(2) a steadily increasing level of cosmic anxiety;

(3) the realization that formal learning is meant to, and can, be used to alleviate one's cosmic anxieties;

(4) steadily increasing competence in the basic intellectual and academic skills that are necessary for undertaking problem-solving, cosmic-anxiety-reducing learning projects;

(5) the continuation and extension of the previous stage's feelings about self and world;

(6) continuing development and integration of the inner and outer aspects of self (cultural, including school, values and practices should *not* make 5 and 6 incompatible with 4, as they far too often do, unfortunately).

Developmental Stage 7 covers eleven to fourteen years, and is characterized by changes in both the outer and the inner components of self (the fourth of the five neurally mediated phases in the development of self). The gross physical changes associated with the onset of puberty, together with one's (sub-) culture's attitudes to and evaluations of sexual maturation, the respective social sex-roles, and the degree of one's own sex-appropriateness of bodily development, result in alterations in one's body-image. At the same time, the physiological changes of puberty, subserved by the Intraorganismic short circuit, lead to a rediscovery of one's inner world of feeling and reactivity — an awareness subserved by the Intraorganismic long circuit. Girls achieve dependable emotional control the earlier part of this period. These physical and experiential changes lead to the break-up of established patterns of polarization and differentiation in the T-O-P perceptual field, Intraorganismic short and long circuits functioning, and CI circuits functioning. Some sections of the PF association area have begun to function through layer 3c (?). The carryovers of this stage conducive to continuing normal development is the psyche's survival through this stressful (in most complex societies) period: twelve to fifteen years is the third "critical period" in the incidence of childhood schizophrenia!

Developmental Stage 8's age-boundaries are sufficiently different for girls and boys, it is necessary to give two age-spans: thirteen to seventeen years for girls and fifteen to twenty years for boys. This period is characterized primarily by reintegration of the outer and inner aspects of self, which succeeds the earlier phase of change in both dimensions of self; this is the fifth and protracted-last of the neurally mediated phases in the development of self. Maturation of kinesthesis and of the ability to discriminate all parts of one's body coincides with achievement of adult levels of conception of far space and distant time. With the achievement of these additional perceptual discriminations and of personality reintegration, cognitive abilities and processes reach nearly mature levels. Boys acquire dependable emotional control near the beginning of this period. The Intraorganismic subsystem reaches maturity at the beginning of this period, as does the Transactional subsystem at its end, and all three neural systems become restabilized. Development in the most central parts and upper layers of the T-O-P area and in the upper layers of the PF area is still occurring. The presence of the theta rhythm in anterior-frontal areas from fifteen to twenty years suggests that cortical dominance over the thalamus does not yet obtain in this section of the cortex; it may also reflect the unstable initiation of the CI "long circuit."

Carryovers of this stage conducive to the subsequent achievement of personality maturity (integration and autonomy) include: advancing self-integration, which involves acceptance of both the intellective and the feeling-reactive aspects of self, and the initial stages of deliberate development of a personal value-system and a life-style that provide for both in a balanced manner.

One should enjoy and have a fair degree of competence in activities which capitalize on the integration of both the inner and the outer aspects of self: that is, are whole-self fulfilling, rather than outer-appearance dominated. Mature personal relationships, including the heterosexual, are attainable by the end of this period, *if* previous development is felicitous and the influencing social environment is an enabling one.

Developmental Stage 9, from sixteen to the mid-thirties, is characterized by attainment of full neural maturity, which means that especially these two "life themes" are now possible from the inside out, as well as optimal for continuing personal fulfillment and integration: "beyond-self" activities — i.e., acting as an "enabler" of others' lives (own children, own community, human race) ; and continuing acquisition of high levels of cosmic anxiety, accompanied by systematic and creative cognitive attempts to reduce them. A mature EEG pattern in the prefrontal areas is achieved during the latter part of this period (in all other areas by twenty years). Continuing development of the PF area, stabilization of the functioning of the CI long circuit and of the entire CNS, together underlie this EEG development.

The carryovers of this period of early adulthood should be, at least in technologically advanced societies:

(1) a degree of vocational or avocational competence and involvement that will allow one to spend long, absorbed and productive hours in a self-integrative, "central-motif" activity;

(2) sufficient self-acceptance and self-integration to take the declining vigor of middle and old age with equanimity, along with

(3) skill and pleasure in activities and relationships which are minimally affected by the aging process.

This discussion does not, by design, go past the period of full neural maturity. Nevertheless, reference to the findings of a recently published series of studies on personality in the middle and late years in our culture (137) is being made because they appear to provide indirect confirmation of a number of this inquiry's formulations. The most pertinent findings follow, in excerpted form:

Different modes of dealing with impulse life seem to become salient with increasing age. Preoccupation with the inner life becomes greater; emotional cathexes toward persons and objects in the outer world seem to decrease; the readiness to attribute activity and affect to persons in the environment is reduced; there is a movement away from outer-world to inner-world orientations (p. 189).

. . . the increase in interiority has the characteristics of developmental change in much the same sense as do changes in earlier periods of life — that, as a result of the life history with its accumulating record of adaptations to both biological and social events, there is a continually changing basis within the individual for perceiving and responding to new events in the outer world. . . . Although there is undoubtedly a circular process between psychological and social elements of disengagement, the implication is that the psychological changes described here as increased inward orientation and decreased cathexes for outer-world events seem to precede, rather than to follow, measurable changes in extent of social interaction. . . . There is the implication in these data that certain of the changes associated with age are deteriorative. There are losses of efficiency in cognitive processes — certain breakdowns of control over impulses observable in TAT protocols, certain perceptual impairments, certain inabilities to deal with wide ranges of stimuli (p. 194).

These findings imply, rather clearly I think, that deteriorative changes occur in the functioning of the three neural networks postulated in this inquiry: branches 6 and 5 of the CI circuits, the most advanced cortical components of the Transactional subsystem, the upper-cortical components of the Intraorganismic subsystem, all appear to become nonfunctional with advancing age; whether they perhaps do so in the actual order given — which is the reverse order to their ontogenesis — is not deducible from the data provided by Neugarten.

PRINCIPLES OF HUMAN DEVELOPMENT

The accumulated data and analyses of this inquiry, when viewed in the perspective of previous examinations of the concept and the nature of development, also yield the following five developmental principles.

Principle 1 concerns the consequences of the way in which our species' dual genetic endowment — a human principle superimposed upon a mammalian foundation — expresses itself in ontogenesis. The neural and the behavioral data indicate that:

(1) At birth, man is functionally a decorticate mammal; his humanity is present entirely as maturational potential.

(2) The development and expression of that potential is dependent upon the growing normal individual human organism's suitably enabling transactions with its environment.

(3) The "suitability" of these transactions is a function of each unfolding stage of development.

These inter-related species circumstances jointly comprise the first developmental principle; they make human development a very complicated and hazardous enterprise indeed.

Circumstance 1 implants two apparent contradictions in human development:

(1) In order for the human principle eventually to become dominant and to express itself fully and in undistorted form, the mammalian-level needs of the early life periods must be taken care of appropriately. If they are not, there is abundant clinical evidence that further neural and behavioral development is either entirely arrested, or aspects of the neural organization and associated psychological needs of the mammalian-dominated early periods are carried over into later developmental stages and hamper or distort their expression — that is, that cortical dominance, especially PF cortex dominance, is incompletely or variably established.

(2) But, paradoxically enough, the environmental conditions which make appropriate provision for the mammalian endowment are quite different from the environmental conditions which make appropriate provision for the human endowment! Thus, the fundamentally important firm establishment of the prerequisite basic-mammalian aspect requires responsive and consistent physical handling and care cued by the infant's body-centered needs and the individually unique way in which a particular

infant expresses those needs (176), with externally imposed interference or pressures kept to a minimum. But the optimal development of the *human* principle requires firm and consistent imposition of limits on certain categories of behavior on the one hand: the child's reliable self-control of emotional reactivity and of some physiological processes are examples of outcomes of such impositions; and the provision of a richly stimulating environment — sensory (tactual and distance-receptive), social-emotional, verbal, sensorimotor and language skills, ideas, values — on the other hand.

Whether the mammalian and the human principles in human development actually do work at cross-purposes or not in individual development is largely dependent upon the child-rearing values and practices of the culture in which the individual human being grows up, as these values and practices are refracted through the personalities of those who care for the child. A culture's child-rearing goals and practices can serve to place these two fundamental influences on human development in opposition to each other by poorly timed overemphasis on one or the other: Freudian theory constitutes documentation of the effects on individual development of such a child-rearing approach; *or* can make them complementary by the wisely timed and executed catering to *both* principles, with the complementarity contributing to personality integration — to cite only the two ends of what is actually a continuum of possible cultural practices.

Circumstance 2 may be termed the "if-then" or "open system" principle. It stems from the character of human post-natal nervous system development, which *allows* the individual member of the human species to express the behaviors associated with each succeeding developmental stage but *does not ensure* their provision. *If* at a particular stage of neural maturation, the environment provides one with the sorts of experiences one requires in order to go on to the next developmental stage, *then* the integrative apparati of the nervous system can perform their coordinating job and move the organism on to its next higher level of development. If these "enabling" experiences are not available to the growing individual, the integrative processes will have incomplete or distorted subprocesses to coordinate — and the next functional stage does not emerge at all *or* does so in incomplete or distorted form. If the environment continues to be nonenabling, the distortions may become cumulative to the point of *later* arrest in psychological development; at the least, inappropriate handling of the early, mammalian-dominated period of human development creates an underlying vulnerability to later stress.

The expression of this contingency principle is analogous to the physical mechanisms which implement genetic inheritance: these develop in a chain of successive links, the emergence of the last link dependent upon the one just prior to it; if one link should fail to develop or be defective, all subsequent links are in some way defective.

Here the idea of an "enabling" environment," that is, one which supplies the experiences most appropriate to each human-developmental stage and so fosters integrated progression to the next stage — Circumstance 3, suggests itself and raises the possibility of rating cultures and subcultures according to the *species-appropriateness* of their child-rearing practices, relationships, values, secondary institutions. This concept also raises the issue of the role of culture in promoting personality disorder. Both these implications will be further explored in the last section of this monograph.

Principle 1 may be (over-) summarized thus: Functionally, man is born a decorticate mammal; behaviorally, he becomes a human being *if;* he becomes an integrated, mature human being *if-if!*

Principle 2 has already been consistently pointed to by students of human development. It is the epigenetic maturational-mode principle: as development advances, successively more complex and higher order behaviors within the same behavioral category emerge progressively — behavioral categories such as a particular sensory-modality, sensorimotor coordinations culminating in such complex motor skills as locomotion and manipulation, sensation-perception-conception, cognition, intelligence, feeling and emotion. This inquiry has made clear that the epigenetic developmental mode is neurally based. It is a function both of the hierarchical-reduplicative — i.e., vertical — organization of the three basic neural networks of the CNS *and* of the functional relationships between the integrative circuits and the two analytic subsystems. As each neural system develops, it successively incorporates progressively higher forebrain levels into its functioning (postnatally, successively higher cortical layer-levels are chiefly involved), and as it does so, more complex *and* refined levels of behaviors subserved by the particular neural system emerge. The seventh developmental pattern hypothesized in Chapter IV *does* appear to be borne out by the postnatal data!

The correspondence of these successively higher levels with the phylogenetic history of our species is noteworthy. As cortical layers *through layer 3* in a particular functional area are incorporated into its related mediating neural system, *human levels* of that particular behavior emerge. As the PF association area, the last cortical area to develop phylogenetically and ontogenetically, becomes functional, *solely human behaviors* emerge. And the T-O-P association area has its own lower-to-higher developmental patterning, a shrinking-concentric, peripheral-to-central one: as the outer-boundary, sensory-area-adjoining sections become functional, more refined sensory discriminations appear; as more central sections become functional, perception and progressively more differentiated perceptual discriminations appear; and as the (higher layers of the) most central T-O-P area sections become functional, abstract concepts are formulatable. The highest cognitive processes emerge as all parts of the brain are incorporated into the functioning of the CI circuits.

Principles 3 and 4, following, relate to the communication aspects of human interaction, *aspects which are postulated as fundamental to the undistorted development of the "human principle" in human development.*

Principle 3 concerns the circumstance that there are two relatively discrete avenues or "levels" of interpersonal communication among human beings, the "gut" or somatic level, and the verbal level: a circumstance deriving from the operation of the mammalian and the human genetic principles in the development of individual members of our species. At birth and for some months thereafter, the infant experiences his world primarily through direct somatic contact; hence others' communications with him occur through direct-physical, usually skin-to-skin, contact. As his mother cares for him, she communicates to him *her* "gut-level" reactions; *the words she coincidentally speaks represent sound-patterns which have meaning for him only in relation to what is occurring at her somatic-motor level.*

As speech emerges and develops in the child, it becomes a meaningful avenue of communication *for him* to the extent that the words he learns actually express his feelings — and the degree to which they do is a function of two factors: the appropriateness and promptness of his mother's responses to his *pre*verbal efforts to communicate his needs and feelings, as well as of the degree of coincidence between her gut and verbal reactions to him during his first several months of life. This proposition implies that speech and language development proceed more smoothly and with fewer regressions in the child whose mother's responses to his pre-verbally expressed needs have been both prompt and appropriate and whose gut and verbal levels of reaction to him have coincided closely, than in the child where these circumstances have not obtained. This implication must be stated as a reasonable hypothesis, pending its focused investigative testing.

Beyond childhood, the degree of convergence and/or divergence between the individual's gut and verbal levels of expression bears a relationship to this order of his early experience. Generalized, cultural and subcultural factors also have an impact here, but not as potent a one.

Principle 4 is a further elaboration of the gut or mammalian level of communication enunciated under Principle 3: it is the "interpersonal-feedback" or "resonance" principle. As the growing person relates to his immediate environment, primarily his immediate human environment, he alternates between taking into self what is occurring "out there" *and* going towards the other person, adjusting to his reactions. This alternating process has been noted and analyzed by various theorists; we shall refer only to Piaget's and George Mead's analyses.

Piaget terms the former process "assimilation" and identifies make-believe play as the key childhood process through which it occurs; the latter process he terms "accommodation" and identifies imitation as the key childhood activity through which *it* occurs (86). George Mead conceptualizes this alternation within a more subjective framework, speaking of the two phases of the self, the "I" and the "me" (120). The "me" comprises the organized set of attitudes of others which the individual has internalized (and continues to internalize throughout life); the "I" depends upon one's awareness of one's own reactions and is the spontaneous response of the organism to these internalized attitudes. The "I," that is, is the inner answer the person makes to the attitudes others take toward him when he assumes an attitude toward *them*. There is a constant inner alternation between these two phases of the self-process.

Interestingly, Piaget's and Mead's concepts, when placed in sequence, can be readily related to the functional roles of the three basic neural networks postulated in this inquiry. Accommodation corresponds to the functional role of the Transactional subsystem; the "I" is related to the Intraorganismic long circuit; assimilation seems to depend upon the integration of the Transactional and Intraorganismic subsystems (i.e., on CI circuits functioning); and the "me" can be seen as the ongoing psychological outcome of this integrative process.

I prefer to place this alternation of environment $\longrightarrow$ individual and individual $\longrightarrow$ environment within the broader framework of the process of human communication, conceived as a *mutually regulative* process which is directly analogous to the operation of the feedback principle in complex automated systems. This approach applies especially well to the nonverbal, somatic or gut or mammalian level of communication. In any interactive human diad, the incipient, unverbalized, somatic reactions of the one ordinarily call forth a similar set of incipient, "answering" responses, also somatic, on the part of the other, which in turn evokes a reactive, gut-level response in the first member of the diad — and a fundamental *communication-tie* is established, a tie which determines whether communication also occurs at the verbal level — or only words are exchanged.

As the prototype for all later human interaction and communication, such a tie must be established between the mother and her newborn, *as yet only mammalian,* infant. At this early stage of cortical functioning, the tie is established through direct somatic contact of the mother with her child, since the infant is able to experience the external world only through the skin senses. Studies of the effects of early sensory deprivation, Harlow's skin-comfort concept (70), clinical evidence, all lend credence to this formulation. This prototypical communication-tie is the foundation for the child's unconscious, gut-level attitudes towards self and for later meaningful verbal communication.

It also appears to serve an even more basic role. The infant member of the diad has at this early stage no objective awareness of his own identity; but he *is* able to register *upon others* that he exists. He does so through his demands for satisfaction of his urgent vegetative needs — needs and demands of which he is not aware and over which he has no control, however. The adult member of the child's first communication system has a very special and a very fundamental responsibility in this situation. When she reacts to her newborn child's demands responsively and appropriately, she is not merely keeping him alive physically: she is also reflecting back to him *that he exists;* the mother's appropriately responsive reactions to her babe's first overtures to the external world which he has so recently entered constitute *for him* his first — and at this stage *his only* — concrete source of information that he has identity.

If one member of this first interaction-system does not react responsively and appropriately habitually, the result is similar to one key component of a feedback system not "feeding back" accurately: cumulative distortion in the system occurs — and although the original defective component may be either the adult or the infant, it is usually the immature half of the diad who is "wrecked" as a result.

A not-atypical example, unfortunately, in the middle-class subculture of a defective adult component of this first communication system is a young woman who has been taught all her life not to express, nor even to acknowledge to herself that she experiences, strong spontaneous emotion, especially strong negative feelings. Such a person has typically also acquired a *verbal posture* of warmth towards, and acceptance of others because of the sex-role stereotyping of her subculture.

But behind this socially accommodating facade is confusion about her own identity and her own feelings; that is, her gut-level reactions are frequently at variance with her verbalized posture (a split which can occur only in the human species) and she is not even aware that this is so. When a person with this personality organization has a child, especially her first child, she is very often unable to accept any of the normally negative feelings she may have towards her infant because "mothers are supposed to love their children." As a result, she is very likely to feed back contradictory reactions to her child: she maintains for others *and* for her cognitive self a verbal posture of love and acceptance, but at the somatic level she is communicating very different feelings to her infant — *who is exclusively dependent upon her for reflection of the fact and the nature of his existence.* It is not difficult to visualize — but may be very hard to establish experimentally — the effect that such a dual set of behavioral cues has on her child.

I am reminded here of the study of the role of auditory feedback from one's own voice in meaningful, coherent speech; the experimenter was able to delay the speaker's reception of his own voice by a fraction of a second and the result for the speaker was utter confusion — so much so, he was unable to continue speaking (33, I believe).

Or, this prototypical communication system may not be established at all because of deprivation of responsive human contact during infancy — as occurs too often in children's "shelters" and among the very poor, where the infant is left completely alone for long periods and is fed and cared for according to a schedule determined by external exigencies rather than by the infant's own cycles of need and feeling.

Autism's essential etiology may lie here, at least some cases of autism; the unhappy plight of the "unwanted child" also acquires additional meaning in this context. (When oh when shall those in the mental health professions come to recognize that the most fundamental individual preventive-mental-health starting-point is the psychological health of the expectant mother — and that by far the greatest concentration of psychiatrists and consulting psychologists and other psychotherapeutic personnel should be in group practice with obstetricians and pediatricians and in public-health sponsored prenatal and early postnatal well-baby clinics?)

Subsequent human communication even at advanced developmental levels rests upon this gut-level communication substrate — or lack of it. Successful psychotherapy undoubtedly depends upon the creation of a good "gut-level communication" situation. It is also interesting to note that when two human adults wish to be in especially close communication, as when in love, they employ frequent mutual touching. Typically in the adult years also, one feels most intensely alive *and* oneself while interacting with another in whom one evokes a strong, unique-to-oneself emotional reaction. I recall here the perceptive report of a woman in her middle years of the impact on her of one of her brief, infrequent meetings with a friend of many years' standing who had never lost a complex and intense feeling for her; it was: "He makes me feel I *exist*." Her comment suggests that the operation of the resonance principle is the core reason for the lower incidence of mental illness among married, as compared with single, adults. The universally human institution of having animal pets also constitutes an expression of this principle.

This "interpersonal resonance" principle of human development is essential, I believe, for the undistorted development of the human personality. The original version of the foregoing sentence continued as follows: "and constitutes the core reason young children cannot be raised by an unresponsive machine nor habitually 'taught' by machine and still become 'whole' human beings." Introduction to the Edison Responsive Environment Learning System as a means of treating schizophrenic children has necessitated a revised way of making essentially the same point. According to a *New York Times* report of March 12, 1965, a *responsive* machine, built at the instigation of Professor O. K. Moore of Rutgers, has been working therapeutic wonders with autistic and schizophrenic children at the Bassett Hospital in Cooperstown, N. Y. The machine's manner of functioning is described as follows:

> It is almost as much human as it is machine. It talks, it listens, it responds to being touched, it makes pictures or charts,

it comments and explains, it gives information and can be set up to do all this in any order. . . . The computerized typewriter allows its user to explore freely. It has infinite patience. There are no punishments when a wrong key is punched. There is no competition. It has inflexible logic. It never varies. It never, never, makes a mistake.

The machine consists of a computer about the size of a small, upright piano with a typewriter keyboard in front. It has a speaker and a frame above the typewriter for printed matter.

The first thing a child does is press one of the standard typewriter keys. This prints the character in large type. At the same time, a soft voice automatically identifies it through the speaker. The computer can be programmed vocally and visually, or both together. When a letter is selected by a recorded voice, all the remaining keys are locked. The machine waits indefinitely while the child punches away until the right letter is hit before it calls automatically for the next one. Then letters lead to words and words to sentences. Sentences lead to stories.

It appears that this *super*-human machine consistently provides these withdrawn children with the *undistortedly resonant experiences* that they were unable to derive from their first human environment — and the positive effect on them of their interaction with this machine presents corroborative evidence for Principle 4.

Individuals who have not had adequate resonance experiences during infancy and early childhood are thereafter vulnerable psychologically to conflicting or overly complex and demanding social stimuli. Such persons as adults with some awareness of their vulnerability and some freedom of choice typically structure a socially isolated style of living for themselves. If they are unable so to do and instead, are bombarded unremittingly with social pressures that cannot be avoided, they may at some point beyond childhood react explosively *or* withdraw into schizophrenia. The crowded, stressful urban environment which is becoming increasingly typical of the American way of life is particularly difficult for such persons to tolerate psychologically, and there may well be a relationship between the trend towards urbanism and the rise in the rate of schizophrenia in the United States. Formerly, farming, small-town living, and the frontier provided living conditions which were more suitable, psychologically, for such vulnerable persons.

Principle 5 assumes the validity of Tinbergen's dictum (here paraphrased) that the study of human behavior must be preceded by a study of underlying neural mechanisms in man — and goes beyond it. Not only is such "moment in time" knowledge necessary; the developmental status and functional organization and characteristics of the neural mechanisms which underlie successive *earlier* stages in the human being's development of a particular category of behavior constitute equally essential knowledge.

If the thalidomide tragedy does not provide evidence on behalf of this principle, perhaps the following more complex set of data does. The development of the electrical activity of the macaca mulatta brain has been systematically studied with the EEG and has been compared with the same aspect of development in man (32); the following table of developmental correspondence, here reproduced in abbreviated form, has been drawn up by the investigator:

The EEG of a: *Monkey aged*	roughly corresponds to that of a: *Man aged*
2 weeks	3 months
6 weeks	9 months
3 months	18 months
6 months	3 years
1 year	6 years
1½ years	9 years
2 years	12 years
4 years	24 years

That is, the developmental ratio is a consistent *six to one* between man and monkey. (Some may consider the very consistency of the ratio as justification for direct extrapolation from monkey to man: for some common-mammalian categories of behavior, perhaps; for uniquely human behavior . . ?)

Such a prescription obviously raises major methodological problems. Greater development and use of such *in situ* techniques as the EEG and focal-action drugs are two promising approaches. Perhaps more promising is a shift by the psychological investigator towards the medically-related professions, along two lines: (1) close collaboration of the neurophysiologist and psychologist with obstetricians, pediatricians, pathologists; (2) the establishment of such new investigative specialties within developmental psychology as: a combined PhD in developmental psychology and neurophysiology; a PhD in developmental psychology plus an MD in pediatrics.

Psychologists who continue to prefer animal experimentation on its own merits rather than as but one useful preliminary method for checking on hypotheses concerning human behavior, should consider seriously Tinbergen's (implied) invitation to help develop a systematic phylogeny of behavior — that is, that they become ethologists, and thereby provide data which will serve the science of psychology very well indeed.

PART E

A TREE-TRUNK, A WALL, A SNAKE —
OR THE WHOLE ELEPHANT?

Chapter XIII

SOME IMPLICATIONS

FOR INDIVIDUAL DIFFERENCES

A CONSISTENT THEME of nearly all the neural research reports consulted for this inquiry was the wide range and subtle shadings of individual differences in every aspect of neural structure and every index of neural development investigated. Williams has documented the circumstance of "biochemical individuality" (194); neural variations provide an even more basic organismic source of individual differences, since the nervous system, from reception through mediating mechanisms to reactions, is *directly* involved in behavior: other sources of individuality, such as the biochemical, express themselves in behavior through their influence on neural functioning.

Answers to this question are needed: How do the observed individual differences in microscopic neural structure and development express themselves in behavior: directly, or primarily through their effects on the functioning of the three macroscopic neural systems postulated in this inquiry, the Intraorganismic, the Transactional, the CI circuits? There may well be identifiable genetic differences in individual potentialities for the patterns of structure and functioning of each of these networks. Individual differences in stability-instability of the basic vegetative functions and in reactivity to stress may be at least partially a function of individual genetic differences in the Intraorganismic subsystem; it has already been indicated that the ANS shows such inherited individuality of functional patterning (95). Sensory sensitivities, perceptual and conceptual capacities, ease of motor control and coordination may reflect the influence of individual genetic differences in the Transactional subsystem. And the strength and stability of neural integrative mechanisms may also have an individual-genetic foundation.

Since the individual nervous system acts as the "intervening variable" in any postulated relationship between a particular physical trait and individual differences in personality, the key investigative issue in such relationships must become: is this physical trait associated with certain individual patterns of neural functioning? I am thinking here not only of such traits as "maze brightness" and "maze dullness" in rats, but of Sheldon's physique-temperament theory, and of Freud's assumption that sex differences in personality stem directly from the configuration of the sexes' respective genitalia. Is bodily endomorphy perhaps associated with a nervous system in which the Intraorganismic subsystem inherently plays the more dominant role? Is ectomorphy associated with a nervous system in which the Transactional subsystem inherently plays the more dominant role? Does the mesomorph inherently tend to have a balance between both subsystems, as well as more stable CI mechanisms? Do these relationships hold *within* each sex? As for Freud's Victorian-era formulation, both appreciation and criticism of facets of Freudian theory are being held over to a later section of this chapter.

When individual differences in the experiencing mechanism are further related to variations in the environment which is the source of stimulation and experience, and that mechanism is in turn affected by these experiences, the possible individual permutations and combinations become still more complex. One such relationship well worth exploring is embodied in this question: When a baby with a certain innate "style" of neural functioning is born to a mother with a very different style *or* who has reacted negatively during the course of her own development against a basic pattern originally very similar to her child's, what is the effect on her child's development? Perhaps the very first source of emotional difficulty and/or poor personality integration lies here.

Even though individual differences in behavior tend to decrease as one grows up because of the "uniforming" influence of culturally provided and imposed learnings, the fundamental circumstance that one's diversely unique nervous system forms the substrate for one's unique ways of sensing, perceiving, feeling, reacting, thinking, should not continue to be overlooked: it forms by far the richest, most varied physical basis for individual differences that psychology can consider.

FOR SEX DIFFERENCES

As the field of developmental psychology has grown, research documentation of the developmental lag of the male human organism has, as we have seen, grown together with it. The evidence that this lag rests on a neural base would seem to confirm these data's indication that this developmental difference between the sexes is as biologically determined a matter as is the XX and XY chromosome arrangement. Yet there is an apparent lack of systematic exploration by psychologists of the implications of this biological difference for individual development, for personality theory, for child-rearing and educational practices, for society. Concerning the last area especially, such an exploration could well point the way to better comprehension of many long-standing questions of psychiatry, criminology, comparative anthropology, the anatomy of war, the "battle of the sexes" — and even of religion and philosophy and the human condition in general. Such an omission suggests that psychologists' reactions to their own findings have not been as objective as geneticists' have been.

Let me begin my attempt at such an exploration where this inquiry began: with relevant phylogenetic information. *Item #1:* According to evolutionary criteria of morphologically higher and lower forms (degree of organ specialization, particularly), the human male organism is slightly less advanced phylogenetically than the human female organism. *Item #2:* organs and organ-systems acquired recently in phylogeny are less stable and more vulnerable to environmental exigencies than organs and organ-systems acquired earlier. *Item #3:* the Transactional subsystem, which subserves the organism's transactions, sensorimotor and perceptual, with its environment, is, according to Romer's analysis, the newer acquisition phylogenetically, of the two subsystems postulated in Chapter VII. It follows from Item #2 (and clinical data are corroborative) that the Transactional network is inherently the least stable and most vulnerable of the three systems — with the probable exception of those CI circuits dependent upon the functioning of the Transactional subsystem. I shall return to this phylogenetic "groundwork" in a moment.

On the essentially positive side of the ledger of sex differences from the male point of view, behavioral data as well as general knowledge inform us that on a group basis, in our culture at least, boys-men, in comparison with girls-women perceive space more accurately, are better at mathematical reasoning, are more overtly aggressive and more oriented towards competition and achievement (whether *this* difference should be considered positive or negative is acknowledged to be debatable), are given to occupational and avocational pursuits which express a drive for mastery over the environment — whether such pursuits be direct-physical (e.g., manipulative), indirect-physical (i.e., gadgetry and technological), *or* cognitive, in the form of coherent, complex ideational systems devoted to explaining what is "out there" and why. These cognitive systems may be religious, scientific, mathematical, moral, political in orientation. The last-cited proclivity suggests, in line with the analysis of anxiety previously given, that the human male is not only prone to higher levels of existence anxiety but also to higher levels of cosmic anxiety.

The almost total preponderance of men as the formulators of the great ideational systems of recorded history comprises the most frequently utilized argument — and a potent one — for a basic male superiority. A possible counter-argument — that since men have traditionally set the values of historically known cultures (that is, have decreed which human activities and personal characteristics are to be considered superior, which inferior, which more laudable socially and which less laudable) all we have actually established is a logical tautology — is also a potent one. But creative thought, it is generally agreed, is one of the highest activities of the highest species, and certainly on the basis of past performance, men appear to be the more gifted *thinkers* of our species.

On the negative side of the ledger of sex differences, again from the male point of view, proportionately more men than women in our society die younger, suffer from mental illness and stress-related maladies, commit crimes and more violent and sadistic acts, show homosexual and psychopathic (and/or sociopathic) tendencies, commit suicide, and are homeless drifters.

A useful tool for the interpretation of some of these characteristics is provided by one of Werner's postulations. On the basis of a developmentally oriented analysis of forms of symptom-expression among emotionally disturbed children and adults, he has concluded that symptoms characterized by immediacy of overt reaction are displayed by persons who function at developmentally lower levels, while symptoms representing displacement to more mediated forms of behavior are displayed by persons who function at developmentally higher levels (192, page 145). Thus, in accordance with Werner's analysis:

Developmentally Lower Level Symptom	*Developmentally Higher Level Symptom*
Directly assaultive	Threatening to assault.
Overt sexual perversions	Fearful of reacting perversely sexually.
A serious suicidal attempt	Threatening to commit suicide.

Both psychiatric and normal-range behavior-problems data (*viz.*, 113, utilized extensively in Part D) show that boys and men, when compared with girls and women of the same chronological age, consistently express more of the developmentally lower type of symptom. (It would seem that Freud's and Werner's respective explanations of girls' "greater masochism" are very different: it may not be a function of the configuration of their reproductive apparatus at all; rather, their nonacting-out tendencies may instead represent a more mature reaction made possible by their neural acceleration!)

Also, the lopsidedness of our modern technological era — high in productive efficiency and conquest of the physical environment and low in consideration for the worth of the individual — has made it the "age of anxiety," more anxiety than increasingly more people can cope with psychologically. Is it an exaggeration to suggest that this era is essentially the product of some men's drive for control over the environment converging with other men's drive for power and status?

All of the more-or-less positive male behaviors earlier enumerated are heavily dependent upon the functioning of the Transactional neural subsystem. All the more-or-less negative tendencies referred to reflect the behavioral outcomes of a lack of integration of the outer and the inner aspects of self — or, in this inquiry's neural terminology, of overcultivation of the Transactional sub-system, undercultivation of the Intraorganismic subsystem, and consequently poorly coordinated CI circuits. Is this apparent tendency towards greater use of the Transactional subsystem among men due to innate-species factors or to cultural pressures — or, perhaps, to a convergence of both species *and* cultural factors?

There seem to me to be three possible — and reasonable — explanatory approaches to the apparently greater role of the Transactional subsystem in male than in female behavior. The first is that although the female has been made the more biologic-ally stable and viable organism for good and sufficient preserva-tion-of-the-species reasons, nature has been more daringly experi-mental with the male organism and has endowed it with a poten-tially more advanced Transactional subsystem than that possessed by the female organism. Consistent with the phylogenetic princi-ple of the greater instability of more recently acquired and more advanced organ-systems, among males this neural potential takes longer to develop, has more hazards along the developmental way, *and* its eventual full expression is greater.

The second explanation is directly opposite from the first in its biological assumptions: not advancement but deficit in the male's Transactional subsystem may well obtain. That the human male has a greater drive for sensory stimulation and perceptual novelty than the human female has been observed both experi-mentally and generally: studies on perceptual isolation have shown that male subjects begin to have perceptual anomalies well before female subjects (188) ; stereo and hi-fi sound systems are much more of a male than a female "addiction" and have been attributed to the smaller range of auditory sensitivity among men. This active seeking among males for perceptual novelty and sensory stimulation may be seen as compensatory; as due to an innately *less* sensitive Transactional apparatus and to less stable associated CI circuits. Sir Winston Churchill's reported last words seem to me to epitomize the foregoing point; indeed, it was a news item reporting them that precipitated this analysis. The last paragraph of the item (139) reads:

> Sir Winston was unconscious virtually all the time until his death Jan. 24, the [Feb. 1 *London Evening*] *Standard* said. He

spoke only once, during a restless period on Jan. 15 when he opened his eyes and said to his son-in-law Christopher Soames, "I am bored with it all." [True, he had a right to be, at 94!]

The third feasible explanation is a good bit more complex. It departs from the circumstance that the human male is born with a less mature nervous system, which implies that the (incomplete-) mammalian principle is dominant in a boy-child's development for a longer period after birth. The less mature male nervous system at birth undoubtedly has much to do with boy-babies' greater difficulty in getting a firm grip on life, attested to by their greater mortality rate during the first few hours, days and weeks of life. Those who survive are likely to have a more physiologically unstable organism for a longer period than the girl-babies who survive, and are therefore prone to the development of higher levels of existence anxiety. Boys, that is, are *especially* needful of the kind of relaxed and responsive care that has already been described as vital during this period, and furthermore, *they need it for a longer period*. Since the distance-receptor components of the male nervous system start to develop later (also because of maturational lag), a boy-baby's externally derived experience is dominated by his skin-senses for a longer period, and he is therefore more affected, both physically and psychologically, by his early, skin-mediated experiences. He is as a result, more affected by the kind of mothering he receives, especially by his mother's gut-level feelings towards him. We now know these feelings may have already had a *congenital* influence upon how sturdy an organism he is at birth (54): the "old wives' tales" have turned out to have a good deal of implied meaning, after all!

If his mother's immediate life-space is not unduly stressful to her, if she is fundamentally accepting of her child, and if culturally sanctioned child-rearing practices permit the kind of quickly responsive, consistent and unsmotheringly supportive care her little mammal needs at this early period — *and* she gives such care, her son, if he *is* a sturdy child, will very likely get a firm grip on life quickly and go on to the next functional stage with minimal difficulty. (Also, since some children are constitutionally less sensitive than others, they will not be as much affected by the subtler maternal reactions as will a more sensitive brother or sister.) Among such fortunate children, this early, highly vulnerable life-period will not play a major role in the negative sense in subsequent personality formation; and a positive external environment is likely to have maximal influence. Such a child will be able to approach the external world with zestful adience during the next functional stage — and *if* his world subsequently provides him with widely varied, unprohibited, and steadily expanding opportunities for interaction with people and with things — which is generally more the case for boys than for girls in most cultures, *if* he continues to be given emotional support by those close to him, and *if* he has a high Transactional subsystem potential, he will relatively uncomplicatedly acquire a wide range of perceptions and experiences — and so develop the high levels of cosmic anxiety that provide the most effective motivation for sustained, high-level intellectual effort.

In such positive developmental instances, the Transactional subsystem plays a greater role in individual-male development than in individual-female development because boys and men: (1) are given greater cultural encouragement and opportunity to develop the potential inherent in their particular Transactional subsystem, and (2) ordinarily acquire greater motivation to make maximum use of it, again because of primarily cultural factors. (Yet this greater male tendency towards development and use of the Transactional subsystem at the same time makes personality integration more difficult for them: it encourages an escape from self into the external world; and may men's greater "product" creativity represent an exteriorization of their greater struggle for personality integration?)

Unfortunately, the ideal picture just presented describes a male life-career which is the exception rather than the rule, not only in the less privileged sections of the world but in our own country as well. What about "the rule"?

Let us return to the early postnatal period. What if, instead of a warmly supportive, stable, early maternal and physical-environmental situation, such variations as the following obtain?

(1) The young infant is left completely alone for long periods of time, which is not at all uncommon in orphanages or among

large numbers of the world's urban-poor, where the mother must work to keep herself and her children alive.

(2) The infant is born into war and/or famine conditions, which not only make food-supply inadequate but impose great and sustained emotional and physical stress on his primary caretakers.

(3) His mother, very often still in her teens, is deeply ambivalent towards her mothering function, or is unhappy in her marital situation, and as a consequence consciously or unconsciously rejects her child — and so does *not* give responsive care to the vulnerable organism in her charge, and/or as she does, communicates to him at the gut-level her anxieties and/or ambivalence and/or rejection?

Among infants consistently subjected to such early experiences, especially when these experiences are reinforced beyond infancy, pervasive feelings of weakness and helplessness, of fears and tensions not one's own, of reactive rage (a primitive-mammalian secondary reaction to threat to one's existence, especially when flight is impossible), are very likely to become the core factor to varying degrees in subsequent personality formation. Recall that the male child's greater neural immaturity makes him more vulnerable to, and therefore more influenceable by, such negative situations.

There are several ways in which this "core factor" thereafter expresses itself in personality formation. Which one is adopted by the young person depends firstly on such individual factors as the extent and length of the early exposure to deprivation and/or to maternal stress *and* the infant's degree of constitutional sturdiness and sensitivity; and secondly on such subsequent factors as his later, extrainfancy and extrafamilial experiences and the behaviors and roles valued and rewarded by his (sub-) culture. Probably the most common normal-range individual-male reaction-patterns among the North American middle-classes next to conversion to psychosomatic symptoms represent an escape from one's painful inner self into one's culture (85); as such, these patterns depend upon excessive utilization of the Transactional subsystem. Examples of such common male patterns in our society are as follows:

(1) Conversion of the original primitive reactive rage into expressions of intense, adaptive competitiveness — adaptive because they are rewarded by our middle-class subculture; *un*converted aggressivity is more common among boys growing up in the slum-culture. (But this latter reaction-pattern is spreading to some sectors of the middle class as middle-class familial dynamics show a growing correspondence, in our increasingly mass society, with those of the slum culture.)

(2) Systematized reaction-formations involving adoption of behavior-patterns rewarded by one's culture, such as a strong drive for dominance or for power over others, or for achievement motivated by "personal status" anxiety (129).

The concept of "personal status" anxiety rounds out the "species theory of anxiety" previously cited. This aberrant form of anxiety is converted from existence anxiety as a result of the coming together of two contributory factors, the first intraindividual and the second culturally determined: high individual levels of "leftover" existence anxiety, converging with one's subculture's high valuation of competitive achievement and status, characteristics which are in turn equated with masculinity. Herewith the postulated dynamics of this process:

> At the time that the child first becomes an object to himself, his body is coincident with his self. His degree of existence anxiety, as a basic part of his bodily functioning, automatically becomes an integral part of his feelings about himself. Concurrent with his differentiation of himself from others, he becomes aware of and psychologically sensitive to his parents' attitudes towards him, of his personal meaning to them. If his existence anxiety is already fairly high because of inappropriate early care, and if his parents put constant obvious and subtle pressures on him to be a bigger, better, smarter, more successful child than he is, his anxiety over his physical existence is broadened to anxiety over his psychological existence.
>
> As a result, his status in the eyes of others of personal importance to him becomes of central concern to him. With continuing subsequent beyond-family cultural reinforcement, which is typical in our society, this functionally neurotic kind of anxiety becomes the motivation behind his constant attempts

to maintain, enhance, defend, his always-vulnerable personal status. When he perceives this status as being threatened, he reacts just the same physiologically as he did when an infant to threats to his physical existence. The role of personal status anxiety in learning and in personal development is as negative as is existence anxiety (Adapted from 129, p. 235).

Although the first explanation of the greater role of the Transactional subsystem in male behavior, that of the inherently more advanced nature of this subsystem in the human male, is the most attractive one because of its relative simplicity, medical and psychological and criminal data — and the recorded history of the human race — make the second and third explanations in combination probably the more correct one. Actually, although explanations 1 and 2 are mutually exclusive, the third one is compatible with either 1 *or* 2.

Many of the psychological characteristics traditionally associated with girls and women may also be related to the neural formulations of this discussion. Their typical underdevelopment of their Transactional subsystem potential often leads to poor personality integration: underused Transactional network capacity can create its own kinds of personality-integration difficulties. The high emotionality and/or the psychological absorption of their children typical of many middle-class women may well be a reflection of their lack of constructive, disciplined mental-activity outlets, a lack stemming from the limitations imposed on them from birth onward by the subculturally approved feminine sex-role.

Still more profound societal implications stem from traditional cultural prohibitions on women's open expressions of their aggressive and hostile feelings and of achievement as an expression of independent self-hood: do women who live within this culturally imposed pattern of repression transfer these "forbidden" feelings and drives to their children at a mutually unconscious level, and may there, as a consequence, be a direct relationship between the degree to which a particular culture forces women to live vicariously rather than directly and the degree to which that culture embraces institutionalized aggressiveness — e.g., a high degree of competitiveness in the economic and occupational spheres, and/or militarism and war as an instrument of national policy?

Serious research consideration needs to be given to the possibility that consistently expressed psychological differences between the sexes stem much more from the greater role of the external environment, for good and/or for ill, in male behavior on the one hand, and from the underawareness and underutilization of the beyond-family environment by many women on the other hand, than from the secondary variable of the differences in the configuration of the respective genitalia as postulated by Freud. As neo-Freudians such as Karen Horney have pointed out (84), it is the symbolic meaning of these differences, accrued from cultural values and practices, which has made them psychologically significant to both sexes.

The contradiction between the circumstance that the female organism is developmentally accelerated *and* the long-standing institutionalized subordination of women in most societies is so intriguing as to invite speculation concerning its possible etiology. The two halves of the contradiction seem to me to be dynamically related, expressing another kind of male reaction-formation, an order of male reaction also evident in the intermittent witch-hunts of Western history and in periods of open male hostility against women such as the present: in cultures and subcultures which employ highly restrictive and/or coercive methods of child-rearing, or during historical periods when (or among groups where) infants and young children are chronically neglected, physically and psychologically, a reactively hostile need is engendered in the individual to subjugate and "put down" the order of being who made him feel so weak and helpless so often during his dependent and vulnerable early years.

This order of male reaction-formation is indeed ironic from both the societal and the individual points of view because of its strongly self and socially defeating character. A vicious circle is set up and kept in constant generation-to-generation motion by it. As girls grow up, their evaluations of themselves and their feelings towards the male sex are strongly influenced by institutionalized expressions of their subordination as well as by conscious and unconscious male (and female) ambivalence towards their sex-group. These feminine self-evaluations and unconscious counterhostilities almost ensure that *when many young women become mothers, they will handle their biologically and psychologically fundamental mothering function in such a way as to generate in their sons continuing reactive ambivalence and/or hostility towards girls and women in general!*

Such generalized male displacement of hostility is at least partially a product of cultural taboos which make conscious awareness of hostility towards one's own mother — as well as towards *Mother* — impossible. Because of spreading recourse to psychotherapy, there are recent — but limited — signs of a break in this dike. As for investigation on a controlled, sampling basis into the relationships among men between their degree of fear and hostility towards their mothers and their fear and hostility towards women in general, we have a major cultural terra incognita so far as existing attitude-research data are concerned; we seem to have only individual-clinical information in this area. This continuing omission would seem to stem from the circumstance that awareness of both these areas of fear and hostility is typically inadmissable, culturally, among investigated and investigator alike. It is noteworthy in this connection that Freud not only harbored just such a reaction-formation as has been postulated here, but that cultural reinforcement of it both prevented him from unearthing it during his self-analysis *and* contributed to its major influence on key aspects of his theoretical system.

Ostensibly only for the increasing numbers of women in technically advanced societies who wish to become distinct persons and personalities in their own right but actually also for men and the entire society, this whole area of the fundamental influence of a woman's practice of the mothering function on her children poses a most difficult — because apparently contradictory — choice. When the maternal role was accorded high social recognition and status, a woman's exercise of the mothering responsibility more easily allowed her to satisfy within the *same* social role both her children's needs *and* her own desire for recognition as an important person in her own right. Now, because of our society's current value-system that one's occupational attainments and/or consuming power are the *really* significant, even exclusive, sources of personal status and feelings of worth (127), the role of mother no longer affords especially the better educated young woman feelings of unique personal value in and of itself. As a result, girls and young women who wish to become and to be self-fulfilling, autonomous individuals typically harbor two sets of attitudes which are in direct contradiction to one another in their individual and social implications. Such young women tend to be particularly demanding of maturity in the opposite sex: as growing individuals, as lovers and as wives, they want the boys and men in their lives to be mature, integrated individuals, friends, lovers, husbands, fathers. Yet these same young women, primarily because of our culture's current devaluation of the traditionally feminine roles and overvaluation of the traditionally masculine ones, tend to relegate to a secondary position in their scale of worthwhile, self-fulfilling activities, maternal responsibilities and preoccupations — even, among many of them, to resent the temporal and emotional demands their young and growing children make upon them.

They — and our terribly short-sighted society — appear to have overlooked that if little boys are to grow up to be adequate partners for the *next* generation of emancipated young women, they will have to be acceptant of themselves, which necessarily includes a "gut-level" acceptance of their male identity and of their sexual *and* familial roles — all of which requires that women so function as mothers as to foster such self development and such attitudes in their sons! Other than intrafamily factors are of course influential here: for example, *all* persons, both male and female, tend to be devalued in a mass, overpopulated, technology-dominated society — but the dynamically fundamental factor lies here, in the mother-child relationship.

To overcome the contradiction, it would seem that nothing less than a revolution in cultural values — and associated practices — would seem to be necessary, a revolution resulting in an almost complete reversal of present evaluations of the *really* important activities of adult men and women. Both for the individual and the society, the *parental* functions, maternal *and* paternal, need to become the more highly valued, and occupational and conspicuous-consumption roles secondary, in social *and* individual-psychological importance. This in spite of the voluntarily limited size of families that will shortly become the approved norm in those "advanced" countries which wish to remain so. Certainly Margaret Mead's classic study on sex-associated personality patterns in three simple societies (121) has rather definitely demonstrated that, beyond sheerly sexual and procreative functions, considerations of "appropriately" feminine or masculine behavior are largely, if not entirely, a culturally determined matter.

Such a cultural reversal may be much nearer in time than is generally realized. The rapid spread of automation and cybernation is pushing us, willy-nilly, in just this direction: when all routine physical and mental work is performed by machines, and large numbers of the population have very little work in the traditional sense to do, one must hope that a speculation attributed to Hallock Hoffman will turn out to have been prophetic:

> Suppose mothers and fathers had all the time and affluence they needed to make babies happy, to bring them through those infinitely demanding first years without harsh and premature discipline? Might this not allow us to break with the heritage of neurosis which in the past each love-lacking and harried generation has passed on to the next (158, p. 347) ?

FOR THE ROLE OF "MOTHERING" IN HUMAN DEVELOPMENT

A major implication of this inquiry is its affirmation of the fundamental importance of the mothering function in individual human development. But it does a good deal more than merely affirm what the "tough-minded" psychological investigator has traditionally dismissed as a piece of sentimental, near-mystical semantics. Much of this chapter's immediately preceding section, data in Part D, and the first, third and fourth principles of human development constitute documentation in *operational terms* as to why the responsive child-caring function termed "mothering" is so essential, not merely for "normal" human development, but for the *very possibility that each newborn human-mammal will become, be transformed into, a human being* (as each particular social group defines human). For a society which has devalued this traditionally feminine function to a socially and individually disastrous degree, the societal and individual implications of this circumstance are major.

The first implication has already been referred to in the foregoing section: the need for a reversal in present cultural values concerning the *really* important activities of adult men and women. The recent retreat of a whole generation of women to domesticity and the rearing of larger families than their parents had, represents in many — if not most — instances *not* a renewed inner affirmation of the worth of the maternal role, but the response of immature personalities to strong external influences. The sharp increase in competitive economic and social pressures on American men has made them especially vulnerable to anything they perceive as a threat to their traditional sex-role prerogatives, and these girls as they grew up became thoroughly aware of the hostile reactions of the boys and men in their lives to women who had equal or superior intellectual or job status. Add the constant echoing of this hostility in the popular mass media and parents' projection onto their daughters of their own unresolved sex-role ambivalences and fears, and it is not difficult to understand this feminine reaction.

The second implication is that societies as cultural entities, as well as individual men and women, need to recognize far more than they do at present the fundamental *societal* implications of the personal development of girls and women. The fullest development of women as complex individual personalities and their being accorded ample grounds for feelings of inner worth can no longer be considered a parochial, feminist, concern, but as fundamental to the well-being of all, since a society which "diminishes" women, through the impact of their exercise of the mothering function on their children, automatically diminishes men and the entire quality of life in that society.

Implementation of both these implications will require changes not only in the relatively easily developed and carried out "practical programs" level; a challenge to deeply entrenched — and quite unconscious — ways of thinking is also involved, and *this* level is a much more subtle and difficult one to cope with. Further discussion of both the practical and subtle levels of needed change is being held over to the section on "preventive measures" in the next chapter.

FOR FREUDIAN CONSTRUCTS

Freud's contributions to our understanding of human psychological development emerge more clearly when his postulations are first placed in their (a) methodological and (b) cultural cum historical-period, settings. Thus, (a) he did not study children directly, but rather, his neurotic patients' verbalized recollections of, and free associations to, their childhood experiences. Since these persons had grown up in (b) a particular culture (western European), subculture (upper middle-class), and historical period (later nineteenth century), their childhood experiences reflected the impact on the growing individual of a particular family structure and intrafamily relationships *and* of a particular set of child-rearing aims, values and practices. Beyond his true "breakthrough" postulation of the fundamental influence of early stress and deprivation on later behavior (since corroborated by impeccable animal and other research), and the related concept of unconscious motivation, most of Freud's constructs have been personally and philosophically meaningful and psychotherapeutically useful in other places and times in direct proportion as these other cultural settings share similar family structure and relationships and values, and employ similar child-rearing practices.

So placed in social-anthropological perspective, Freudian theory provides vivid documentation of what happens (a) psychologically to the individual when he is reared in a (sub-) culture which holds a particular conception of "human nature" and which, as a consequence, seriously mishandles from the point of view of overall personality growth and integration the "mammalian principle" in its child-rearing practices (as outlined in Chapter XII));[1] and (b) within societies in which the culturally and politically dominant groups are the products of such a conception and associated practices. As Theodore Roszak has put it in his provocative essay, "The Historian as Psychiatrist" (158):

> From the concept of sublimation we derive an exciting sense
> of the wholeness of human nature, but at the same time the

---

[1] Indeed, this inquiry may on this score be interpreted as providing the neurological "underpinnings" for many of Freud's personality constructs.

bitter knowledge that our highest cultural achievements are of a piece with the dark and wicked deeds of history, the Parthenon of a piece with the Melian dialogue and the mines of Laurion, Bayreuth of a piece with Auschwitz; the one cannot be understood without the other. . . . Don't we all dimly realize that it isn't simply a series of 'bad breaks' that has descended upon us in the years since 1914, driving the proud self-confidence of the Enlightenment from our society? Nasty things like world wars and concentration camps and Hiroshimas don't just happen. Human beings, the same decent human beings who build cathedrals and draft constitutions and subscribe to symphony orchestras, make them happen, and for reasons that sound far-fetched (p. 343-4).

What is history? It is the piece-by-piece assassination of the infant's polymorphously perverse body. So far has this unrelenting repression of physical joy gone that now only an overworked genitality is left to us" (p. 345).

Especially Freud's picture of the id's overriding influence on personality formation and on individual behavior, including the use of the intellect, throughout life, *and* his concept of sublimation of the primitive id-drives as the fundamental factor behind civilization, alike reflect in the terminology of this inquiry (1) his conclusion that the "mammalian principle" in our species' (phylo) genetic inheritance is the fundamentally, even solely, significant factor in human personality formation; and (2) his apparently total oversight of the "human principle" in our species' genetic inheritance, which is as much a part of that inheritance as is the mammalian principle: *viz.*, data in Chapter III. He was, however, very right in his implied proposition that optimum development of the higher, uniquely human behaviors is conditional upon the prior proper "serving" of our mammalian inheritance.

Both his conclusion and his oversight reflect the tremendous influence of Darwin's revolutionary contribution on nearly all late-nineteenth century western-European thought. They are also, more specifically, a function of the experiences and the data from which he derived his theory. Both Freud and his patients had been subjected, as products of their common culture, to early experiences that militated against the undistorted development of the human principle — that is, that handicapped the uncomplicated emergence of neocortical, especially prefrontal cortex, dominance. Also, Freud's own anthropological investigations were tainted by a preconceived bias: he singled out for attention very early and/or simple cultures in which un-self-conscious expressions of the emotional life in art and in religious practices created permanent artifacts, while the more subtle evidences of the human principle, expressed in direct communication and in the regulation of social relationships, were, in these prerecorded language cultures, unavailable to the archeologist.

Freud's explanation of the emergence of "civilization" needs to be seen in the light of the two influences itemized above. This explanation departed from the postulation that suppression of the mammalian-inheritance libido is *the* motive-force behind man's use of his intellect: the influencing relationship between man and society, that is, is unidirectional, *viz.*, man's biological nature $\longrightarrow$ society or civilization. When primitive man began to inhibit his direct instinctual expressions and to "sublimate" them in the form of increased use of the intellect, civilization began to emerge; civilized man is inescapably discontented because organized society with its various institutions exists at the expense of his free expression of his libido (55).

Only if a *particular set* of cultural traditions and forms is substituted for "civilization" does Freud's analysis have a degree of validity — a degree that Roszak makes much of in his essay earlier cited. But I am led by the data and the insights of this inquiry, as well as by biological and anthropological knowledge which has accrued subsequent to the late nineteenth and early twentieth centuries, to explain the relationship between impulse-repression and distinctive characteristics of western civilization in a somewhat different way.

At the point in evolutionary time when our species emerged, it did so not merely in group form but in groups rather advanced in the social-organization sense, as studies of our nearest primate relatives in their natural habitat have been strongly suggesting. As these early social groups' culture — the product of our species' human principle — slowly accumulated from generation to generation, the benefits to the entire group of each member's control of his first heedless reactions became manifest to the group's "wise elders" and led them to place taboos on certain categories of spontaneous impulsivity, especially on expressions of intratribal aggression and intrafamily sexuality. Some of Moses' Ten Commandments in all probability codified formally what had already been preached for centuries by established authority in most early cultures.

Unfortunately, early propounders of social ethics within the Judaeo-Christian tradition began to apply these restrictions on impulsivity not only to adults but also to children, not realizing that the young child's neural immaturity makes impulsivity as natural — and as psychologically valid — as breathing. They projected, that is, an adult level of understanding and of capacity for impulse-control onto the child — even, in some Christian sects, onto the infant. It became parents' *religious* duty — here I am accepting much of Durkheim's thesis of the social-group origins of organized religion (44) — to impose a dedicated suppression of impulsivity on their children. This Judaeo-Christian child-rearing tradition has served to initiate, and through reaction-formation to maintain, a schizoid split between the inner and the outer aspects of the self, especially in the slower developing male. This split manifests itself in three reaction-patterns widespread among the chief inheritors of that tradition, the middle classes of Europe and America: an ejection of impulsivity outside of self into two types of institutionalized aggressiveness — interpersonal competitiveness and outgroup hostility, cruelty and war; a high level of personal-status anxiety; neurotic "escape" into the intellect — i.e., overuse of the Transactional subsystem with accompanying poor personality integration.

As was suggested at the close of the discussion of sex differences, what if we were to break this long-entrenched vicious circle and employ the child-rearing approaches implied in Chapter XII: the *age-graded* catering to *both* the mammalian and the human principles in human development? Would such a shift in adult values and practices create a new personality norm and in turn, new, more adaptive and psychologically satisfying varieties of societal forms and values?

Certainly, other, relatively recent cultural changes are demonstrating that Freud's developmental constructs are *not* innately predetermined. Because of the family structure and parental sexroles and relationships typical of the "slum culture," a structure and relationships quite different from those of the "old" middle-class, the neuroses stemming from the clash between the id and an overly repressive superego have always been rare among these social groups. Rather, defective, even lacking, superego formation, with all the *social* problems such a family situation engenders, has been the hallmark of such population groups. Traditional psychoanalysis has been notoriously ineffective with delinquents and psychopaths of lower lower-class[2] origins; in such instances, superego-building experiences are much more likely to be effective, provided they are instituted early (preferably in the preschool years).

As initially lower lower-class persons have moved up into the middle-class, carrying many lower-class values and practices with them; as the traditional middle-class social sex-roles have changed, partially but nevertheless inescapably because of the economic and social impact of technology; and as increasing population and urbanization have combined with archaic value-systems to intensify the competitive and psychological pressures on the success-driven middle-class male and his consort (127), many middle-class parents have abdicated from nearly all aspects of the parental role except that of material provider. In such instances, intrafamily dynamics much like those for the slum-culture frequently obtain, with a similar effect on the children growing up in such families — and psychoanalytic constructs and therapeutic approaches are having similarly limited applicability.

A critique of Freud's elevation of the psychological role of the overt physical differences between the sexes from an intermediate-symbolic one to a biologically fundamental, directly causal one, has already been presented in the section on sex differences. Again, when Freud is related to his place and time, western Europe and the Victorian era — *and* to the circumstance that many of Freud's own oedipal anxieties and hostilities remained unresolved — one can more readily understand why this particular formulation has

---

[2]As defined by Warner's *Index of Status Characteristics* (189).

proved to be probably the most vulnerable of his constructs (but the one most likely to be emphasized by more contemporary young men with similarly unresolved oedipal anxieties and hostilities).

If there are indeed biologically based psychological differences between the sexes, their sources are more likely to be found first, in somewhat different hormonal balances and physiological rhythms; second and third, in different physiological reactions to sexual tension *and* in degree of control thereof; and fourth, in somewhat different neural endowments and different developmental timing thereof. The possibility that all four of these variables may be *genetically interrelated* deserves investigation.

FOR PERSONALITY THEORIES — AND THEORY

As the title of the last section, E, of this inquiry implies, the diversity of extant theories of personality is at least partially due to the circumstance that each focuses upon a particular aspect or aspects of a process that is truly elephantine in its complexity. As a result, each has validity when considered within its own particular perspective or frame of reference, and each is also limited, even misleading, when considered from another perspective or a broader frame of reference.

Current theoretical approaches may be grouped into the following general categories — those focusing on:

(1)   the instinctive-biological or subjective-depth dimension; e.g., orthodox-Freudian and Jungian concepts;

(2)   the role of culture and of specific facets of the social environment in personality-formation; e.g., 'cross-cultural and social-role theories;

(3)   the process of interaction between the (growing) individual and his (cumulative) social environments, either situationally or over time; e.g., Lewinian field theory, George Herbert Mead's "social act"; theories of social learning and socialization;

(4)   the ongoing, cumulative behavioral outcomes of the growing human organism's transactions with its various influencing environments; this category may in turn be divided into three overlapping subclassifications:

(a)   social-psychological theories; e.g., some neo-Freudians such as Horney, Kardiner, Erikson; also Fromm and later Margaret Mead;

(b) normative-developmental (i.e., theories stressing the individual's progression during the life-career from lower-simpler-immature behaviors to higher-complex-mature behaviors) ; e.g., Rogers, Maslow, Erikson, Piaget; also aspects of Freud and Lewin;

(c) existential theories, which include explicitly the individual's own functioning and reactivity as the most important component of the "influencing environment."

The psychometric approaches to personality — trait-cataloguing and factor-analytic — are not included because they are considered to represent specialized investigative tools rather than theories *per se*.

Since the neural formulations of this inquiry describe the physical mechanisms that underlie both personality functioning at any one moment in time *and* the process of personality formation and change over time, it is possible to relate psychological concepts and processes central in each of the various theories to the neural organizations which appear to mediate these processes.

Thus, Freud's *id* represents the functioning and the functional role of the Intraorganismic short circuit. The emergence of the infantile *ego* is dependent upon the onset and spread of functioning in the sensorimotor neocortex and hence upon the Transactional long circuit. The mature ego depends upon the integrated functioning of the Intraorganismic and Transactional subsystems. The *superego* represents certain of the perceptual structurings (phase sequences?) within the T-O-P area. Freudian theory, as has already been pointed out, does not adequately provide for the functional role of the PF area, although the capacity to sublimate may be conceived as dependent upon its functioning. The layering organization of the neocortex and its developmental and functional relationships with the two subsystems and CI circuits (of which the ARAS is a part) provide for the conscious-unconscious continuum, including the layers 6 and 5 unconscious-level reservoir of early memories — i.e., for the "depth" orientation so fundamental to Freudian theory.

Since the Transactional subsystem provides for the individual's environmentally derived experience and for individual selectivity of perception, 'cross-cultural and social role theories accord it, by implication, the dominant role in personality formation and expression. Theories which attempt to conceptualize the organism ↔ environment interaction process *per se* are addressing themselves primarily to the functioning of the Transactional subsystem, the T-O-P "perceptual field" association area as an important part of that system, and the CI circuits.

As for normative theories, the progression from the lower, simpler, uncoordinated behavior and personality patterns of the infant to the higher, complex, controlled and integrated behavior and personality patterns of the neurally mature adult, is dependent upon the vertical pattern of development of the two subsystems, with especial emphasis on the neocortical layers' lower to higher order of emergence to function, plus the gradual postnatal establishment of forebrain integrative circuits which bring these two disparate networks into intimate functional relationship.

As for personality theory in general, the formulations derived through this inquiry have shown that complex psychological constructs covering

— person to person, and person to physical environment interactions, both situationally and over time;
— developmental accretions in behavior and cognitive structures, including the self;
— circular self-reactions,

all very probably have a neural basis. This summation presumes the discussion in Chapter VI of the implications of the new knowledge of the human nervous system for *behavioral* theorizing. When further research enables us to relate each of these constructs to the developmental changes in organization and functioning of the neural mechanisms mediating these events more exactly than the beyond-the-data projections of this monograph have been in the position to do, we shall have taken a giant step towards a fuller and richer and more scientifically respectable picture of that complex configuration, the human personality, than the ones we as yet have.

Psychological investigators' eventual willingness to take into account the many factors influencing individual development in all their interactive intricacy poses not only a sheerly methodological, research-design challenge. It also — and perhaps more so — poses a mathematical challenge: the necessity to develop new mathematical systems, or adaptations of existing systems

> . . . increasingly better suited to the study of a class of phenomena, each *one* at least as complex as the entire physical cosmos: the developing individual human being. When shall we in the behavioral sciences become aware of the need to develop *our own* Einsteins (128, p. 257) ?

Von Bertalanffy has made some useful observations in this connection, stating that science represents a "hierarchy of statistics," that is, of probabilities (19) : the statistics utilized by the various sciences differ in their respective "degrees of freedom;" in their extent, that is, of possible variation in structure, function, reaction. He groups the sciences into four levels of complexity according to their increasing degrees of freedom (p. 172) :

> (1) At the first level is the statistics of microphysics.
> (2) A second level is constituted by the laws of macrophysics; that is, of those phenomena where a great number of elementary physical units is involved. [These laws appear to be deterministic but are actually probabilitistic or statistical.]
> (3) A third level is represented by the "biological realm." [I shall have further comments to make concerning this level presently.]
> (4) Finally, there are laws that apply to supraindividual units of life [e.g., population and insurance statistics].

The size of the difference in degrees of freedom between the first and the third levels foregoing is tantamount, in functional terms, to the size of the difference between von Bertalanffy's "closed" and "open" systems, a fundamental functional difference already referred to in Chapter I. Further implications of this qualitative difference having special relevance for research and statistical methodology are highlighted in these two additional passages by von Bertanlanffy:

> The increase in degrees of freedom is also shown in equi-finality. Whereas the development of closed systems to the final state is determined by the initial conditions, the same end state can be reached in open systems in different ways (p. 175).
>
> In physical systems, events are, in general, determined by the momentary conditions only. . . . In contrast, organisms appear to be historical beings. For instance, when the human embryo displays gill clefts at a certain stage, it reveals that mammals evolved in geological times from fish-like creatures. In a similar way, we find "historicity" in organic behavior: the reaction of an animal or a human depends on the stimuli and reactions that the organism met with or produced in the past (p. 109).

This inquiry's area of concern is entirely subsumable under von Bertalanffy's third, "open system," level. But the biological realm itself represents, as was pointed out in the first chapter, various subhierarchies with ascending degrees of freedom in precisely von B's sense. For example, changing "levels of function" up the phylogenetic scale are directly paralleled by increasing statistical degrees of freedom. The subhierarchy represented by the increasing levels of complexity of processes within the living organism is another example: from the biochemical to the cellular to the tissue to the organ and organ-system to inter-system co-ordinations (e.g., homeostasis) to the reflex to the purposive-behavioral. A consistently overlooked factor with regard to this particular hierarchy, one with major implications for measurement, is the unavoidable relationship between the rate of the organismic process/function/behavior being observed and the temporal factors inherent in the human observer's perceptual processes. Thus, such concepts as growth and maturation and development embody organismic events occurring at rates which are very slow in relation to the processes of human perception, while organismic processes which occur at rates directly comprehensible by the human observer are considered physiological or reactive-behavioral: *there is a qualitative difference or discon-*

*tinuity between these two orders of organismic functioning only
in the mind of the perceiver, not in the living organism itself.*

Hence, the preliminary suggestion that we need to develop one
type of mathematical approach for studying behavior that occurs
at a moment in time, i.e., situationally, and another approach for
the study of behavior over time, i.e., developmentally, must be
immediately qualified. Such separate mathematical approaches
will have to be complementary, or, better still, the former approach should be *susceptible to incorporation within* the latter
approach.

As for the measurement of behavior occurring situationally
specifically, Lewin's conceptual formula, B = fPE (107) provides
us with a perceptual-psychological "lead," while von Bertalanffy
provides us with a more comprehensive, biologically oriented
approach in these excerpts from the same source already cited:

> If we were ever able to put the whole process in an organism
> into one formula, it would be an integro-differential equation,
> indicating the spatial and temporal whole at the same time (p.
> 113-4).

> Many of the most essential questions of biology are not a
> matter of quantities but of "pattern," "position," and "shape."
> For instance, in the hierarchical order of the organism, it is not
> quantities that are interesting but relations of subordination
> and superordination, of centralization and the like. . . . [There
> is a] possibility that a nonquantitative or gestalt mathematics
> could have an important bearing for biological theory. It would
> be, as Bauink has put it, a system of mathematics where . . . the
> *notion of form or order would be fundamental* (p. 159).

For studying the development of behavior, and especially for
studying the development of the individual personality, which is
partially a function of others and of outer events, a complex "contingency" mathematics involving a hierarchical chain of probability formulae, each higher formula in the hierarchy dependent
upon the results derived from those below, would seem to be
necessary. Norbert Wiener has set a precedent for this approach
in his development of a very simple kind of contingency math,
used in the first computers:

With the aid of this technique [related to the calculus of variations] we were able to obtain an explicit best solution of the problem of predicting the future of a time-series, given its statistical nature. . . . In the case of communication engineering . . . the transmission of information is impossible save as a transmission of alternatives. . . . To cover this aspect, we had to develop a statistical theory of the amount of information, in which the unit amount of information was that transmitted as a single decision between equally probable alternatives (193, p. 17) .

This sort of statistics is reducible to the binary system, in which each operation of a computing machine represents a series of yes-no decisions, each succeeding question determined by the answer to the previous one; here is the methodology underlying computer "programming."

Perhaps a similar statistical approach, but one somehow providing for a decision based on many more than two alternatives will be developed by a future mathematical genius having both intensive and extensive background in the behavioral sciences. Certainly psychological experimenters will have to discard their habit of selecting only those problems which can be adapted to mathematical approaches originally developed by the physical sciences.

FOR ADDITIONAL RESEARCH

The basic formulations of this inquiry, as embodied especially in Chapters VII and XII, are essentially all hypotheses awaiting focused research testing. Several specific investigative problems were also suggested in context throughout Part D.

Further suggestions for additional research studies of a programmatic nature follow:

In connection with the developmental history of the brain's electrical activity, answers to these questions should be sought:

(1) Are the developmental changes in patterning of electrical activity related to the structural maturation of — and onset of function in — specific neural loci (such as the thalamus) and/or interconnections?

(2) What changes in behavior, if any, accompany or follow closely maturational changes in electrical activity?

(3) Which aspects of the developmental changes in electrical activity are innately determined and which are dependent upon the individual's opportunities for experience — and what kinds of experience?

> Suggestions for research designs suited to answering question 3 include: a longitudinal comparative study, from birth to five years of age, of the electrical activity patterning of blind and of sighted children; a similar study of children born without hands and handed children; a birth to fourteen years longitudinal study of children growing up in very different child-rearing milieus such as (a) the slum-culture and the upper middle-class in our own society, holding "race" constant, and (b) the nonacculturated Eskimo family, which employs very permissive child-rearing practices, and the large-urban lower middle-class North American family.

Does successful psychotherapy alter the functional relationships among the treated individual's Transactional and Intraorganismic subsystems and CI circuits? For example, are there detectable electrical and biochemical post-therapy differences in especially thalamic and PF area functioning during specific situations which prior to therapy aroused unadaptive reactions such as marked anxiety?

As to whether there may be a relationship between (sub-) cultural patterns of child-rearing and the medical/behavior-disorder histories of individuals growing up in that subculture, the following research-design is suggested:

> The child-rearing practices of lower lower-class samples from birth to sixteen years, with sex held constant (preferably a white and a Negro group, at least), should be studied by a group of developmental psychologists, while a medical and psychiatric team not in communication with the first set of investigators keeps thorough medical and behavior-disorder records of the same samples — with periodic comparison of these two sets of data made by still a third set of investigators (who would suggest needed changes in approach to each of the

first two sets). A similarly designed study of middle-class samples should also be done. The results of the first study should be compared with those of the second study, in such a way as to keep ethnic and/or racial (as well as sex) factors constant — for example, middle-class white boys should be compared with lower lower-class white boys, and middle-class Negro girls should be compared with lower lower-class Negro girls.

Are behavior disorders or difficulties which manifest themselves during infancy and early childhood due to the convergence of externally induced stress (*or* lack of needed stimulation) with the neurogenic period when a particular neuraxial center is in active process of establishing its neural dominance?

More specifically, if stress is imposed while hypothalamic coordination of the ANS is in process of being established, will an infant respond with homeostatic and other vegetative disturbances? If stress is imposed *or* sensory deprivation occurs while intrathalamic connections are being established, will sensory and perceptual anomalies be manifested both at the time and subsequently? If stress occurs while cortical centers which provide for voluntary control over strong negative emotion are in process of functional emergence, will the child respond with unpredictable and disproportionate emotional outbursts?

One of the very first EEG signs of aging, cited in Chapter XI, is a recurrence of theta rhythms in the temporal poles, a pattern which is strongly reminiscent of that of the highly emotional early childhood period. This circumstance prompts this research-begging question: Do people who had a stressful infancy and childhood, either because of deprivation or over- (or contradictory) stimulation, tend to show this EEG pattern (as well as other "deteriorative" neural and behavioral changes) *younger* than do persons who had more positive childhood experiences (with genetic factors held constant, if at all possible)?

FOR PSYCHIATRY'S PRESENT "PRE-PASTEUR" PERIOD

Except for a minority in the psychotherapeutic professions, American psychiatrists, social workers, consulting psychologists, approach individual cases of psychological disorder in very much the same way that the medical profession approached a patient suffering from an infectious disease in its pre-Pasteur days. Their rationale is directly comparable to the "pre-Pasteur practitioner's belief that his professional responsibility did not extend beyond efforts to treat the infected individual" (127, p. 131). This comparison is particularly applicable to those who are committed to the medical school of psychological therapy, that is, to the use of drugs, shock-treatment, and so on, and to continuing research into the development of related means of "control" and treatment. If and when societal factors contributing to the patient's disorder — e.g., early family influences — *are* taken into account (as do all psychoanalytically oriented practitioners), such factors are not perceived as "epidemiological," but solely as part of the particular patient's background of thoroughly individualized experience.

So long as the total professional frame of reference is treatment of the *already afflicted,* the foregoing are defensible, indeed essential, orientations and procedures. But what of the professional responsibility that must be of equal, if not of greater, importance, that of *prevention?* So far as I am aware, medically oriented therapists do not concern themselves with this broader professional obligation except to point to the advantages of early individual diagnosis and treatment — and sometimes to urge and to work towards increased medical facilities therefor. Psychoanalytically oriented therapists are more likely to have a preventive concern, but as heretofore represented by individual practitioners as well as by representatives of the organized mental health movement, this concern is typically expressed either in exhortations to parents to mend their ways and/or in educationally motivated enunciation and interpretation in popular terminology of Freud's psychosexual stages *as if they were as biologically determined as physical growth itself.*

In light of the implications of the findings of this inquiry, such preventive approaches are shockingly inadequate, even diversionary. Not until psychiatry and clinical psychology and related research disciplines ask, and systematically set about answering the following first-order question, will they at last have opened the entry-door to a professional period analogous to physical medicine's present post-Pasteur era.

Given this particular newborn biological form, the human organism, which, like any other biological entity has certain implanted potentialities for development and is dependent upon its environment for provision of the materials that will allow these inherent potentialities *to* develop, what kinds of growth-enabling materials need to be provided by its environment at each of its succeeding stages of development so that its full range of potentialities will be expressed at maturity without stunting or distortion?

The basic preventive question, above, has been deliberately expressed in generalized biological phraseology. To avoid misunderstanding, interpretation of its key terms in light of their specific meaning for the human species is necessary. "Implanted potentialities" include those for physical structure *and* for behavior in the broadest sense; once the latter order of potentialities is included, then both the "mammalian" and the "human" genetic legacies of the nervous system must be taken into account. The environment upon which the human organism is dependent includes not only such physical factors as air and temperature and nutrition but also the cumulative social environments which accrue from birth to neurological maturity, at least: from mother to rest of family to play-group to neighborhood-bounded contacts to school-related contacts to — etc. The influence upon these immediate social environments of further-removed societal variables such as economic trends, cultural value-systems, work-life, is also involved. "Growth-enabling materials" include not only food and warmth, but also opportunities for experience relevant to each developmental stage: it is essential to keep in mind that for the human organism especially, to be alive is not only to breathe and to digest but equally as surely, *to experience.*

When the broad-applicability order of question cited above is answered, individual reactions to environmental provisions which are known to be generally conducive to optimal human growth at the succeeding developmental stages can be dealt with as *variations within a known range of reactions,* much like physical medicine today approaches individual-physiological reactions to the standard treatment for a particular infectious disease.

Thus, those doing psychotherapy in our complex society need to know, in detail:

(1) the child-rearing patterns of the various identifiable subcultures — social class, ethnic, religious, etc. — in our society, as well as the generation-to-generation changes in these patterns;

(2) the physical and the psychological impact of these patterns on the growing individual at the succeeding stages of development in each of these subcultures;

(3) concerning young women of various subcultural backgrounds, the influence of their earlier, culturally based experiences as well as of current events in their life-space on their attitudes towards, and preparation for, the mothering responsibility;

(4) the cumulative effects of the entire sequence of experiences associated with growing up in our society for each of the various population categories of: middle-class boys and girls, lower-class boys and girls, middle-class Negro boys and girls, lower-class white boys and girls, etc., etc.

Not until psychiatry and allied professions have begun *as a matter of course* to think in the culture ⟷ individual interaction terms here enunciated, and such organized-yet-changing bodies of information as the foregoing have been acquired, and continue to be as regularly "researched" as new drugs, can the psychotherapeutic practitioner fulfill with any real degree of sophistication and effectiveness his *dual* responsibility of (1) treating individual cases of psychological and psychosomatic illness, and (2) urging the institution of preventive measures, *even measures which may necessitate changes in specific social or economic or other cultural practices.* This second, preventive, responsibility necessarily leads to overlap with the professional concerns of those in educational and legal and religious and social welfare occupations, and the consequent need to develop effective cooperative working relationships with them.

Chapter XIV

SOME APPLICATIONS

IT MIGHT HAVE BEEN anticipated that a discussion centered on the role of the nervous system in the development of behavior would conclude with a declaration of the obviously overriding importance of implanted-physical factors in human behavior and development. The findings of this inquiry do not permit such a conclusion. Rather, the time-graded interaction of environmental, especially social, influences with biological potentialities is the fundamentally significant dimension for human development. The implications of such an interactive postulate are being carried one step further in this final chapter; its material is even more influenced than the foregoing sections' by knowledge other than that yielded by the data presented — as well as by the author's own individual value-system.

THE POSSIBILITY OF A "CULTURAL RATING-SCALE"

It is the contention of modern cultural anthropology that the diverse cultures of the world cannot validly be compared on a single scale of value because each culture or a related grouping of cultures represents a particular society's uniquely elaborated, coherent manner of dealing with the basic and recurrent demands of the biologically human condition in a particular physical setting, gradually developed over long periods of time. This dictum, which has been a fruitful one for the orderly growth of this field of study, is a product of social anthropology's reaction against its sterile initial period as a discipline, a period when Darwinian theory was considered to apply to the world's cultures as well as its species, and when western European upper middle-class ways of believing and behaving were taken to represent the apex of cultural evolution by the first, upper middle-class western European, anthropologists.

Yet the more recent studies of "cultural personality" that anthropologists have undertaken show not merely that the adult end-result of growing up in various cultures are widely diverse. They also show that a wide range and degree of expression of our species' potentialities for uniquely human behavior and for personality integration are the outcomes of these diverse orders of growing up experiences. A particular culture's or subculture's *practiced* values, secondary institutions, child-rearing practices and mothering styles may be classified, that is, as serving to promote the greater use and development of one or the other of the Transactional and Intraorganismic subsystems; more rarely, they may serve to promote the balanced development and integration of both subsystems, a balance which is conducive to the maximum development of the human-principle genetic potential.

The implication here is that there may well be a *biological basis* for evaluating the adequacy of a child's growing-up environment, as implied by the first "principle of development" enunciated in Chapter XII. The neural postulations of this inquiry suggest that a human adult who expresses a large repertoire of uniquely human behaviors *and* a high degree of personality integration is utilizing to a major extent the "higher" behavioral potentialities implanted in our species. On this basis, such an adult pattern can be considered not merely one culture's ideal goal of individual human development but a *universally* ideal goal because it is *species* based. It then becomes possible to examine specific cultures and subcultures with a view to determining the degree to which each is, first, *en*abling of this ideal adult pattern at the various stages in the individual life-career as well as over the entire sequence of growth to maturity. They may also be examined in light of the degree to which each is, second, *un*abling of this ideal species pattern — that is, the degree to which its customs and its institutions promote personality disorder.

On the basis of the foregoing value-orientation, which at the same time embodies a preventive philosophy, it is suggested that the following questions, answerable in terms of degree rather than of discontinuous absolutes, be included in a universally applicable "cultural rating-scale":

(1) To what extent do the (sub-) culture's primary and secondary institutions prepare those to whom it delegates the child-rearing functions — the direct physical care of infants and young

children and their basic socialization — for the competent exercise
of those functions?

Competence is here being defined in terms both of individual psychological adequacy for the parental or child-caring
role *and* of relevant knowledges and skills. Suitability on the
basis of these characteristics is in turn to be judged in light of
the degree to which the children reared manifest at maturity
the ideal species characteristics enunciated. See also questions
4 and 5 below.

(2) And to what extent do they accord both emotional and
practical support for these persons' exercise of these functions?

Translation of the foregoing generalized questions into
terms more specific to our own society yields these supplementary questions:

(a) To what extent do the (sub-) culture's primary and
secondary institutions prepare girls, psychologically and in
knowledges and skills, for the mothering function; and to what
extent does it give girls and women practical and emotional
support in the exercise of these functions?

(b) To what extent do the (sub-) culture's primary and
secondary institutions prepare boys, psychologically and in
knowledges and skills, for the exercise of the fathering function;
and to what extent does it give boys and men practical and
emotional support in the exercise of the fathering functions?

(3) To what extent does the (sub-) culture provide parentless
babies and children (or children with manifestly incompetent
parents) with adequate mothering and fathering?

(4) To what extent, and for what proportions of its socially
various childhood populations, does the culture's physical living-
patterns and primary and secondary institutions take into balanced account the "mammalian" and the "human" legacies in
man's neural inheritance and as a result provide experiences
which are suitably enabling of each successive developmental
stage?

(5) To what extent does the (sub-) culture's values and practices promote personality integration? That is, does it employ
infant-care practices which permit the individual's development

of a "future" orientation and is there some correspondence between the expectations and personal aspirations developed during childhood and the adult activities and roles (a) rewarded by the culture and (b) achievable by the majority of adult men and women in that society? Are the individual's various social roles and related behaviors as he/she grows up in successive harmony, or discontinuous, even in conflict, with each other: is there a gradual and consistent transition from the status and responsibilities of the child to the status and responsibilities of the adult, with appropriate learning experiences provided by the primary and secondary institutions at each transitional stage?

(6) Having contributed to establishment of stable dominance of the human genetic principle during the growth-to-maturity phases of individual development, do (sub-) cultural values *and practices* promote its continuing dominance throughout the periods of physiological maturity, later maturity and old age?

For purposes of both clarification and illustration, a tentative formulation of enabling environments suited to each of the first five of the developmental stages postulated in Chapter XII is herewith presented. It is intended to be illustrative rather than prescriptive; nor is it meant to be all-inclusive. It departs from the value-orientation earlier enunciated: that the universally ideal goal of human development is an adult who expresses at the same time a high degree of the species-implanted potentialities for human behavior *and* a high degree of personality integration. It is influenced by the implication of the first principle of human development, given in Chapter XII, that it is crucial to such an end-result for child-rearing practices to take both the mammalian and the human neural legacies explicitly into account during especially the early stages of human development.

The circumstance that appropriate ways of so doing are ostensibly at cross-purposes can be taken either as evidence of a biologically built-in, essentially unresolvable, fundamental conflict inherent in the human condition — or more positively, as a challenge to our species' capacity for complex problem-solving and long-term planning. The resolution of this contradiction would seem to necessitate a philosophy and practice of child-rearing which, having a thorough awareness of the biological basis for the problem, is able to conceive, and flexibly to practice, an approach of balanced opposites: on the one hand, to be responsively and practically alert to the varied physiological, sensory and basic motility needs of the very young "human mammal," and to impose initially only those behavioral controls which are necessary for the safety of the child and of others; and on the other hand, to provide — *not* to force or to coerce — the emerging member of the human species with a human environment which is responsive to his unique patterns of response, with a steadily widening variety of opportunities to experience and to learn, and also, as the child's capacity for self-control develops, with the clear indication that he is but one among others and that others (including his mother!) have rights he must respect just as they (hopefully) respect his.

There is no claim to universality beyond the fifth developmental stage. Even for these early stages, use of the term "mother" and "parents" assumes the biological family-structure, which is by no means a universal type of family organization. If it is understood that for "mother" may be substituted the person (or persons) who has the direct responsibility for the physical care of the dependent infant and young child, and that for "parents" may be substituted the nuclear family-group, then the claim to universality for these early stages is strengthened. (Other applications specific to our own culture are occasionally interjected in parentheses.)

Developmental Stage   *Postulated Enabling Environment*

1st: Getting a firm hold on life (first several weeks after birth).

Establishment of a firm symbiotic tie to the "giver of life," usually the mother, as a substitute for the physiological symbiosis of uterine life is conducive to, if not essential for, the establishment of stable vegetative processes. Accordingly, the mother's handling of her infant should be perceptively and quickly responsive to the babe's expressions of need, and her basic emotional state should be relaxed as well as acceptant of her child and her mothering function, since she communicates her affective reactions to her child through direct skin-to-skin contact. The promptness with which the external world responds to the infant's expressions of inner need is an indication to him, literally at the gut level, whether his first attempts to establish communication with the external world are effective — or not.

2nd: Development of firm ties to one's immediate social and physical environment (one to nine months).

(1) A conducive environment consists pirmarily of a caretaker who understands *and accepts* the fundamentally important role in the child's development of his/her safe and unhampered opportunities for direct physical contact with the immediate physical world and his own body, *and* for establishing psychological contact with his human environment. Who, so understanding and accepting the role of these experiences, sees to it that they are provided.

(2) Child-caring routines should be stable, the surrounding family-living routines should have some sort of regularity of time-pattern, and the mother's emotional reactions should not be highly labile and should have some degree of consistency. All these external factors contribute to the child's development of patterns of expectancy and predictability at the gut (i.e., ANS) level — the substrate for the eventual full development of the "human" genetic potential. As Erikson has so sensitively described one aspect of this fundamental "learning set,"

"At the beginning, some kind of organized faith must provide the mother with a periodic restoration of that basic trust through which she can become trustworthy — so that trust may be created in the baby" (50, p. 147).

(3) Ready, responsive verbalization should accompany caretakers' interactions with the waking infant.

(My present hunch is that the later intellectual handicaps of the Negro lower lower-class child who is the inheritor of slavery's fragmented-family tradition, have already been implanted by the end of the second developmental period: typically for this population group, the foregoing conducive environments are either minimally provided or nonexistent.)

3rd: Emergence of awareness of self as a separate entity, together with a keen reactivity to the immediate external world (eight to twenty-four months).

(1) Parents who are ready, willing and psychologically able to — and do — practice their parental (i.e., responsive child-caring) responsibilities. Their seeing their child as a unique, important person should be a fundamental aspect of their "ableness" because of this attitude's contribution to an ultimately strong and stable ego in him or her.

(2) There should be continuing exposure to rich opportunities for experience — including verbalization — which the child can take advantage of as he becomes maturationally responsive to them; imposed expectations and over-stimulation should be avoided.

(3) Extensive opportunities for responsive, nonpunitive social relationships are especially desirable during this period; here the extended family can play an important role. (The urban ethnic-tradition child is especially advantaged here.)

4th: Emergence of the awareness of an inner world of reactivity and feeling (one and one-half to four years).

(1) Since the emergence of this developmental stage is dependent upon the prior emergence of the second and third stages, then the con-

ducive environment is cumulatively the same as for stages 1, 2 and 3.

(2) Adult respect for the child's spontaneous expressions of his/her fantasy-life, including those with overt sexual connotations.

(3) Contact with children older, younger and the same age under conditions of minimal adult intrusion or manipulation, plus

(4) availability of play materials some of which are low in structure and some of which are related to adult roles and activities.

5th: Beginning phases of integration of the outer and the inner aspects of self (three to six years).

(1) The conducive environment for this nodal period places a premium on parents' own degree of self-acceptance and self-integration (which probably dates back to this period in their own lives). The parent(s)' unresolved and denied-to-consciousness conflicts, or deep but unacknowledged marital conflicts and tensions, can be disastrous for perceptive children, who are often those with the greatest creative and intellectual potential: the unconscious parental conflict(s) between feeling and doing and feeling and saying may be passed on to such a child at the unconscious level; he serves, that is, as his parents' "emotional garbage-pail."

(2) Since especially the connotative meanings of basic words are being acquired by the child during this time, parental (and other adults') attitudes and child-rearing practices should not inadvertently promote a spilt between saying and feeling, saying and doing.

(3) So far as a "philosophy of discipline" is concerned, parental formulation of realistic behavioral expectations — realistic, that is, in terms of *this* child's capacities and individuality, *and* parental firmness and consistency of enforcement of these expectations, are equally relevant.

(4) The natural curiosity of this period should be reinforced not only by taking the child's questions seriously, but by raising others the child has not yet thought of, at appropriate times. It is parents' inner attitudes towards the value of people, of books, of creative self-expression, rather than their verbalized strictures, which influence the child.

(5) Parental and institutional encouragement of whole-body activities which promote integration of the somatic and the feeling aspects of self — self-expressive dance and song, the plastic arts, handcrafts — can play a constructive role not only at this time, but provide outlets for later tensions which living in a complex and enlarging world will inevitably arouse.

(The advantage of the suburb over the slum so far as provision of conducive experiences is concerned narrows during this period, primarily because many middle-class families are also lacking in such experiences at this time. But the relative disadvantage of the slum-culture child continues to be considerable.)

"UNABLING" VARIATIONS IN OUR OWN SOCIETY

To examine systematically a number of different cultures in light of such a species-derived yardstick as the foregoing rating-scale would undoubtedly be a worthwhile enterprise, but one too far beyond the scope of the present inquiry to be undertaken here. However, exploration of "unabling" variations in our own complex society in at least thumbnail sketch form may provide a concrete illustration of the nature of the postulated relationship between (sub-) cultural patterns and personality disorder.

Some aspects of *the slum-culture as a growing-up environment* are common to nearly all of its members; others are more particularly related to specific population subgroupings. Contrary to popular conception, lack of adequate mothering during infancy is not necessarily a slum-associated characteristic: many poor children experience warm mother-child relationships during their babyhoods. Rather, such physical and psychological accompaniments of poverty and its urban correlate, population congestion, as these are common to most children of the slums:

The constant close physical proximity of different generations, which makes the normal, necessarily overt motor and vocal expressions of the growing "human mammal" a distracting nuisance to his elders, and therefore something to be curtailed, even prohibited, through punishment — with the minimal result that many children are unable to make the developmental transition from the early motor tendency of whole-body involvement in manipulative and mental activity to the later more differentiated and focused motor and mental approach, ordinarily evident by five to six years;

The young child's lack of safe privacy both at home and in the street, which handicaps the make-believe play so central to the fourth developmental stage — with consequent negative effects on mental and personal development;

The great emotional and temporal drain on parents associated with the family's precarious economic situation: the father's, and often also the mother's, long hours of work outside the home, the mother's usually sole responsibility for the care of a large family, unremitting anxiety over the basic exigencies of daily living, parental inability to make and to keep rewarding promises to their children — all combine to hinder parents' giving each one of their youngsters the responsive, individualized attention so fundamental to the growing child's optimum development of language, of a positive self-picture, of eventual emotional self-control, of a "future" orientation, of cognitive grasp of the immediate environment, and of the desire to identify with adult behavior-models.

By the beginning of the fifth developmental stage, these poverty-related experiences serve to imprison the child in a narrowly immediate "here and now" life-space — at just the developmental period when more physically and psychically privileged children's perceived world begins to expand markedly. So long as the slum child remains within his limited world, he ordinarily functions adaptively, even happily, within it. But as soon as his social contacts extend beyond his family and neighborhood play-group to institutions such as school and TV, which represent the values and expectations of the broader — and culturally dominant — society, the discontinuities between the school culture and his home culture, as well as between the behavioral requirements of these middle-class institutions and his own past life experiences and learnings, are alike so great as to be unbridgeable, except, possibly, for the bright and personable few who attract the positive interest of their middle-class teachers and recreation workers.

From school-entrance on, many slum children feel themselves to be "strangers in their own land" and, understandably, cling tenaciously to the familiar, in both locale and associates. They also develop fears of and strong resentments towards the culturally dominant middle-class world which so overtly — as well as covertly — rejects them. These feelings of psychological isolation when in contact with middle-class persons and institutions, on top of their actual physical isolation in the slum, militate effectively against their development of a desire to learn the different values and ways of behaving which the dominant, rewards-monopolizing middle-class society sets up as a prerequisite to its acceptance of them. Indeed, a vicious circle!

Typically for these children, existence anxiety remains high and cosmic anxiety is only minimally developed. Poor personality integration at neurological maturity is usual for individuals who have grown up in the slum-culture setting, for primarily two reasons. Whatever future orientation a basically good babyhood may have given such a person is seldom retained beyond adolescence, when his exclusion from the material and psychological rewards of the dominant culture has its full impact. Also, associational deprivations and the discontinuities in his life experience prevent him from developing a personally meaningful and/or realistic picture of the "ideal self."

The unique social history of the lower lower-class American Negro adds influencing variables which go beyond the generalized "culture of poverty" situation described above. The social and individual-psychological legacy of slavery which they have inherited provides a vivid illustration of the exorbitant price succeeding generations of an entire society are obliged to pay for earlier generations' privileged groups' unhampered exercise of immediate economic self-interest: an object-lesson from which we continue not to profit!

The institution of slavery stripped the captive African tribesman and woman of whatever social controls and obligations the tribal culture had provided, prevented the development in their place of the biological family-structure of the enslaving culture with its distinct male and female social sex-roles, and imposed other unilateral restrictions which infantilized the slave, especially the male. Aside from the biologically imperative maternal responsibilities, parental roles were minimally elaborated by adults and minimally acquired by the child-apprentice through the indispensable means of identification, imitation and deliberate tutoring; nothing approaching responsible male-adult and related paternal roles was available for the boy-child's emulation. The weak and irresponsible male who is the inevitable outcome of such a social legacy is not merely of no assistance to the harassed mother of several children; frequently he adds to her burdens and resentments by "donating" one or more children to her brood before he moves on to a less argumentative liaison.

With the migration of members of this population-group from the relatively undemanding — and hence, from the child's viewpoint, relatively stable — environment of the rural south to competitive and impersonal and congested large-urban centers, the instability of the urban Negro lower lower-class "family" has become endemic.

Such a demoralized lower lower-class (*not* working class) family situation is able, typically, to provide very few of the enabling physical and psychological experiences conducive to the first three developmental stages. The physical and interactive neglect of the young infant results, predictably, in minimal development of a "future" orientation, unstable establishment of the basic homeostatic controls — physiological functioning disorders and psychosomatic illnesses are especially common among persons who have had such a babyhood — and disproportionate incidence of childhood schizophrenia. When the tendency of male adults to inflict brutal punishment on the "interfering" child converges with poor to nonformation of affective ties with the immature and/or irresponsible mother, superego development among such children is rendered difficult if not impossible, as is stable ability to inhibit strong emotional reactions such as those of aggression and later also of sexual need. It should come as no surprise that crimes of violence against women — rape and murder — are disproportionately committed by adolescent and adult males with such a background of growing up experiences, nor that overt homosexuality is another relatively frequent development among persons with such a background.

But, contrary to the selective perception of most middle-class persons, the slum culture is not the only example of an "unabling" growing-up environment in these United States. Subcultural blinders have led many in the middle-class to overrate the psychological importance of the physically privileged infancy and childhood of the middle-class child and to underrate the psychological role of more subtle types of deprivation and pressure associated with *growing up in a middle-class world.*

As was elaborated in Chapter XII, the basic characteristic of developmental stage 7, the pubertal period, is change in both the outer or body-image aspects of self as well as in the inner or reactive-feeling components; while adolescence, stage 8, is characterized by reintegration of the self, with achievement of a self-acceptable, integrated personality the ultimate aim of this interrelated neural and psychological process. Accomplishment of this goal has become a very complicated and difficult matter indeed for the middle-class individual in complex technological and urbanized societies, for a number of subcultural and individual reasons.

Puberty is universally a harbinger of adult status, but the ways young persons react to these maturational changes are not. By early adolescence in these United States, the immature and inexperienced young person is brought smack up against — and expected to cope adaptively with — such fundamental subcultural contradictions as these:

(1) In the U.S. middle-class, there is a marked difference between the adult personality and responsibilities most highly rewarded by one's social group and the infancy and childhood behaviors and personality fostered by family relationships. Further, experiential opportunities for a graded transition from childhood status, responsibilities and behavior, to adult status, responsibilities and behavior are not consistently provided (17).

(2) Technological, and resulting social, changes have become so rapid, the adult world's picture of approved adult roles and behaviors is itself in a state of confusion. As a result, and thoroughly bewildering to the growing young person, there is frequently a marked gap between his social group's espoused adult-ideal and the actual adult behaviors rewarded by his society.

(3) The rapidity of social change also contributes to the circumstance that what the older generation learned while growing up has little carryover value for the younger generation, resulting in poor intergeneration communication: another kind of "cultural discontinuity." Rather, intergeneration communication is frequently subliminal and negative, expressing parents' own unresolved adolescent conflicts. For example, the current adolescent peer-group's high valuation of early sexual sophistication may well represent an unconscious acting out of their parents' own unfulfilled adolescent-period desires, the result of prohibitions imposed on them by *their* parents.

(4) Patterns of urban and suburban living and child-rearing almost ensure that the young child of both sexes will form a primary identification with the parent whose sex and sex-role

is accorded secondary cultural status — that is, with the mother. Because of TV, children are being made aware of our culture's ambivalence in this area at increasingly younger ages. *For the boy, it is not the cross-sex identification as such that creates psychological difficulties, but rather, his eventual realization that such identification is considered "bad" by his society.* This contradiction is compounded by the mother's own personal stresses stemming from the circumstance that cultural values have led her to feel ambivalent about the social value of the child-rearing role and responsibility and consequently about her own worth as an individual.

Since the gap between childhood and adulthood in the American middle-class subculture is of a somewhat different nature for each sex, each sex is affected by, and reacts differently to, the confrontations of adolescence. The conflict between the actual preadolescent self and the emerging aspirational adult self is typically more intense among boys than among girls because the psychological gap between the little-boy self and the subculturally prescribed adult-male roles and responsibilities is as yet greater than the psychological gap between the little-girl self and the subculturally approved female adult roles and responsibilities — although the gap has begun to widen for girls as well, especially among college-educated, upper middle-class girls, as Bettelheim has recently pointed out (20).

Consider the extent of the break between the boy-child's early, family-centered experiences and the public roles and behaviors of the "successful" American man. The middle-class adolescent is expected not only to transform himself from a dependent and loving and obedient son into a self-reliant, unremittingly and resourcefully competitive, authoritative top-dog in an occupational status-hierarchy. Even more incompatible is the fact that he is expected to assume an adult style of life which is among the most stressful in recorded history *on top of an early psychological foundation which is excellently designed to make him especially vulnerable, both physically and psychologically, to later stress:* prior to about 1945, subcultural patterns of child-rearing hurried him through each phase of his early development, affording him minimal opportunities for the basic, body-centered gratifications, and often also in urban settings, for mastery of his physical environment.[1]

American men born before 1935 to 1940 have tended to solve this inner-psychological contradiction in a rather uniform manner; young men born after this period have been showing more variable reactions. The reaction-patterns of the older group have already been described in a previous publication (127); the following paragraph is a summarized adaptation of this earlier discussion.

Members of the older group have usually resolved the conflict, if they resolved it at all, by elaborating their preadolescent reactions against the dependent and "feminine" components of their personality into the structured, prototypically masculine reaction-formations referred to in the previous chapter. They maintain this culturally adaptive adjustment by splitting their lives into two clear-cut categories of relationship: the personal, family and friends centered category, where the dependent and tender aspects of self can be freely and "safely" expressed; and the public, occupationally centered category, where the culturally approved "masculine front" is assumed. Those who have not been able to achieve this stably split style of personality functioning are at best left with neurotic defense mechanisms (i.e., incompletely structured reaction-formations), accompanied by the periodic generation of disorganizing amounts of anxiety, and at worst with deep feelings of alienation and/or overt homosexuality. Many ostensibly successful men have resolved the conflict only partially: they have achieved the approved occupational, public, aspect, but have failed miserably in their personal relationships; in such instances, the latter failure is a direct function of the former accomplishment.

As for the younger group, the same personality conflict is continuing in intensified form; but many, perhaps most, do not

---

[1]Since about 1945, a shift on the part of the middle class to greater permissiveness concerning body-centered gratifications during infancy (27A) has been more than counterbalanced, so far as the generation of stress is concerned, by the collision of this pattern of early relaxation with even stronger pressures than formerly for acceleration of growth and for competitive achievement *beyond* infancy.

appear to be resolving it as their fathers and older brothers have done or have tried to do. This change has occurred partly because the conflict *has* intensified and partly because of the greatly increased external, social, pressures on them. Those who find themselves failures at sixteen because they cannot meet or adapt to the intense competitive demands of the high-school college-preparatory single standard, are reacting in ways heretofore considered typical only of their lower lower-class counterparts, as earlier described — and with similar underlying psychological dynamics. Some are simply remaining psychologically at the preadolescent, same-sex gang stage, unable to go on to adult heterosexual relationships and to assume the responsible-parent role. Others, psychologically immobilized by the convergence of competitive subcultural demands they cannot meet with leftover tensions stemming from unmet infantile dependency needs, have surrendered their "future" orientation: either they retreat to drug addiction or other momentarily conflict-obliterating sensory "kicks," and/or to an obsessive preoccupation, engendered by their body-centered infantile deprivations, with the basic bodily functions. This fixation, when combined with another previously chiefly lower lower-class behavior-pattern, of overt hostility and aggression against constituted authority, is expressed through the verbally hostile avenue of obscenity — an expression formerly confined, at least among middle-class boys, to only the middle-childhood and early-adolescent periods. And what was a relatively rare phenomenon in these United States heretofore, overt, active male rejection of women as objects of affection and of sexual need, is becoming, if not more common, then far more openly expressed (*viz.,* 164).

Although unadaptive reactions have been deliberately singled out for attention in this section, such consistently negative younger-group instances need to be balanced by at least one positive one, lest the impression be mistakenly created that only negative instances are believed to exist. Many upper middle-class urban adolescents are showing much more open acceptance of their basic — and unavoidable — feminine identification than has been typical heretofore, and are not doing so in the old either/or form of overt, passive-role homosexuality. Rather, they are *adding* an

inner acceptance and open expression of those personality tendencies and related interests and activities traditionally considered
feminine, to proclivities traditionally labeled as masculine, and
are building the richer, individualized and integrated personality
cum life-style that has hitherto been rare among American men:
only a few men, chiefly of European upper middle-class and upper
class backgrounds, have heretofore manifested it. It would seem
that the young avant-garde of each sex is converging towards the
other in interests and in personality traits: men are openly accepting their "feminine" characteristics and are assuming more and
more of the traditionally feminine vocations and avocations, while
women are more openly accepting their "masculine" traits and
pursuing traditionally masculine vocations and avocations. This
development is particularly noteworthy because of its possible
bellwether character: it may well be signaling a new middle-class
male — and also female — personality norm, in which *individual*
differences, rather than culturally stereotyped and unadaptive sex-
role differences, are the core motif.

Will the eventual outcome be that the growing child will
have a much wider range of personality characteristics and
activities to "try on" for compatibility, none of them marked
"verboten" or "out of bounds" because of rigid sex-typing —
and that, as a result, not merely individual differences will become the ruling personality principle, but also, for *both* sexes,
much richer personalities and better personality integration?

Another positive instance is those boys and men who, because
of culturally *now-atypical* family experiences, are still developing
the traditional, comfortably masculine personality from the inside out; reaction-formations have not been resorted to. The
middle-class subculture is currently faced with a difficult question
in this connection, whether or not we are aware of it: Should the
relative handful of male personalities who easily and integratedly
express *the ideal of a past era* continue to serve as the aspirational
model for the great majority of boys who as adults must expend
most of their energy maintaining merely the external semblance of
the old ideal?

As for the negative effects on the middle-class girl of the various cultural contradictions enumerated, one of the most important

of these has already been described in the previous chapter in the section on sex differences: their growing ambivalence towards the role of the mothering function in their lives. Bettelheim, in the perspicacious paper already referred to (20), points to an additional discontinuity in the middle-class culture which particularly affects the adolescent girl: the inconsistency in our attitudes concerning the role of marriage in the female life-career versus its role in the male life-career. In Bettelheim's words,

> Many young men show little interest in marriage, even through their early thirties and are allowed to go their way. . . . In brief, a man is considered a failure if he does not support himself, does not achieve in work, but his marital status little affects people's estimate of him. All this is very different for the girl. A woman, no matter how gifted or successful in her work life, is judged a failure if she does not marry fairly soon. From adolescence on, therefore, the pressure to marry interferes with her ability to find self-realization in her own personal way. Discrimination usually begins in youth, when there is some indulgence for the boy's nonconformity or revolt . . .; much less tolerance is accorded the girl who seeks to find herself through such a period of nonconformity (20, p. 96) .

But beyond this particular inconsistency,

> . . . the problems of youth have become nearly the same for both sexes; the sexual difference counts for less, because *the conflicts of growing up are so much more psychosocial than sexual* (p. 86) . (Italics EM's.)

If mankind survives its present period of intense, hydrogen-bomb-backed nationalisms and its emerging period of suffocating overpopulation, it will be because we have at last begun to identify ourselves first and foremost as members of the human species whose habitat is a very small planet — albeit holiday jaunts to outer space may not be too far off! In such a small world, the interrelated concepts of a *species* basis for uniquely human behavior and personality integration *and* of growing-up environments that can hinder *or* promote men's potentialities for humanity and for integration can be very useful indeed. We can go beyond cultural anthropology's non-normative, sheerly relativistic frame of reference, and as a planet Earth society take steps towards the deliberate creation of environments that are more "species suitable" to growing-up than those that obtain in most areas of the world (including our own).

If this suggestion sounds as though I am following in B. F. Skinner's footsteps (168, 169), then I have been thoroughly misunderstood. The "human principle model" that has been proposed in this monograph is at the opposite end of the conceptual and values spectrum from Skinner's "mammalian principle model." Unlike Skinner's goal of a compulsively and unreasoningly "adaptive" adult, the behavioral goal here advocated is an open, changing, constantly emergent one, as this passage from a previous publication makes clear:

> The overall developmental trend from dominance of maturational forces to dominance of learning in individual behavior has an innate basis directly related to the pattern of development and functioning of the human nervous system. As such, *this trend is biologically characteristic of the human species.*
>
> Our humanity is a constantly emerging phenomenon, in both a social and an individual sense, in the light of this circumstance. History and anthropology document that specific societies throughout the course of their existence gather up and pass on to each succeeding generation — and to succeeding societies — the cumulative experience of that society and of the societies before it. In so doing, they increase constantly the available "cultural reservoir" of uniquely human expression and the products of that expression. Man, as Korzybski has put it, is the only "time-binding" form of life (100).
>
> Our humanity is constantly emergent in the individual in three senses. It tends to accumulate throughout our life span. We may approach, but we seem never quite to reach our individual upper limits for learning and expressing the higher human behaviors. These limits themselves seem to be receding for mankind in general as an increasing depth and range of human expression is gathered up and passed on through the cultures of human societies. *Particularly creative people, who*

are able to make the jump from the already known and experienced to the previously unknown and unexperienced, contribute to the enlargement of the common reservoir of human expression (127, p. 149).

Further, Skinner's *means* of achieving his goal is to apply to human beings methods of conditioning successful in training animals: immediately to reinforce, from birth onward, those (originally spontaneously emitted) behaviors which are considered by some superordinate authority to be desirably adaptive, and *only* those behaviors. The result of such capitalization upon the mammalian principle in man's species inheritance is compulsively stereotyped, conforming behavior as unamenable to the control of the higher thought processes as the early stress experiences of the emotionally disturbed person. The constant guiding principle behind the concept of an "enabling environment," on the other hand, is diametrically opposed. It is: will it contribute to the eventual stable dominance of the "human principle" in adult behavior?

PREVENTIVE MEASURES

If it is accepted, at least provisionally, that

(1) the goal of individual human development is an adult in whom the human biological principle is stably dominant, and who, as a result, expresses a wide variety of uniquely human behavior and a high degree of personality integration;

(2) individual experience subsequent to birth plays a fundamental role in the secure establishment of the dominance of the human genetic principle (i.e., of cortical, especially PF area, dominance);

(3) among the most important of the experiences subsequent to birth for individual human development are those provided during the first few-to-several years of life within a responsively interactive mother-child relationship — i.e., experiences provided by the mothering process;

(4) there are sex differences in the timing of neural maturation and that these differences have psychological and social ramifications,

then it becomes pertinent to make suggestions concerning measures which are conducive to the prevention of psychological disorder.

Most of the suggestions following have been influenced by what is probably the most serious of our society's many cultural contradictions or discontinuities: our country's current tendency to devaluate the child -rearing and -caring roles and responsibilities collides head on with the wealth of evidence documenting the fundamental importance for individual human development of the mothering and fathering processes.

This tendency expresses itself overtly as well as covertly at both the individual attitude and mass communications levels; two of its more concrete manifestations are the lower social status accorded those occupations which are child-care centered, *and* educated women's own reactions concerning the relative worthwhileness of traditionally feminine versus traditionally masculine roles and responsibilities. The former manifestation was succinctly expressed in a letter from a professional nursemaid of British background in the May 1965 *Harper's,* from which the following passage has been drawn:

> . . This is a thing-oriented culture. Growing is not tangible. One cannot chart the child on a sales-graph. People who care for children are not social equals and are not to be paid salaries comparable with those of other professions (p. 14) .

There is a great irony in the latter manifestation. Educated American women are "caught in a bind" between their own attitudes concerning the lesser merit of the traditionally feminine functions and the circumstance that if and when they do act out their culture's values and assume occupational roles traditionally the province of men they rather quickly find that a double standard of evaluation and of rewards of their work obtains — a circumstance that a number of recent discussions have begun to air openly; Doctor Ruth Kundsin's article (101), is an especially articulate example.

My placing of emphasis on the fundamental importance of women's mothering function may give the impression that I am in favor of women's "return" to their traditionally restrictive venu of "kinder, kirche und kuchen." Not at all. When girls and women have full access to all the social and occupational and intellectual opportunities of their society and, as a direct consequence, freedom of individual choice, they will be much more likely to develop the mature, integrated personality-mode that is prerequisite to adequate exercise of the mothering function. They will then be able to evaluate realistically the relative merits of the various occupational and personal roles available to them — and a great many will, as a result, rediscover *for themselves* the tremendous personal satisfactions accruing from "growing" a human being. Increasingly more women will so arrange their individual lives and, through appropriate political activity at local and national levels, help so to arrange the economic and occupational and educational practices of their society that they will be able to do full justice to both their *time-limited* biological and related-social responsibilities *and* the continuing cultivation of other facets of self.

Voluntary programs of population control are, and will increasingly, aid and abet the implementation of this cultural change. It will shift the emphasis in child-rearing even more towards quality rather than quantity, and will so not only place a premium on the greater participation of women of all social levels in the decision-making processes of their society, but will allow them more time for such activities.

In the meantime and *in addition,* there is a genuine need for practical programs which will serve to assure all children a physical and emotional environment of a minimal level of stability for the first six years of their lives. In this country, the extension of already existing agencies which are intended to strengthen and to supplement the role of the family is undoubtedly a more acceptable approach to our citizenry than the creation of entirely new child-nurturing institutions. On the dual proposition that our present niggardly practices in this area largely provide for picking up the pieces *after* young lives have been wrecked (if even that much!) and that much more emphasis on a preventive philosophy is needed than has heretofore obtained, several quite-specific suggestions of a relatively limited and practical nature are herewith offered:

(1) Free "well baby" clinic services should be upgraded and expanded both in quality and quantity of personnel and in scope of services offered. Individual and group psychotherapy should be routinely available, as the need is indicated, of pregnant girls and women regardless of marital status, such therapy to be continued as long as it is needed and/or sought; as well as of cohabiting parents, whether they are legally joined or not. All professional personnel working in such centers in non-middle-class areas should have a basically positive attitude towards women, extensive sociological, anthropological, and developmental psychology background, and skill in communicating effectively with their constituents. Similar services should be available in middle-class areas through the group practice of obstetrician, pediatrician and "family" psychiatrist and/or consulting psychologist; these self-employed professional persons should be no less equipped in attitudes, sociological and psychological knowledge and in communication skills than their public-service counterparts.

(2) At all social levels, the value system that *no child who is unwanted need be born* must come to prevail over the present community power-structure's rejecting and punitive attitudes towards sexual promiscuity and/or immoral and irresponsible parenthood. Informed concern for the kind of life the child who might be conceived or has already been conceived will have, should be practically implemented by readily available conception-preventing measures and by legal abortion for psychological as well as physical reasons. The latter is at present accepted practice in private mental hospitals: is it consistent with this country's espoused ideals that only the children of the economically privileged have ready access to such consideration?

Even as this question was written, a truly remarkable cultural breakthrough came to my attention. The June 26/65 issue of the *New York Times* reports that the New York Court of Claims has granted the father of a state-mental-hospitalized girl who was raped by a fellow inmate, the right to sue the state on behalf of the infant who has been born as a result of that rape, the state having earlier refused the girl's father's request for an abortion. The Court's grounds for granting the father this right was that the baby was "stigmatized with illegitimacy!" The Court even went so far as to comment that *if* the state can be proved to have been negligent, "then the child could recover damages, for such things as deprivation of a normal childhood and home life and proper parental care and supervision"!!

(3) But what of those unwanted children who have already been born and remain unwanted after birth? Much more adequate provision than we now have for parentless and neglected children *of all economic levels* is urgent. Voluntary surrender of unwanted children by their parents should be made a socially accepted practice involving a relatively simple procedure; perhaps then the "battered child syndrome" will become a historical curiosity in the medical literature. Suitable foster-homes continue to be the optimum solution, but the waiting period for a great many children's placement in such ideal situations has become so long, large, centralized, chronically understaffed facilities have developed, with all the proven shortcomings for the proper nurture of the infants and children who are packed into them. Instead of this "swept under the rug" approach, there should be decentralized, *neighborhood* facilities which recruit their nonprofessional staff from such residents of that neighborhood as "born mothers," high school and college students who either need a part-time source of income or practical experience in social responsibility or both, and parents with grown children who miss having children around. Such neighborhood facilities should be governed by boards made up jointly of residents of the area and of their professional staffs.

(4) Neighborhood recreational, health, guidance, and social welfare services should be expanded markedly and should function on an explicitly cooperative basis with each other; and such cooperative organization, planning and programming should be symbolized by these agencies' actual physical proximity in imaginatively planned, professionally staffed community-service centers. The policy board of each component agency should be composed jointly of representatives of residents of the area they serve and of the professional persons who staff them. The greatly expanded numbers of community service personnel this approach implies provides a major area of new job opportunities to replace occupations displaced by automation and cybernation.

(5) Special programs in addition to the foregoing, generally applicable suggestions are required in areas populated by large numbers of demoralized families with a lengthy history of disorganized family life. The assimilative record of European ethnic groups indicates that something in addition to such oft-cited economic and social factors as poverty and social isolation and distinctive physical features are contributing to the high incidence of academic and social and psychological problems among a great many slum-culture Negro children. As was pointed out earlier in this chapter, the psychological inadequacy of their first social (i.e., family) environment; more concretely, of the low quality of the mothering and fathering, if any, they have received and are receiving, is a more fundamental contributing factor. It is also a far less easily remedied factor than poverty *per se,* since such parental behavior constitutes a culture-pattern handed down from generation to generation since the days of slavery; a pattern since continually reinforced (*not* "caused") by social isolation and poverty.

Negro leaders and other concerned persons who wish to upgrade the lives of their fellow human beings at the very bottom of the heap need to face the real possibility that pressures and programs suited to the aspirations of those in the working and middle classes — better job opportunities and school and housing integration — simply will not provide enough of the remedial muscle required to release the catch of the trap in which each successive slum generation is caught. Two programs aimed at building such muscle are herewith proposed:

(a) Some means are needed of involving the adolescents and adults of these areas in the planning and carrying out of programs of family-life education intended *for themselves,* programs designed to get across, without the distracting static of middle-class moralizing, these two essential orders of information and understanding:

(1) that only *wanted* children should — *and need* — be born;
(2) that from the moment a child is conceived, he must have certain kinds of physical, emotional and basic-socialization experiences if he or she is to develop into "somebody."

The tendency of present thinking to aim programs for the upgrading of the Negro lower lower-class family at the adoles-

cent boy, on the thesis that the strengthening of the traditionally weak male role among this population group is *the* key, is
not nearly fundamental enough: beginning at this level is
akin to closing the barn door after the horse has been stolen.
An additional — and much more basic — target must be the
little and big *girls* of this group, whose acquiescence in the
lower lower-class pattern of limited education and early child-
bearing — that is, in the early domination of their lives by
their biological role — contributes most directly and most
fundamentally to the generation-to-generation social immobili-
zation of members of the slum subculture. Creative attempts
on the part of very specially qualified persons to develop a
participative family-life education program might well be
included along with present community organization approaches of the domestic peace corps and other "anti-poverty"
efforts.

(b) The previous program is intended primarily for the
near-parent and parent groups, both Negro and white, in both
urban *and rural* slums. A coincident program aimed at the
young child should also be undertaken as an integral part of
the public-school curriculum. Preschool programs are at last
being instituted in slum areas as a means of filling in the gaps
which have been found to exist in lower lower-class children's
verbal and cognitive experiences by the time they begin their
formal schooling and which handicap them in their subsequent
school performance (125). These programs should be broad-
ened to include as well "enabling" emotional and basic-
socialization experiences. Married couples with special personal and educational qualifications should be utilized in such
extensions to the neighborhood public-school curriculum. In
this connection, nothing could be more irrelevant than the
present ban, imposed by some school systems, on the employ-
ment of male teachers in nursery school, kindergarten, and
the primary grades! It is much more likely that remedial measures instituted at this early period, reinforced by such additional community programs as those already suggested, will
"take hold" than those undertaken during the after-the-fact
drop-out period of mid-adolescence.

(6) Our schools — and a *socially responsible* air mass media — are the logical avenues for another, more broadly serving, preventive undertaking. When parents' present competitive drive for having their children read at four, speak a foreign language at seven, and achieve high-school grades that will ensure their Ivy League college acceptance at seventeen, has run its course, they may be receptive to the radical notion that the basic responsibility of the public school is to help children learn how to live, how to think, and what is worth valuing. The high school and junior college years (thirteen to nineteen for most) comprise the age period in the individual life-career when, ideally, transition from dependent child to responsible and autonomous young adult is accomplished. Yet, in the present high school curriculum which is essentially an adaptation of the European university curriculum of the eighteenth century with science grafted on, American and English literature seems to be the only school-sponsored means by which adolescents can learn anything about the human condition in an organized manner — and that only hopefully, from the teacher's point of view! There is little to no widespread provision for the data of the behavioral sciences of sociology, psychology, cultural anthropology, and human physiology, which have been rapidly accumulating during the past fifty years. "Social studies" in the secondary school typically comprises only history and economics and geography, with the merest smattering of sociology, if any. Even present-day biology is still, in René Dubos' words, "almost completely irrelevant to the study of the nature of man" (43). If and when psychology and sociology *are* taught in high school, they are typically perverted into courses in "life adjustment," which essentially constitute indoctrination in how to conform to middle-class parental expectations.

The interdisciplinary study of human development by now comprises a rich body of objective and impeccably researched data and should be introduced into the secondary school curriculum on a four-year basis as universally as American history, English, the natural sciences and mathematics. Those who teach it should either have solid background in all of the behavioral sciences, or the course should be organized by such a person and team-taught.

To play a maximum preventive function, such a formal, required course should serve as the subject-matter point of departure for supplementary *and voluntary* group-guidance activities. Personal implications for understanding of self and others, for child-rearing and the responsibilities of parenthood and citizenship (including family-planning information) should be freely explored in small-group discussions guided by a fully professional person having both skill in the techniques of group psychotherapy and informed-critical understanding of both the relevancies *and* irrelevancies of orthodox-Freudian theory. Either the school psychologist (a full PhD in clinical and developmental psychology), or qualified personnel from such community facilities as those described in suggestion 1 working in close cooperation with school personnel, only, should undertake such supplementary activities. Individual-student participation in them should, of course, be *neither graded nor recorded in official school records.*

(7) My next suggestion is more of a question than a recommendation, since it is as yet so tentative in its suggester's mind. Our culture and our social institutions have yet to face up squarely to the implications of the circumstance that the growing young person is sexually and procreatively mature many years before he is neurally — and therefore intellectually and personally — mature. Further, that the most sexually urgent decade in the entire male life-career is from fifteen or sixteen to twenty-five or twenty-six years of age, precisely the period when our complex, technologically advanced society requires that its boys and young men put forth a most intense and sustained intellectual effort in preparation for adult occupational and citizenship roles. Boys' personal management problems are further compounded by the circumstance that hard physical labor, an effective former means of siphoning off sexual and emotional energy, has become irrelevant in a technological, urban world, and that the population congestion coincident with urbanization — plus the commercialized messages of our mass media — have served to increase sexual stimulation well out of proportion to the increase in psychologically as well as physically satisfying opportunities for sexual release.

Many middle-class boys are solving at least part of the problem by marrying, or by establishing a fairly stable liaison with a fellow student, during their early college years. But this "male solution" is not necessarily the best answer from his partner's — nor our society's — point of view. For girls, the hazards of regular sexual expression during the early, middle and later teens are not just the social risk of pregnancy. They also entail the strong possibility of premature emotional involvement and/or of premature domesticity, both of which can have negative effects on her continuing development as a person. Subjectively, it very frequently means a permanent arrest in the girl's potentialities for intellectual and for personal growth: her typically more generalized emotional involvement in her sexual attachment diverts her emotional energies from her continuing self exploration and development, at a time when her neural and psychological readiness is greatest for it; and if domesticity is assumed, the duties of housekeeping and of motherhood divert her time from continuing her formal education. The early domination of the female life-career by her biological role has always made a major — if not *the* major — contribution to the limited intellectual development of the lower-class girl, and to her consequent passing on of her "lower classness" to her children. This pattern appears to be emerging also among many middle-class girls who marry in their teens. But in the latter case there is a strong possibility of a *later* arousal of interest in, and sustained effort towards, a continuation of formal education and other avenues of self-development.

The ready availability of conception-prevention measures *and* the development of the value-system among young people that one does not marry for sheerly sexual reasons but only when one is ready to assume the responsibilities of parenthood, may together prove to have a constructive impact. But they do not get at the essential contradiction of our time between biological readiness and socially imposed unreadiness: in today's complex societies, the adolescent is physiologically suited to procreation and has the greatest physical resilience to cope with the exhausting demands of infants and young children, well before he or she is ready for the psychological and economic aspects of parenthood.

Perhaps our society should condone middle teens' free sexual exploration, and then subsidize later-teens marriage, making sixteen to twenty-six an easygoing period when young people's *paid occupation* consists of attendance at high school, college, and postgraduate specialization, achievement of sexual stability, service to one's local community, and getting one's two or three child family started. Then, at the point when one's youngest child is five or six years old (having been in half-day nursery school since four) *and* when one is a "settled" and level-headed young adult of twenty-six or so, the active child-rearing functions are given over to the children's grandparents, freeing the parents to embark on their individual careers and personal interests — even their divorces! — in a thoroughly self-centered fashion. After fifteen years spent in career-centered and self-expressive pursuits, it should be a welcome responsibility, beginning at about forty, for them to undertake to pass on, in turn, what they have learned to *their* grandchildren. Child-rearing is in any case much too important a societal responsibility to be delegated, as we now frequently do, to immature and irresponsible adolescents. By fifty-five, when one's physical powers have begun to wane, one will be free to resume a less taxing self or community centered way of life.

Such a three-generation arrangement would not only take full social and individual advantage of man's increased longevity, it would also help to solve at least these four current social problems:

(1) it would provide children with stable and mature parent-figures at a point in their development when they can most profit from such association;

(2) it would make sixteen to twenty-six an individually and socially meaningful period and so eliminate many of the current negative reactions of this age-group to their present social and occupational displacement (which will continue to increase steadily because of technological trends) ;

(3) it would make the period of middle-maturity, one now filled with occupational and personal anxieties among many, a period of personal regeneration and great social utility;

(4) it would serve to minimize the impact on the developing child of overrapid social change and so contribute to greater family stability.

And finally:

(8) The present killingly competitive way of life of the American middle-class male begins very early and quite unknowingly in our culture's expectation that little boys surpass little girls in developmental and intellectual accomplishments from infancy onward — a thoroughly unreasonable expectation in most instances in light of boys' biologically determined lag in general development and in neural maturation. School practices have contributed to boys' stress experiences in several ways, some of them known and accepted as unavoidable, such as competition for high grades, especially at the secondary school level. But at least one practice of our coeducational schools is unknowingly imposed and relatively easily avoided: the requirement that boys and girls begin their formal schooling at the same age — in spite of the circumstance that the maturational gap between boys and girls is greatest during the early years. More attention should be paid to the datum that a great many of the boys who drop out of high school and college share in common an antipathy for the school situation that began with their kindergarten and primary-grades experiences.

Three preventive approaches seem feasible in this area; I favor the third one:

(1) Cater to the boys' developmental pattern by delaying the beginning of formal schooling until seven years of age (as is done in Sweden), and then permit the acceleration of girls who are both maturationally and intellectually advanced.

(2) Go back to the educational practice of segregating the sexes throughout the formal-schooling period, as is still done in many European church-connected schools.

(3) Adopt our culturally-approved marriage-age-differential pattern and have boys begin their formal schooling one to one-and-one-half years later than girls: boys start at, say, six-and-one-half to seven, and girls at five to five-and-one-half, years of age. Then at either or both of two later age-periods, later-childhood (ten to twelve years) and/or post-puberty adolescence (fifteen to seventeen years), boys who are more maturationally advanced

should have the explicit opportunity to telescope two years of schooling into one, providing they are also intellectually advanced.

As for the more global — and obviously more difficult to implement — *international* level, general-social and familial stability on our shrinking and increasingly crowded planet would seem to require the elimination not just of adverse physical conditions such as famine, but also of major social upheavals, because their accompanying physical and psychological hardships make physically and psychologically deprived babyhoods inevitable for whole populations. Accordingly, a *minimal* preventive program would appear to entail not only the elimination of starvation and malnutrition, but also the abolition of war and the institution of voluntary programs of population control in all countries, including our own — no less!

But it is obvious that the kinds of babyhoods present and future national groups are having and are likely to have is not the sort of consideration which motivates the foreign policy of little and big nations, past and present. The fruits of the dragon's teeth sown by self-righteous and narrowly self-interested power-blocs of previous generations have been showing up profusely in international events, not just before the founding of the United Nations, but also after, including the past few years and months. Unfortunately, there is every indication that *today's* self-righteous power-blocs, instead of profiting from the wise old dictum that "the sins of the fathers shall be visited upon the sons," are busily sowing whole *new* crops of dragon's seed! There is a significant difference *this* time, however: today's dragon's teeth are not likely to grow up to plague future generations, since there is a strong likelihood there will be no future generations of the human species to be so plagued.

POSTSCRIPT: A WORD TO STUDENTS IN THE BEHAVIORAL SCIENCES

Let me conclude this free-wheeling last chapter with some advice to students who intend to go on for advanced degrees in one or another of the behavioral, and related physiological, sciences — advice not likely to be heeded, however, because it flies in the face of current trends and biases of the academic and professional "establishments" of the various related disciplines.

The implications for students of the changing levels of neural integration thesis, presented in Chapter I, seem to me to be two-fold. First, they imply that individual psychological investigators need to focus their investigative glass much more than they have in the past on the third category of behavior itemized on page 11 — that is, on those behaviors which are unique to man. And as a direct corollary, to develop research designs and mathematical techniques increasingly better suited to the study of such behaviors. Second, it implies that behavioral scientists must discard that aspect of the research-applications value-system which was intended to apply solely to physical and lower-species phenomena: the goal of *control*. In its place must be substituted an aim which is suited to the phenomenon being studied, the human species: the provision of accurate and *relevant* information — and ways of communicating such information — which will permit members of that species, individually and collectively, to make *their own wiser choices and decisions about their own destiny.*

My last item of out-of-the mainstream counsel is related to the present academic push towards earlier and earlier science-area specialization. In spite of its currently flourishing state,[1] this trend is a serious mistake, on two scores: from the point of view of the discipline itself, and from the point of view of the student as a self-developing individual.

Especially in the behavioral sciences, the aegis of which is the study of the most complex phenomena known — the individual human being *and* his interactive relations with his social organizations, early specialization constitutes an error both for the optimum growth of the discipline and the eventual worth of the individual investigator's contributions to his chosen discipline; obviously, the two are interrelated. In these youngest of the sciences, what is most needed is a wider range of meaningful problems, the expression of these problems in clearly formulated and testable hypotheses, the development of fresh and imaginative research designs to test these hypotheses, and the formulation of

---

[1] A state which is, fortunately, sowing the seeds of its own demise.

mathematical systems which can provide for the scientific study of exceedingly complex, interdependent phenomena. The greatest research contributions will be made by those who have taken the time to acquire a rich and varied background in fields one does *not* intend to "major" in and to reserve one's field of specialization for postgraduate concentration: such a catholic orientation is the most likely soil for the growth of original hypotheses and overall fresh approaches.

Early specialization is also a mistake for personal-advancement reasons, although it is on these very grounds that most students have been going along with it: in the present highly competitive industrial and academic "rat-race," to have piled up all those specialized credits and published a few papers by the time one has graduated — *and* to graduate as young as possible — would appear to give one the competitive advantage. In so accommodating unquestioningly to whatever economic and social patterns confront them, regardless of such a pattern's impact on their society and on themselves as individual human beings, these "bright young men" are behaving according to the adaptive-Skinnerian, sheerly mammalian model. If they were instead to exercise their uniquely human capacities for "intelligent foresight" (103), they would put this order of question to themselves — and conduct themselves in accordance with its gradually developed answer: "What sort of person would I like to be, what sort of world would I like myself and my children to be living in, what sort of life would I like to have, when I am forty — with thirty-five more years of living ahead of me?"

Appendix A

SOURCES FOR BEHAVIORAL
DEVELOPMENT DATA OF PART D

Category of Development	References
Sensory, Motor, Sensorimotor	GESELL, A.: The ontogenesis of infant behavior, in L. Carmichael, ed., *Manual of Child Psychology*, 2nd ed. New York, Wiley, 1954, 335-373. MUNN, N. L.: *The Evolution and Growth of Human Behavior*. New York, Houghton Mifflin, 1955. ZUBEK, J. P., and SOLBERG, P. A.: *Human Development*. New York, McGraw-Hill, 1954.
Speech and Language	JERSILD, A. T.: *Child Psychology*, 4th ed. Englewood Cliffs, Prentice Hall, 1954. McCARTHY, D.: Language development in children, in L. Carmichael, ed., *Manual of Child Psychology*, 2nd ed. New York, Wiley, 1954, 492-630. MUNN, N. L.: *op cit.*, 1955. PARMELEE, A. H. JR.: Infant speech development, *J. Pediat.*, 46:447-450, 1955. ZUBEK, J. P., and SOLBERG, P. A.: *op cit.*, 1954.
Emotional	JERSILD, A. T.: *op cit.*, 1954. JERSILD, A. T.: Emotional development, in L. Carmichael ed., *Manual of Child Psychology*, 2nd ed., New York, Wiley, 1954, 833-917. MUNN, N. L.: *op cit.*, 1955.
Social	BOEHM, L.: "The development of independence: a comparative study," *Child Development, 28, 1957*, 85-92. JERSILD, A. T.: *Child Psychology*, 4th ed. Englewood Cliffs, Prentice-Hall, 1954. MUNN, N. L.: *op cit.*, 1955. RUSSELL, D. H.: *Children's Thinking*. New York, Ginn, 1956. ZUBEK, J. P., and SOLBERG, P. A.: *op cit.*, 1954.

Memory   MUNN, N. L.: Learning in children, in L. Carmichael,
              ed., *Manual of Child Psychology,* 2nd ed., New York,
              Wiley, 1954, 374-458.
              RUSSELL, D. H.: *op cit.,* 1956.

Perceptual AMES, L. B., LEARNED, J., METRAUX, R., WALKER, R.:
              Development of perception in the young child as
              observed in response to the Rorschach test blots. *J.
              Genet. Psychol., 82*:183-204, 1953.
              AMES, L. B., and LEARNED, J.: Developmental trends in
              child kaleidoblock responses. *J. Genet. Psychol., 8:*
              247-270, 1954.
              HEMMENDINGER, L.: Perceptual organization and devel-
              opment as reflected in the structure of the Rorschach
              test responses. *J. Project. Tech., 17*:162-70, 1953.
              PIAGET, JEAN: *The Construction of Reality in the Child,*
              New York, Basic Books, 1954.
              PIAGET, J., and INHELDER, B.: *The Child's Conception of
              Space.* New York, Basic Books, 1957.
              RUSSELL, D. H.: *op cit.,* 1956.

Interests,   JERSILD, A. T.: *op cit.,* 1954.
Esthetic and RUSSELL, D. H.: *op cit.,* 1956.
Imaginative   ZUBEK, J. P., and SOLBERG, P. A.: *op cit.,* 1954.
Activities

Reasoning,   AEBLI, H.: *The Development of Intelligence in the
Problem-   Child:* A summary of the works of Jean Piaget from
solving,   1936 to 1948. Minneapolis, University of Minnesota
Learning,   Inst. of Child Welfare, 1950.
Tested   BAYLEY, N.: Mental growth during the first three years.
Intelligence   *Genet. Psychol. Monogr., 14*:92, 1933.
              BAYLEY, N.: On the growth of intelligence. *Amer.
              Psychol., 10-12*:805-818, Dec., 1955.
              INHELDER, B., and PIAGET, J.: *The Growth of Logical
              Thinking from Childhood to Adolescence.* New York,
              Basic Books, 1958.
              MUNN, N. L.: Learning in children. *op cit.,* 1954.
              PIAGET, J.: *The Origins of Intelligence in Children.* New
              York, Basic Books, 1952.
              RUSSELL, D. H.: *op cit.,* 1956.
              ZUBEK, J. P., and SOLBERG, P. A.: *op cit.,* 1954.

Conceptual HUNT, J. McV.: *Intelligence and Experience.* New York, Ronald, 1961.

JERSILD, A. T.: *op cit.,* 1954.

KATCHEN, A., and LEVIN, G. M.: Children's conceptions of body size. *Child Develop., 26:*103-110, 1955.

MOTT, S. M.: Concept of mother — a study of four and five year old children. *Child Develop., 25:*99-106, 1954.

MUNN, N. L.: *The Evolution and Growth of Human Behavior.* New York, Houghton, Mifflin, 1955.

RUSSELL, D. H.: *op cit.,* 1956.

SIGEL, I. E.: Developmental trends in the abstraction ability of children. *Child Develop., 24:*131-144, 1953.

SPRINGER, D. J.: Development in young children of an understanding of time and the clock. *J. Genet. Psychol., 80:*83-96, 1952.

Values and JERSILD, A. T.: *op cit.,* 1954.
Attitudes   RUSSELL, D. H.: *op cit.,* 1956.

UGUREL-SEMIN, R. J.: Moral behavior and moral judgment of children. *J. Abnorm. Soc. Psychol., 47:*461-74, 1952.

ZUBEK, J. P., and SOLBERG, P. A.: *op cit.,* 1954.

Sex   MILNER, E.: Effects of sex-role and social status on the
Differences early-adolescent personality. *Genet. Psychol. Monogr., 40:*231-325, 1949.

TERMAN, L. M., and TYLER, L. E.: Psychological sex differences, in L. Carmichael, ed., *Manual of Child Psychology,* 2nd ed. New York, Wiley, 1954, pp. 1064-1114.

Behavior   BENDA, C. E.: Psychopathology of childhood, in L. Car-
Problems   michael, ed., *Manual of Child Psychology,* 2nd ed., New York, Wiley, 1954, 1115-1116.

KANNER, L., and EISENBERG, L.: Notes on the follow-up studies of autistic children, in P. H. Hoch and J. Zubin, eds., *Psychopathology of Childhood.* New York, Grune & Stratton, 1955, 227-239.

KANNER, L.: General concepts of schizophrenia at different ages, in 1954 *Proc. Ass. Res. Nerv. Ment. Dis., 34:*451-3, 1956.

MacFarlane, J. W., Allen, L., and Honzik, M. P.: *A Developmental Study of the Behavior Problems of Normal Children.* University of California Publ. in Child Devel., 2, 1954.

Physical and Psychological Self, and Personality

Benton, A. L.: Development of finger localization capacity in school children. *Child Develop., 26:225-230,* 1955.

Jersild, A. T.: *op cit.,* 1954.

Russell, D. H.: *op cit.,* 1956.

Fink, M., and Bender, M. B.: Perception of simultaneous tactile stimulation in normal children. *Neurology,* 3-1, 27-34, 1953.

Swanson, R., and Benton, A. L.: Some aspects of right-left discrimination. *Child Development, 26:123-133,* 1955.

General Developmental

Bayley, N.: Normal growth and development, in P. H. Hoch and J. Zubin, eds., *Psychopathology of Childhood, op cit.,* 1-14.

Bayley, N.: Individual patterns of development. *Child Develop., 27-1:45-74,* Mar., '56.

Werner, H.: The concept of development from a comparative and organismic point of view, in D. B. Harris, ed., *The Concept of Development.* Minneapolis, University of Minnesota Press, 1957, 125-148.

REFERENCES

1. ADRIAN, LORD: Sensory mechanisms—an introduction. In American Physiological Society, *Handbook of Physiology,* 1959, vol. 1, pp. 365-7. **(Orientation Supplement 6, 146)**

2. AEBLI, HANS: *The Development of Intelligence in the Child.* Summary of the works of Jean Piaget published between 1936 and 1948. Institute of Child Welfare, Minneapolis, Minn., 1950. **(Appendix A)**

3. AMASSIAN, V. E.: Interaction in the somatovisceral projection system. *1950 Proc Ass Res Nerv Ment Dis, 30,* 1952. **(236)**

4. AMES, L. B.; LEARNED, J.; METRAUX, R., and WALKER, R.: Development of perception in the young child as observed in responses to the Rorschach test blots. *J Genet Psychol, 82:* 183-204, 1953. **(Appendix A)**

5. AMES, L. B., and LEARNED, J.: Developmental trends in child kaleidoblock responses. *J Genet Psychol, 84:*247-270, 1954. **(Appendix A)**

6. AREY, L. B.: *Developmental Anatomy,* 6th Ed. Philadelphia, Saunders, 1954. **(Tables IIA, IIC; 71, 78, 79)**

7. ARIENS-KAPPERS, C. U.: The (evolutionary) development of the cortex and the functions of its different layers. *Acta Psychiat Neurol, 3:*115-132, 1928.

8. ARIENS-KAPPERS, C. U.; HUBER, G. C., and CROSBY, E. C.: *The Comparative Anatomy of the Nervous System of Vertebrates Including Man.* New York, Macmillan, 1936, vol. II. **(Tables IB, IC; 111, 115, 116, 173)**

9. ARIETI, S.: *Interpretation of Schizophrenia.* New York, Robert Brunner and Basic Books, 1955. **(106, 227, 273-8, 248).**

10. ASCH, S. E.: *Social Psychology.* Englewood Cliffs, N.J., Prentice-Hall, 1952. **(10)**

11. BAILEY, P., and VON BONIN, G.: *The Isocortex of Man.* Illinois Monographs in the Medical Sciences, Urbana, U. of Ill., 1951. **(109)**

12. BARCROFT, J.: *The Brain and Its Environment.* New Haven, Yale, 1938. **(174)**

13. BAYLEY, N.: Mental growth during the first three years. *Genet Psychol Monogr, 14:*92, 1933. **(Appendix A)**

14. BAYLEY, N.: Normal growth and development. In P. H. Hoch and J. Zubin (eds.) : *Psychopathology of Childhood.* New York, Grune, 1955, pp. 1-14. (**Table IIC; Appendix A**)

15. BAYLEY, N.: On the growth of intelligence. *Amer Psychol, 10* (No. 12) :805-818, Dec. 1955. (**Appendix A, 254**)

16. BENDA, C. E.: Psychopathology of childhood. In L. Carmichael (ed.): *Manual of Child Psychology,* 2nd Ed. New York, Wiley, 1954, pp. 1115-1161. (**Table II; Appendix A, 204**)

17. BENEDICT, RUTH: Continuities and discontinuities in cultural conditioning. *Psychiatry, 1:*161-7, 1938. (**337**)

18. BENTON, A. L.: Development of finger localization capacity in school children. *Child Develop, 26:*225-230, 1955. (**Appendix A**)

19. VON BERTALANFFY, L.: *Problems of Life.* New York, Wiley, 1952. (**Preface, 16, 317-8, 319**)

20. BETTELHEIM, BRUNO: The problem of generations. In E. H. Erikson (ed.) : *The Challenge of Youth.* Garden City, N. Y., Doubleday, Anchor Books, 1965. (**338, 342**)

21. The Bible: Quotation taken from Genesis 2:61.

22. BISHOP, G. H.: Natural history of the nerve impulse. *Physiol Rev, 36* (No. 3) :376-399, July 1956. (**Table IA; 45**)

23. BOEHM, L.: The development of independence: a comparative study. *Child Develop, 28:*85-92, 1957. (**Appendix A**)

24. BORKOWSKI, W. J., and BERNSTINE, R.: Electroencephalography of the fetus. *Neurology, 5:*362-5, 1955. (**Table IIB**)

25. BRAZIER, M. A. B.: The development of concepts relating to the electrical activity of the brain. *J Nerv Ment Dis, 126* (No. 4) : 303-321, Apr. 1958. (**Orientation Supplement 6**)

26. BREMER, F.: Central regulatory mechanisms. In American Physiological Society: *Handbook of Physiology.* 1960, vol. II, pp. 1241-3. (**131**)

27. BRODAL, ALF: *The Reticular Formation of the Brain Stem.* London, Oliver & Boyd, 1957. (**126, 127**)

27A. BRONFENBRENNER, U.: Socialization and social class through time and space. In E. E. Maccoby, T. M. Newcomb, and E. L. Hartley (eds.) : *Readings in Social Psychology,* 3rd Ed. New York, Holt, 1958. (**339**)

28. BROOKHART, J. M.: The cerebellum. In American Physiological Society: *Handbook of Physiology.* 1960, vol. II, pp. 1245-80. (**Table IB; 132**)

29. BRUNER, J. S.: Neural mechanisms in perception. *1956 Proc Ass Res Nerv Ment Dis, 36:*118-143, 1958. **(13-14)**

30. CARMICHAEL, L.: Ontogenetic development. In S. S. Stevens (ed): *Handbook of Experimental Psychology.* New York, Wiley, 1951, chap. 8. **(Tables IIB, IIC; 27)**

31. CARMICHAEL, L.: The onset and early development of behavior. In L. Carmichael (ed): *Manual of Child Psychology,* 2nd ed. New York, Wiley, 1954, pp. 60-185. **(Appendix A)**

32. CAVENESS, W. F.: *Atlas of Electroencephalography in the Developing Monkey* (macaca mulatta). Reading, Mass., Addison-Wesley, 1962. **(288)**

33. CHASE, R. A.; SUTTON, S.; FOWLER, E. P.; FAY, T. H., and RUHM, H. B.: Low sensation level delayed clicks and key tapping. *J Speech Hearing Res, 4:*73-78, 1961. **(285)**

34. CHATFIELD, P. O.: Comparative anatomy and physiology of the frontal lobes. In M. Greenblatt and H. C. Solomon (eds): *Frontal Lobes and Schizophrenia.* New York, Springer, 1953, pp. 18-26. **(103)**

35. CHEIN, ISIDORE: The image of man. *J Social Issues, 18* (No. 4): 1-35, Oct. 1962. **(7)**

36. COBB, S.: *Emotions and Clinical Medicine.* New York, Norton, 1950. **(Table IB; 118, 130)**

37. COGHILL, G. E.: *Anatomy and the Problem of Behavior.* New York, Macmillan, 1929. **(89, 90)**

38. CONEL, J. L.: *The Postnatal Development of the Human Cerebral Cortex.* Cambridge, Harvard, 1939-63, vols. 1-7. **(Tables IIC, IVB, VII, VIII, IX, X; 28, 119)**

39. COOLEY, C. H.: *Human Nature and the Social Order.* New York, Scribner, 1902 and 1922. **(227)**

40. DENNIS, W.: Infant development under conditions of restricted practice and of minimal social stimulation. *J Genet Psychol, 53:*149-157, 1938. **(30)**

41. DENNY-BROWN, D.: Motor mechanisms: general principles of motor integration. In American Physiological Society: *Handbook of Physiology.* 1960, vol. II, pp. 781-796. **(102, 147)**

42. DREYFUS-BRISAC, C., *et al.*: L'electroencephalogramme de l'enfant normal de moins de trois ans. *Etudes Neo-Natales, VII*(No. 4): 143-175. **(Tables IVB, VII, VIII, IX, X; 70)**

43. DUBOS, R. J.: Address to the 1964 annual conference of the American Assn. for the Advancement of Science, Montreal,

Dec. 29, 1964. Reported in the *New York Times*, 12-30-64. **(351)**

44. DURKHEIM, E.: *The Elementary Forms of the Religious Life.* New York, Macmillan, 1926. **(312)**

45. ECCLES, J. C.: Neuron physiology. In American Physiological Society: *Handbook of Physiology.* 1959, vol. I, pp. 59-74. **(Orientation Supplement 6)**

46. EEG Laboratory, Institute of Living, Hartford, Conn., approved practice at. **(Orientation Supplement 6)**

47. EISELEY, L. C.: Fossil man and human evolution. *Yearbook of Anthropology.* 1955, pp. 61-78. **(61, 62)**

48. ELLINGSON, R. J.: Electroencephalograms of normal newborns. *Electroenceph Clin Neurophysiol, 10:*31-50, 1958. **(Table IVB)**

49. ENGEL, R.: Evaluation of electroencephalographic tracings of newborns. *Lancet, 81*(No. 12):523-532, Dec. 1961. **(Table IVB)**

50. ERIKSON, E. H., in J. M. TANNER and B. M. INHELDER, (eds.) : *Discussions on Child Development.* New York, Int. Univ., 1955, vol. 3, pp. 147. **(331)**

51. FESSARD, A.: Brain potentials and rhythms — introduction. In American Physiological Society: *Handbook of Physiology.* 1959, vol. I, pp. 255-59. **(Orientation Supplement 6)**

52. FINK, M., and BENDER, M. D.: Perception of simultaneous tactile stimuli in normal children. *Neurology, 3:*27-34, 1953. **(Appendix A)**

53. FOIS, A.: *The Electroencephalogram of the Normal Child.* Springfield, Thomas, 1961. **(Tables VIII, IX)**

54. FRANK, L. K.: *Individual Development.* Garden City, N. Y., Doubleday, 1955. **(299)**

55. FREUD, S.: *Civilization and Its Discontents.* The International Psychoanalytical Library, No. 17, London, Hogarth Press, 1957. **(311)**

56. FULTON, J. F.: *A Textbook of Physiology,* 17th Ed. Philadelphia, Saunders, 1955. **(Orientation Supplement 3; 51, 103, 104)**

57. GALAMBOS, R.: Neural mechanisms of audition. *Physiol Rev, 34:* 497-528, 1954. **(149)**

58. GALAMBOS, R.: Neurophysiological studies on learning and motivation. *Fed Proc, 20*(No. 2, part I):603-8, July 1961. **(Orientation Supplement 6)**

59. GARDNER, E.: *Fundamentals of Neurology,* 4th Ed. Saunders, Philadelphia, 1963. **(Orientation Supplement 6; 112)**

60. GASTAUT, H.: État actuel des connaissances sur l' electroencephel-ographie de conditionnement. *Electroenceph Clin Neuro-physiol, Supp. 6*:113-160, 1957. **(128)**

61. GELLHORN, E.: *Physiological Foundations of Neurology and Psychiatry.* Minneapolis, U of Minn., 1953. **(Table IC)**

62. GERARD, R. W.: Neurophysiology: an integration. In American Physiological Society: *Handbook of Physiology,* 1960, vol. III, pp. 1919-1965. **(140, 144)**

63. GESELL, A.: The ontogenesis of infant behavior. In L. Carmichael (ed.): *Manual of Child Psychology,* 2nd Ed. New York, Wiley, 1954, pp. 335-373. **(Table IVA; Appendix A)**

64. GIBBS, F. A., and GIBBS, E. L.: *Atlas of Electroencephalography,* 2nd Ed. Reading, Mass., Addison-Wesley, 1950, vol. I, chaps. 7 and 8. **(Tables IVB, VII, VIII, IX, X, XI)**

65. GOODDY, W.: Cerebral representation. *Brain, 79*:167-187, 1956. **(117)**

66. GRANIT, R.: *Receptors and Sensory Perception.* New Haven, Yale, 1955. **(126)**

67. GREENBLATT, M., and SOLOMON, H. C.: In M. Greenblatt and H. C. Solomon (eds.) : *Frontal Lobes and Schizophrenia.* New York, Springer, 1953, chap. 30. **(238)**

68. HAMILTON, W. J.; BOYD, J. D., and MOSSMAN, H. W.: *Human Embryology,* 2nd Ed. Baltimore, Williams & Wilkins, 1952. **(Table IB; Figure 2)**

69. HARLOW, H. F.: The formation of learning sets. *Psychol Rev, 56:* 51-65, 1949 **(269)**

70. HARLOW, H. F.: Affectional behavior in the infant monkey. In M. A. B. Brazier (ed.) : *The Central Nervous System and Be-havior.* Third Conference, New York, Josiah Macy, Jr., Foundation, 1960, pp. 307-357. **(19, 284)**

71. HARLOW, H. F.: The heterosexual affectional system in monkeys. *Amer Psychol, 17*(No. 1):1-9, Jan. 1962. **(62)**

72. HEBB, D. O.: *The Organization of Behavior.* New York, Wiley, 1949. **(110, 119)**

73. HEBB, D. O.: Alice in Wonderland. In H. F. Harlow and C. N. Woolsey (eds.) : *Biological and Biochemical Bases of Behavior.* Madison, U. of Wis., 1958, pp. 451-467. **(14-15)**

74. HEBB, D. O.: The motivating effects of exteroceptive stimulation. *Amer Psychol, 13*:109-113, 1958. **(19)**

75. HEBB, D. O.: *A Textbook of Psychology.* Philadelphia, Saunders, 1958. **(30, 109, 136, 269)**

76. HEMMENDINGER, L.: Perceptual organization and development as reflected in the structure of the Rorschach test responses. *J Project Tech, 17:*162-170, 1953. **(Appendix A)**

77. HENRY, C. E.: Electroencephalograms of normal children. *Child Develop Monogr, 9*(No. 3), 1944. **(Table XI)**

78. HERRICK, C. J.: *The Evolution of Human Nature.* Austin, U. of Tex., 1956. **(Tables IA, IB; 12-13, 45, 46-9, 49, 50, 112, 115, 141-2, 155, 161-2)**

79. HILGARD, E. R.: *Introduction to Psychology,* 3rd Ed. New York, Harcourt, 1962. **(27)**

80. HIMWICH, H. E.: *Brain Metabolism and Cerebral Disorders.* Baltimore, Williams & Wilkins, 1951.

81. HIMWICH, H. E.: The functional organization of the CNS. *Proc Inst Med Chicago, 19* (No. 6) :115-127, 1952. **(104)**

82. HIMWICH, H. E., and HIMWICH, W. A.: General neurophysiology. In E. A. Spiegel (ed.) : *Progr Neurol Psychiat, 12,* 1957. **(Tables IVB, XI)**

83. DEN HOLLANDER, PROF. A. N. J., Director, American Institute, University of Amsterdam: Talk before the Social Science Faculty Seminar, Brooklyn College, Dec. 17, 1962.

84. HORNEY, K.: The problem of feminine masochism. *Psychoanal Rev, 22:*241-257, 1935. **(304)**

85. HORNEY, K.: *The Neurotic Personality of our Time.* New York, Norton, 1937. **(301)**

86. HUNT, J. MCVICKER: *Intelligence and Experience.* New York, Ronald, 1961. **(20, 239, 283)**

87. INGRAM, W. R.: Central autonomic mechanisms. In American Physiological Society: *Handbook of Physiology.* 1960, vol. II, pp. 951-978. **(138)**

88. INHELDER, B., and PIAGET, J.: *The Growth of Logical Thinking from Childhood to Adolescence.* New York, Basic Books, 1958. **(Appendix A; 201)**

89. JACKSON, J. H.: The Croonian Lectures. *Brit Med J, 1:*1884. **(Orientation Supplement 5; 29, 42)**

90. JASPER, H. H.: Thalamocortical integrating mechanisms. *1950 Proc Ass Res Nerv Ment Dis,* 1952, chap. 23, pp. 493-512. **(Orientation Supplement 3; Table IB; 129)**

91. JASPER, H. H., and RASMUSSEN, T.: Studies of clinical and electrical responses to deep temporal stimulation in man. *1956 Proc Ass Res Nerv Ment Dis, 36:*316-334, 1958. **(Orientation Supplement 6; 128)**

92. JASPER, H. H.: Unspecific thalamocortical relations. In American Physiological Society: *Handbook of Physiology.* 1960, vol. II, pp. 1311, 1315. (129)

93. JERSILD, A. T.: *Child Psychology,* 4th Ed. Englewood Cliffs, N. J., Prentice-Hall, 1954. (Appendix A)

94. JERSILD, A. T.: Emotional development. In L. Carmichael (ed.): *Manual of Child Psychology,* 2nd Ed. New York, Wiley, 1954, pp. 833-917. (Appendix A)

95. JOST, H., and SONTAG, L. W.: The genetic factor in ANS function. *Psychosom Med, 6:*308-310, 1944. (293)

96. KAADA, B. R.: Cingulate, posterior orbital, anterior insular and temporal pole cortex. In American Physiological Society: *Handbook of Physiology.* 1960, vol. II, pp. 1345-1372. (130)

97. KANNER, L.: General concept of schizophrenia at different ages. *1954 Proc Ass Res Nerv Ment Dis, 34:*451-3, 1956. (Appendix A)

98. KANNER, L., and EISENBERG, L.: Notes on the follow-up studies of autistic children. In P. H. Hoch and J. Zubin (eds.): *Psychopathology in Childhood.* New York, Grune, 1955, chap. 13, pp. 227-239. (Appendix A)

99. KATCHEN, A., and LEVIN, G. M.: Children's conceptions of body size. *Child Develop, 26:*103-110, 1955. (Appendix A)

100. KORZYBSKI, A.: *Time-Binding, The General Theory.* Lakeville, Institute of General Semantics, 1949. (343)

101. KUNDSIN, R. B.: Where are our women in science? *Harvard Medical Alumni Bulletin,* Winter, 1965, pp. 25-27. (345)

102. LANGWORTHY, O. R.: Development of myelinization of the nervous system in the human fetus and infant. *Contributions to Embryology, 24:*(No. 139), 1933. (Tables IIC, III, IVB, VII; 28, 80, 82, 173)

103. LASHLEY, K.: Persistent problems in the evolution of mind. *Quart Rev Biol, 24:*28-42, 1949. (258)

104. LASHLEY, K.: The problem of serial order in behavior. In L. A. Jeffress (ed.): *Cerebral Mechanisms in Behavior.* The Hixon Symposium, New York, Wiley, 1951, pp. 112-146. (120, 140)

105. LASHLEY, K.: *1950 Proc Ass Res Nerv Ment Dis, 30:*529-552, 1952. (Preface)

106. LEVY, S., and KENNARD, M. A.: The EEG patterns of patients with psychologic disorders of various ages. *J Nerv Ment Dis, 118*(No. 5):416-428, Nov. 1953. (Table XI; 237)

107. LEWIN, K.: *A Dynamic Theory of Personality.* New York, Mc-Graw-Hill, 1935. **(319)**
108. LINDSLEY, D. B.: A longitudinal study of the occipital alpha rhythm in normal children. *J Genet Psychol, 55*:197-213, 1939. **(Tables IVB, VIII, IX, X, XI; 28)**
109. LINDSLEY, D. B.: Psychological phenomena and the electroencephalogram. *Electroenceph Clin Neurophysiol, 4*:443-456, 1952. **(Orientation Supplement 6)**
110. LINDSLEY, D. B.: Attention, consciousness, sleep and wakefulness. In American Physiological Society: *Handbook of Physiology.* 1960, vol. III, pp. 1553-1593. **(Orientation Supplement 6)**
111. LIVINGSTON, R. B.: Central control of receptors and sensory transmission systems. In American Physiological Society: *Handbook of Physiology.* 1959, vol. 1, pp. 741-760. **(107, 148-150)**
112. LURIA, A. R.: The role of language in the formation of temporary connections. In B. Simon (ed.) : *Psychology in the Soviet Union.* Stanford U.P., 1957, p. 116, **(216)**
113. MACFARLANE, JEAN W.; ALLEN, L., and HONZIK, M. P.: *A Developmental Study of the Behavior Problems of Normal Children.* University of California Publications in Child Development, Vol. 2, Berkeley and Los Angeles, U. of Calif., 1954. **(Appendix A; 297)**
114. MACLEAN, P. D.: Psychosomatics. In American Physiological Society: *Handbook of Physiology.* 1960, vol. III, pp. 1723-44. **(130)**
115. MACLEAN, P. D.: The limbic system and emotional behavior. *Arch Neurol Psychiat, 73*:130-134, 1955. **(130)**
116. MAGOUN, H. W.: *The Waking Brain.* Springfield, Thomas, 1958. **(127)**
117. McCARTHY, D.: Language development in children. In L. Carmichael (ed.) : *Manual of Child Psychology,* 2nd Ed. New York, Wiley, 1954, pp. 492-630. **(Table IVA; Appendix A)**
118. McGRAW, M.: *Growth: A Study of Johnny and Jimmy.* New York, Appleton, 1935. **(30)**
119. McGRAW, M.: *Neuromuscular Maturation of the Human Infant.* New York, Columbia, 1943. **(27)**
120. MEAD, G. H.: *Mind, Self and Society.* Chicago, U. of Chicago, 1934. **(238, 283)**
121. MEAD, M.: *Sex and Temperament in Three Primitive Societies.* New York, Morrow, 1935. **(307)**

122. MEER, S .J.: The relationship between auditory blending ability and perceptual and integrative functions related to reading. *Teacher Education News and Notes.* New York City Board of Higher Education, Feb.-Mar. 1963. **(237)**

123. MILNER, B.: Intellectual functions of the temporal lobes. *Psychol Bull, 51:*42-62, 1954. **(113)**

124. MILNER, E.: Effects of sex-role and social status on the early adolescent personality. *Genet Psychol Monogr, 40:*231-325, 1949. **(Appendix A)**

125. MILNER, E.: A study of the relationship between reading readiness in Grade I school children and patterns of parent-child interaction. *Child Develop, 22(2):*95-112, 1951. **(350)**

126. MILNER, E.: New frontiers in personality theory. *J Nat Ass Deans of Women,* March 1954, pp. 105-119. **(Preface; 25)**

127. MILNER, E.: *The Failure of Success, The American Crisis in Values.* New York, Exposition, 1959. **(260, 305, 313, 323, 343)**

128. MILNER, E.: Differing observational perspectives as a barrier to communication among behavioral scientists. *Rev Existential Psychol Psychiat, 2* (No. 3) :249-257, Fall 1962. **(17, 317)**

129. MILNER, E.: A species theory of anxiety. *Rev Existential Psychol Psychiat, 3*(No. 3):227-236, Fall 1963. **(229, 251-2, 302-3)**

130. MILNER, P. M.: The cell assembly: Mark II. *Psychol Rev, 64:*242-252, 1957. **(136)**

131. MONNIER, M., in J. M. TANNER and B. INHELDER (eds.) : *Discussions on Child Development.* New York, Int. Univ. 1956, vol. 4, pp. 133-135. **(Table XI)**

132. MONNIER, M.: Plan d'organisation, continuité, et stades du developpement des activities électriques cerebrales. *Dialectica, II* (No. 1/2):167-178, 1957. **(Table VI)**

133. MOTT, S. M.: Concept of mother — a study of 4- and 5-year-old children. *Child Develop, 25:*99-106, 1954. **(Appendix A)**

134. MUNN, N. L.: Learning in children. In L. Carmichael (ed.) : *Manual of Child Psychology,* 2nd Ed. New York, Wiley, 1954, pp. 374-458. **(Appendix A)**

135. MUNN, N. L.: *The Evolution and Growth of Human Behavior.* New York, Houghton, 1955. **(Appendix A)**

136. MUSSEN, P. H.: *The Psychological Development of the Child.* Englewood Cliffs, N. J., Prentice-Hall, 1963, p. 37. **(253)**

137. NEUGARTEN, B. L., and associates: *Personality in Middle and Late Years.* New York, Atherton, 1964. **(276)**

138. VON NEUMANN, J.: The general and logical theory of automata.

In L. A. Jeffress (ed.) : *Cerebral Mechanisms in Behavior.* The Hixon Symposium, New York, Wiley, 1951, pp. 3-50. **(139)**

139. *New York Times,* Feb. 2, 1965. **(298)**

140. Nissen, H. W.: Phylogenetic comparison. In S. S. Stevens, (ed.) : *Handbook of Experimental Psychology.* New York, Wiley, 1951, chap. 11, pp. 346-85. **(59)**

141. Novikoff, A. B.: The concept of integrative levels and biology. *Science, 101:*209-215, March 2, 1945. **(9)**

142. Olds, J., and Milner, P. M.: Positive reinforcement produced by electrical stimulation of . . regions of the rat brain. *J Comp Physiol Psychol, 47:*419-427, 1954. **(Orientation Supplement 3; 231)**

143. Parmalee, A. H. Jr.: Infant speech development: a report of the study of one child by magnetic tape recordings. *J Pediat, 46:* 447-450, 1955. **(Appendix A)**

144. Patten, B. M.: *Human Embryology,* 2nd Ed. New York, McGraw-Hill, 1953. **(Tables IIC, VIII, XI; 80, 102)**

145. Penfield, W.: Memory mechanisms. *AMA Arch Neurol Psychiat, 67:*178-191, Feb. 1952. **(113, 136)**

146. Penfield, W.: Epileptic automatism and the centrencephalic integrating system. *1950 Proc Ass Res Nerv Ment Dis, 30,* 1952. **(131-2)**

147. Penfield, W., and Jasper, H. H.: *Epilepsy and The Functional Anatomy of the Human Brain.* New York, Little, 1954. **(132)**

148. Piaget, J.: *The Origins of Intelligence in Children.* New York, Basic Books, 1952 (1936) . **(Appendix A; 118, 178)**

149. Piaget, J.: *The Construction of Reality in the Child.* New York, Basic Books, 1954 (1937) . **(Appendix A)**

150. Piaget, J., and Inhelder, B.: *The Child's Conception of Space.* New York, Basic Books, 1957 (1948) . **(Appendix A)**

151. Pond, D. A.: The development of normal EEG rhythms. In J. D. N. Hill and G. Parr (eds.) : *Electroencephalography,* 2nd Ed. New York, Macmillan, 1963, chap. 6. **(Tables VI, VII, VIII, IX, X, XI)**

152. Pratt, K. C.: The neonate. In L. Carmichael (ed.) : *Manual of Child Psychology,* 2nd Ed. New York, Wiley, 1954, chap. 4, pp. 215-291. **(Table IV; 27, 85)**

153. Pribram, K. H.: Comparative neurology and the evolution of behavior. In A. Roe and G. G. Simpson (eds.) : *Behavior and Evolution.* New Haven, Yale, 1958, chap. 7. **(156)**

154A. Pribram, K. H.: A review of theory in physiological psychology. *Ann Rev Psychol, 11*:1-40, 1960. (**29, 130, 151, 156**)

154B. Pribram, K. H.: Some neuropsychological speculations. In G. A. Miller, E. Galanter, and K. H. Pribram: *Plans and the Structure of Behavior.* New York, Holt, 1960, chap. 14. (**137**)

155. Pribram, K. H.: Reinforcement revisited: a structural view. *Nebraska Symposium on Motivation.* Lincoln, U. of Neb., 1963, pp. 113-159. (**29**)

156. Romer, A. S.: Phylogeny and behavior. In A. Roe and G. G. Simpson (eds.) : *Behavior and Evolution.* New Haven, Yale, 1958, chap. 3, pp. 48-75. (**Tables IA, IB; 152-3**)

157. Rose, J. E.: The cortical connections of the reticular complex of the thalamus. *1950 Proc Ass Res Nerv Ment Dis, 30:*454-479, 1952. (**128**)

158. Roszak, Theodore: The historian as psychiatrist. *The Nation,* Nov. 24, 1962, pp. 347, 343-4, 345. (**307, 309-10**)

159. Ruch, T. C.: Motor systems. In S. S. Stevens (ed.) : *Handbook of Experimental Psychology.* New York, Wiley, 1951, chap. 5. (**Table IB; 126, 133**)

160. Ruch, T. C., and Fulton, J. F. (eds.) : *Medical Physiology and Biophysics.* Philadelphia, Saunders, 1960. (**Orientation Supplements 3 and 4; 103, 114, 115-7, 129-130, 133**)

161. Russell, D. H.: *Children's Thinking.* New York, Ginn, 1956. (**Appendix A; 208**)

162. Schecter, D. E.; Symonds, M., and Bernstein, I.: Development of the concept of time. *J Nerv Ment Dis, 121:*301-310, 1955. (**Appendix A**)

163. Schneirla, T. C.: The concept of development in comparative psychology. In D. B. Harris (ed.) : *The Concept of Development.* Minneapolis, U. of Minn., 1957, p. 86. (**22, 63, 265**)

164. Selby, H., Jr.: *Last Exit to Brooklyn.* New York, Grove, 1964. (**340**)

165. Sellars, R. W.: An analytic approach to the mind-body problem. *Philosophical Review, 47:*461-487, 1938. (**9, 11-12**)

166. Sholl, D. A.: *The Organization of the Cerebral Cortex.* New York, Wiley, 1956. (**110**)

167. Sigel, I. E.: Developmental trends in the abstraction ability of children. *Child Develop, 24:*131-144, 1953. (**Appendix A**)

168. Skinner, B. F.: *Walden Two.* New York, Macmillan, 1948. (**343**)

169. Skinner, B. F.: *Science and Human Behavior.* New York, Macmillan, 1953. (**343**)

170. SMITH, J. R.: The EEG during normal infancy and childhood. II. The nature of the growth of alpha waves. *J Genet Psychol, 53*:471-482, Dec. 1938. (**Tables IVB, VIII**)

171. SPRINGER, D. J.: Development in young children of an understanding of time and the clock. *J Genet Psychol, 80*:83-96, 1952. (**Appendix A**)

172. SWANSON, R., and BENTON, A. L.: Some aspects of right-left discrimination. *Child Develop, 26*:123-133, 1955. (**Appendix A**)

173. TASAKI, I.: Conduction of the nerve impulse. In American Physiological Society: *Handbook of Physiology.* 1959, vol. I, p. 116. (**Orientation Supplement 6**)

174. TAYLOR, JAMES (ed.) : *Selected Writings of John Hughlings Jackson.* New York, Basic Books, 1958, vol. 2. (**Orientation Supplement 5; 99**)

175. TERMAN, L. M., and TYLER, L. E.: Psychological sex differences. In L. Carmichael (ed.) : *Manual of Child Psychology,* 2nd Ed. New York, Wiley, 1954, chap. 17, pp. 1064-1114. (**Appendix A**)

176. THOMAS, A.; CHESS, S.; BIRCH, H. G.; HERTZ, M. E., and KORN, S.: *Behavioral Individuality in Early Childhood.* New York, N. Y. U., 1963. (**279**)

177. THOMPSON, W. R.: Early environment — its importance for later behavior. In P. H. Hoch and J. Zubin (eds.) : *Psychopathology of Childhood.* New York, Grune, 1955, chap. 8, pp. 120-139. (**19**)

178. TILNEY, F.: Comparative ontogeny of the cerebral cortex in four mammals. In *1932 Proc Ass Res Nerv Ment Dis, 13*:49-82, 1934. (**Table IC**)

179. TINBERGEN, N.: *The Study of Instinct.* New York, Oxford U. P. (Claradon Press), 1951. (**9-10, 11, 15, 102**)

180. TRUEX, R. C.: *Strong and Elwyn's Human Neuroanatomy,* 4th Ed. Baltimore, Williams & Wilkins, 1959. (**Table IB; Orientation Supplement 4**)

181. TURNER, O. A.: Growth and development of cerebral cortical pattern in man. *Arch Neurol Psychiat, 59*:1-12, 1948. (**174**)

182. TURNER, O. A.: Post-natal growth changes in the cortical surface area. *Arch Neurol Psychiat, 64*:378-84, 1950. (**Tables V, VIII, X, XI**)

183. UGUREL-SEMIN, R. J.: Moral behavior and moral judgment of children. *J Abnorm Soc Psychol, 47*:463-474, 1952. (**Appendix A**)

184. WALTER, W. GREY: *The Living Brain.* New York, Norton, 1953. (**Orientation Supplement 6; Table XI; 237**)

185. WALTER, W. GREY: EEG development of children. In J. M. Tanner and B. Inhelder (eds.) : *Discussions on Child Development.* New York, Int. Univs., 1953, vol. 1.

186. WALTER, W. GREY: Intrinsic rhythms of the brain. In American Physiological Society: *Handbook of Physiology.* 1959, vol. I, pp. 279-298. (**Orientation Supplement 6; 237**)

187. WALTER, W. GREY: In J. D. N. Hill and G. Parr (eds.) : *Electroencephalography,* 2nd Ed. New York, Macmillan, 1963, chap. 1. (**14**)

188. WALTERS, C.; PARSONS, O. A., and SHURLEY, J. T.: Male-female differences in underwater sensory isolation. *Brit J Psychiat, 110:*290-5, 1964. (**298**)

189. WARNER, W. L.; MEEKER, M., and EELLS, K.: *Social Class in America.* New York, Harper, 1960. (**313**)

190. WEISS, P.: An introduction to genetic neurology. In P. Weiss (ed.): *Genetic Neurology.* Chicago, U. of Chicago, 1950.

191. WEISS, P., in L. A. JEFFRESS (ed.) : *Cerebral Mechanisms in Behavior.* The Hixon Symposium, New York, Wiley, 1951. (**140**)

192. WERNER, H.: The concept of development from a comparative and organismic point of view. In D. B. Harris (ed.) : *The Concept of Development.* Minneapolis, U. of Minn., 1957, pp. 125-148. (**Appendix A; 197, 297**)

193. WIENER, N.: *Cybernetics.* New York, Wiley, 1948. (**15, 320**)

194. WILLIAMS, R.: *Biochemical Individuality.* New York, Wiley, 1956. (**293**)

195. WINDLE, W. F.: On the nature of the first forelimb movements of mammalian embryos. *Proc Soc Exp Biol Med, 36:*640-42, 1937. (**91**)

196. WINDLE, W. F.: Reflexes of mammalian embryos and fetuses. In P. Weiss (ed.) : *Genetic Neurology.* Chicago, U. of Chicago, 1950, pp. 214-222. (**91**)

197. ZUBEK, J. P., and SOLBERG, P. A.: *Human Development.* New York, McGraw-Hill, 1954. (**Tables IA, IVA, IVB, VIII; 82; Appendix A**)

ADDITIONAL BIBLIOGRAPHY

ADRIAN, E. D.: *The Physical Background of Perception.* New York, Oxford U. P., 1947.

AKERT, K., and BENJAMIN, R. M.: Regional functioning of the CNS. In E. A. Spiegel (ed.) : *Progr Neurol Psychiat, 12:*43-69, 1957.

ALLEN, R. M.: Continued longitudinal Rorschach study of a child from 3-5 years. *J Genet Psychol, 85:*135-149, 1954.

ANAND, B. K., and DUA, S.: Stimulation of limbic system of brain in waking animals. *Science, 122:*1139, 1955.

ASHBY, W. R.: *Design for a Brain.* New York, Wiley, 1952.

BISHOP, G. H., and CLARE, M. H.: Relations between evoked and "spontaneous" activity of optic cortex. *Electroenceph Clin Neurophysiol, 4:*321-330, 1952.

BRAZIER, M. A. B. (ed.) : *The CNS and Behavior, Third Conference.* New York, Josiah Macy, Jr. Foundation, 1960.

BUCHANAN, A. R.: *Functional Neuroanatomy,* 2nd Ed. Philadelphia, Lea and F., 1951.

BULLOCK, T. H.: Evolution of neurophysiological mechanisms. In A. Roe and G. G. Simpson (eds.) : *Behavior and Evolution.* New Haven, Yale, 1958, pp. 165-7.

CAMPBELL, JOHN: Functional organization of the CNS with respect to organization in time. *Neurology, 4* (4) :295-300, 1954.

CHAMBERS, W. W., and SPRAGUE, J. M.:

(1) Functional localization in the cerebellum. I. Organization in longitudinal cortico-nuclear zones and their contribution to the control of posture, both extra-pyramidal and pyramidal. *J Comp Neurol, 103:*105-129, 1955.

(2) Functional localization in the cerebellum. II. Somatotopic organization in cortex and nuclei. *Arch Neurol Psychiat, 74:* 653-680, 1955.

CHANG, H-T: Functional organization of central visual pathways. *1950 Proc Ass Res Nerv Ment Dis, 30:*430-53, 1952.

CLOAKE, P.: Some aspects of cortical function. *Brain, 75* (3) :273-291, 1952.

COLLINS, E. H.: Reciprocal nature of growth and behavior in fetus and infant. *Growth, 17:*163-7, 1953.

COOLEY, C. H.: *Social Organization: A Study of the Larger Mind.* New York, Scribner, 1909.

CORBIN, H. P. F., and BICKFORD, R. G.: Studies of the electroencephalograms of normal children. *Electroenceph Clin Neurophysiol, 7:* 15-28, 1955.

CRUIKSHANK, R. M.: Animal infancy. In L. Carmichael (ed.) : *Manual of Child Psychology,* 2nd Ed. New York, Wiley, 1954, pp. 186-214.

DENNY-BROWN, D.: Positive and negative aspects of cerebral cortical functions. *North Carolina Med J, 17* (7) :295-303, 1956.

ELLINGSON, R. J.: Brain waves and problems of psychology. *Psychol Bull, 53* (1) :1-34, Jan. 1956.

ERIKSON, J. C. *et al.*: Observations on the post-central gyrus in relation to pain. *Trans Amer Neurol Ass, 77*:57-9, 1952.

ERVIN, F. R.: The frontal lobes, a review of the literature. *Dis Nerv Sys, 14* (3) :2-12, Mar. 1953.

FRENCH, J. D., and KING, E. E.: Mechanisms involved in the anesthetic state. *Surgery, 38* (1) :228-238, 1955.

FRIEDLANDER, W. J.: Electroencephalographic alpha rate in adults as a function of age. *Geriatrics, 13* (1) :29-31, 1958.

FULTON, J. F.: *Frontal Lobotomy and Affective Behavior.* New York, Norton, 1951.

FULTON, J. F.: *Physiology of the Nervous System,* 3rd Ed. New York, Oxford U. P., 1951.

FULTON, J. F.: The limbic system: a study of the visceral brain in primates and man. *Yale J Biol Med, 26*:107-118, 1953.

GLOOR, P.: Autonomic functions of the diencephalon: a summary of the experimental work of Prof. W. R. Hess. *Arch Neuropsychiat, 71* (6):773-790, 1954.

GRAHAM, B. F.: Neuroendocrine components in the physiological response to stress. *Ann NY Acad Sci, 56*:184-194, 1952.

GREEN, J. D., and MACHNE, X.: Unit activity of rabbit hippocampus. *Amer J Physiol, 181*:219-224, 1955.

GROSSMAN, C.: Electro-ontogenesis of cerebral activity. *Arch Neurol Psychiat, 74*:186-202, 1955.

HALL, C. S.: The genetics of behavior. In S. S. Stevens (ed.) : *Handbook of Experimental Psychology.* New York, Wiley, 1951, chap. 9.

HEATH, R. G.: Correlations between levels of psychologic awareness and physiologic activity in the CNS. *Psychosom Med, 17*:383-395, 1955.

HESS, A.: Postnatal development and maturation of nerve fibers of the CNS. *J Comp Neurol, 100* (3) :461-480, 1954.

HILLARP, N-Å: Peripheral autonomic mechanisms. American Psysiological Society: *Handbook of Physiology.* 1960, vol. II, pp. 1000-1.

HOCH, P. H., and ZUBIN, J. (eds.) : *Psychopathology of Childhood.* New York, Grune, 1955.

HOOKER, D.: Early human fetal behavior, with a preliminary note on double simultaneous fetal stimulation. *Proc Ass Res Nerv Ment Dis, 33*:98-113, 1954.

HUGHES, J. G. *et al.*:
   (1) Electroencephalography of the newborn. I. Studies on normal, full-term, sleeping infants. *Amer J Dis Child, 76*:503-512, 1948.
   (2) Electroencephalography of the newborn infant. VI. Studies of premature infants. *Pediatrics, 7* (5) :707-712, 1951.

JEFFERSON, G.: On the organization of cortical mechanisms. *Lectures on Scientific Basis of Medicine, 1*:61-78, 1953.

KAADA, B. R., and JANSEN, J. JR.: Stimulation of the hippocampus and medial cortical areas in unanesthetized cats. *Neurology, 3*:844-857, 1953.

KENNARD, M. A.: The EEG in psychological disorders: a review. *Psychosom Med, 15*:95-115, 1953.

KENNARD, M. A., and LEVY, S.: The meaning of the abnormal EEG in schizophrenia. *J Nerv Ment Dis, 116*:413-423, 1952.

KLACKENBERG, G., and MELIN, K-A: Aspects of the EEG of a group of children with behavior disorders. *Arch Intern Stud Neurol, II*:1-6, 1953.

LINDSLEY, D. B.: Brain stem influences on spinal motor activity. *1950 Proc Ass Res Nerv Ment Dis, 30*, 1952.

LIVINGSTON, W. K.; HAUGEN, F. P., and BROOKHART, J. M.: Functional organization of the CNS. *Neurology, 4* (7) :485-496, 1954.

MELIN, K-A: The electroencephalogram in infancy and childhood. *Electroenceph Clin Neurophysiol,* Suppl. No. 4:205-211, 1953.

MEYER, V., and YATES, A. J.: Intellectual changes following temporal lobectomy for psychomotor epilepsy. *J Neurol Neurosurg Psychiat, 18* (1) :44-52, 1955.

NAGY, M. H.: Children's birth theories. *J Genet Psychol, 83* (84) :217-226, 1953.

NORRIS, A. H.; SHOCK, N. W., and WAGMAN, I. H.: Age changes in the maximum conduction velocity of motor fibers of human ulnar nerves. *J Appl Physiol, 5* (10) :589-593, 1953.

PASAMANICK, B.: The epidemiology of behavior disorders of childhood. *1954 Proc Ass Res Nerv Ment Dis, 32*:397-403, 1956.

PEACOCK, S. M., JR., and HEATH, R. G.: Some sub-cortical motor contributions to the tonal motor outflow in the cat. *Trans Amer Neurol Ass, 78*:183-5, 1953.

PEACOCK, S. M., JR.: Studies of subcortical motor activity. I: Motor activity and inhibition from identical anatomical points. *J Neurophysiol, 17*:144-156, 1954.

RASMUSSEN, A. T.: *The Principal Nervous Pathways.* New York, Macmillan, 1937.

RASMUSSEN, T., and PENFIELD, W.: Further studies of the sensory and motor cerebral cortex of man. *Fed Proc, 6* (2) *:*452-460, Jun. 1947.

REITAN, R. M.: Intellectual functions in aphasic and non-aphasic subjects. *Neurology, 3* (3) *:*202-212, 1953.

ROTHLIN, E., and BERDE, B.: The structure and function of the ANS. *Aerzliche Monat, 5:*865, 1949-53.

RUCH, T. C.: Sensory mechanisms. In S. S. Stevens (ed.) : *Handbook of Experimental Psychology.* New York, Wiley, 1951.

RUSSELL, G. V.: The brain stem reticular formation. *Texas Rep Biol Med, 15:*332-7, 1957.

SELYE, HANS: The Physiology and Pathology of Exposure to Stress. Montreal, Acta, Inc., 1950.

SHEER, D. E.: Psychology. In E. A. Spiegel (ed.) : *Progr Neurol Psychiat, 12:*399-432, 1957.

SINNOTT, E. W.: *Cell and Psyche: The Biology of Purpose.* Chapel Hill, U. of N. C., 1950.

STRAUSS, A. L.: The development of conceptions of rules in children. *Child Develop, 25:*193-208, 1954.

TILNEY, F., and RILEY, H. A.: *Form and Functions of the CNS,* 3rd Ed. New York, Harper, Hoeber, 1938.

VERNON, M. D.: *A Further Study of Perception.* Cambridge, Cambridge U. P., 1952.

WEINSTEIN, E. A.: Development of the concept of flag and the sense of national identity. *Child Develop, 28:*167-174, 1957.

WHYTE, L. L.: A hypothesis regarding the brain modifications underlying memory. *Brain, 77* (1) *:*158-165, 1954.

WILLIAMS, D., and PARSONS-SMITH, G.: Cortical rhythms not seen in the EEG. *Brain, 73:*191-202, 1950.

INDEX

A

Abstract attitude, ontogeny of, 243, 252-3, 258-9, 264, 273

Adam and Eve, biblical story of, phylogenetically interpreted, 61

Adrian, Lord, 146

Amblystoma: see Coghill-Windle controversy

"American cult of method," 6

    Also see Comparative/Experimental branch of Psychology

Anxiety as a human-species characteristic: 228-238

    as affecting cortical functioning, onset of schizophrenia, higher mental processes, speech development, 150, 235-9

    as contributive to glossolalia, 236-7

    as related to development of the self: see "identity" and "cosmic" anxiety

    "cosmic" anxiety, 233-4, 251-2, 274, 334

    "existence" anxiety, 230, 231-3, 268, 270-1, 274, 334

    "identity" anxiety, 234, 271

    "personal status" anxiety, 302-3

    "transactional" (identity and cosmic) anxiety, 230, 233-4

Arey, L. B., 78, 79

Arieti, S., 106, 227, 237-8, 248

Asch, Solomon, 10

Ascending reticular activating system (ARAS) : 118

    as a complex functional subcircuit, 127, 129, 137

    as a component of the postulated Integrative system, 159

    ontogeny of, 187, 268

    role of, in behavior, 145, 150-1

    unspecific thalamocortical integrating system, as rostral portion of, 129

    Also see Brain-stem reticular formation

Attention, as related to central influences on sensory functioning, 149

Autism/autistic child, 160, 198, 202-3, 204, 214, 270, 271, 285

Automation/cybernation:

    as based on the mechanical principle of feedback, 15

    expanded community facilities as providing positions for those displaced by, 348

    possible future influence on child-rearing attitudes and practices, 307

Autonomic nervous system (ANS) : Orientation Supplement 1; 228

    as a complex functional subsystem, 126, 137

    as linked with the pituitary through the hypothalamus, 147

    as related to anxiety, 229-232

    as the short circuit of the Intraorganismic subsystem, 157

    "future" orientation related to, 193, 268, 331

    levels of function of, 103-4, 157

    ontogeny of: see Neural ontogeny *and* Iatraorganismic subsystem

    phylogeny of, 153

    Also see Intraorganismic neural subsystem

B

Bayley's First Year Test, 197, 202

Behavioral ontogeny, human:

    from birth to one month, 178, 180-1

    from one to three months, 182-3

    from three to six months, 188-190

    from six to twelve months, 194-8

    from six weeks to nine months, summarized, 201-2

    from one to two years, 204-8

    from two to six years, 215-221

    from six to eleven years, 240-4

from eleven through adolescence, 253-5

past adolescence, 258-260

last quarter of first year as a major transition period in, 201-4

postulated stages in, 264-277

rationale for selection and organization of data on, 168

respective roles of learning and of maturation in, 169-171, 175

sex differences in, 177, 178, 182, 204, 205, 206, 212, 215, 216, 217, 221, 225, 232, 241-2, 244, 249-50, 254-5, 256

six to twelve months as crucial in speech development, 200

sources of data on, Appendix A

summarized, 261-4

Behavioral sciences:

"control" as a goal of, 20, 357

differing observational perspectives in, 17-18, 22

optimal educational preparation for research-careers in, 357-8

Behavioral theory:

an updated s-C-r model, 144-5

contributions of new data on neural functioning to, 139-151

Gestaltists'/Cognitivists' contributions to, 18, 21, 143-4

Hebb's contribution to, 144

Hull's contribution to, 144

Behaviorism/S-R theory, 14, 18, 20, 30

critique of, in light of new data on neural functioning, 142-151

Berger, Hans, 120, 122

von Bertalanffy, L., xiv, 16, 317-8, 319

Biochemical individuality, Williams' concept of, 293

Bishop, G. H., 44, 45

Boring, E. G., 21

Brain-mapping:

as an outdated approach to the study of the cerebral cortex, 28, 108-9, 114

Brodmann number-system in, 28, 114

Campbell double-letter system in, 28, 114

Brain-stem reticular formation (BSRF) : 126

as a complex functional subcircuit, 126-8, 150

as a component of the postulated Integrative neural system, 159

as coordinating specific and diffuse nerve-tracts, 107-8

as involved in the affective aspects of sensory experience, 135

as related to the mid-brain's unique ontogenetic characteristics, 155

ontogeny of, 187

role of, in perception and behavior, 145, 151

Also see Ascending reticular activating system

Brazier, M. A. B., 212 (footnote)

Bruner, J. S., 14

C

Cájàl, Ramon y., 99, 117, 148

Cannon's "fight or flight" reaction, 229

Carmichael, L., 27, 85, 173

C-A-T (computer average transience,) 15

Caton, R., 122

Caudocephalic pattern of neuraxial development, 76-8, 91-2

Also see Neural ontogeny

Central integrating (CI) circuits: see Integrative neural system

Central nervous system (CNS)/neuraxis: Orientation Supplement 1

as a developmental derivative of the neural tube, Orientation Supplement 2, Table II, Figure 2; 70-7

as functionally interdependent with the PerNS, 109, 144

as functionally intradependent, 109

as organized in a series of functional-dominance levels, 42, 82, 91-2, 98-9

functional contributions of subcortical centers of. Orientation Supplement 3

human subcortical forebrain, anatomy of, Orientation Supplement 4

influences on PerNS functioning

on sensory functioning, 145-6, 148-9

on motor functioning, 146-150

as evidence of teleology/value, 148, 150

major nerve-centers of, Orientation Supplements 1 and 2

rationale for this inquiry's emphasis upon, 95

structural duality, phylogenetic roots of, 44, 49, 52-4

Also see Nervous system, human, *and* Cerebral cortex

Centrencephalic integrating system (CIS): 130-2

as a complex functional subcircuit, 130, 131-2

as a component of the postulated Integrative neural system, 159

Cephalocaudal pattern of development:

as an earlier over-simplification, 78

as applying to the spinal cord as a discrete CNS sub-unit, 78

as related to the Coghill-Windle controversy, 89-92

Also see Neural ontogeny

Cerebral cortex, human

evidence of a phylogenetic quantum-jump in structure of, 58

origin and evolution of, 49-55, 56-8

postnatal area-myelination ontogeny of, as following phylogenetic trends, 173-4

postnatal growth-gradients in, 172-3

role of "oxygen barrier" in onset of functioning in, 174-5

neocortex of:

areal ontogeny of: see Neural ontogeny

brain-mapping approach to, 28, 108-9, 114

diagrams of major functional divisions of, 112

electrical activity of, 120, Orientation Supplement 6, Table VI, 320-1

electrodynamic fields concepts applied to, 140-2, 161-2

equipotentiality vs. localization in functioning of, 109-111

feedback circuits in, 119-120, 125-139

functional correlates of cellular and layering organization of, 117-120

functions of four lobes of, 111-114

internal organization of, 115-117

postnatal surface-area and fissuration growth-patterns of, 174

role of, in voluntary-motor behavior, 147-8

role in behavior of early developmental patterns of, 27, 29

structural and functional characteristics of, 108-124

Also see Central Nervous system *and* Nervous system, human

Chein, I., 7 (footnote)

Child-rearing, a philosophy of:

biological basis of, 329-330

as practiced by child-rearers, 331

Child-rearing, subcultural patterns of:

as related to individual medical/behavior disorder histories, 321-2

as related to psychiatry's preventive responsibility, 324-5

Churchill, Sir Winston, reported last words of, 298-9

Cobb, S., 118, 130

Coghill-Windle controversy: 22, 79

re-examination of, 89-92

role in human n.s. of commonalities between the amblystoma n.s. and human spinal cord, 92

updated resolution of, 92

Cognitive development:

as dependent upon neural ontogeny, 30

as dependent upon development of the self, 250-2

Also see Behavioral ontogeny *and* Relationships between neural and behavioral orders of development

Communication, human, levels of:

mammalian, or gut-level, 281-7

human, or verbal level, 281-2, 286

Comparative/experimental branch of psychology:

critique of, in light of the biological concept of integrative levels, 7, 8-20, 42-3

methodological rationale of, 6, 42

role of, in psychology as a science, 5, 6, 7, 11, 142-3

Conceptual processes as an "integrative"

neural function, 162
Also see Thinking
Conduction modes, dual neural:
  as expressed in the human nervous
    system, 107-8, 155
  as expressed in the human neocortex,
    110, 114-5
  phylogenetic background of, 43-4,
    45-9
  Also see Nerve-tracts
Conel, J. Leroy, 28, 116, 118-9, 171, 173,
  198, 239, 240
  data limitations of studies by, 173
  neocortical maturative criteria and
    trends of, 171-2
Consciousness:
  as related to the biological concept of
    levels of integration, 11-12
  related to ontogeny and functioning
    of neocortical layers, 118, 225-6
Cooley's "looking-glass self," 227
Cultural anthropology:
  contributions to personality theory
    of, 21
  relativistic frame of reference of, 326,
    343
Cultural factors in personality development: 233, 259-260
  concept of an "enabling" environ-
    ment, 260
  Also see Child-rearing, subcultural
    patterns of
"Cultural personality," studies of, 326-7
Cultural rating-scale, a proposed, 327-9
  rationale underlying, 233, 326-7

D

Darwinian theory, 10, 42, 310, 326
Dennis, W., 30
Denny-Brown, D., 102-3, 147-8
Dreyfus-Brisac, C., 70
Durkheim, E., 312

E

Edison Responsive Environment Learn-
  ing System, 286-7
Eiseley, Loren, 58, 62
Electroencephalogram/-graph/EEG:

as a recording technique, 120-1
functional rationale for, 120-1
behavioral correlates of, 123-4
childhood factors in aging changes in,
  322
clinical implications of developmental
  levels of, 175, 177
comparison of development of, in
  mucaca mulatta and human being,
  288
individual differences in development
  of, 175
parameters showing developmental
  change, 175
postnatal developmental trends in
  (human), Table VI; 176-7
postnatal ontogeny of: see Neural ontogeny
prenatal developmental trends in
  (human), 70
sex differences in developmental of,
  175
Also see Cerebral cortex, electrical activity of
Embryology: see Prenatal phase of human ontogeny
Emotional/affective reactions, as mediated by reverberatory circuits centered
  in the hypothalamus. Orientation
  Supplement 4; 134-5
Also see Limbic system *and* Intraorganismic neural subsystem
"Enabling" developmental environment (s) :
  concept of, 260, 327
  as evaluatively applied to Skinner's
    concepts, 344
  tentative formulation of, for first five
    developmental stages, 329-332
  Also see "Unabling" developmental
    environment (s)
Epigenetic maturational-mode principle,
  26, 280-1
Epilepsy, etiology of first attack of, 212
Erikson, E. H., 331

F

Feedback:
  as a mechanical principle, 15, 139

as related to human communication, 282-7

circuits: as a principle of over-all neural organization, 125-139

in cerebral cortex, 119-120

to and from motor cortex, 133

Foresight, as dependent upon the PF association area, 136

Freudian theory/Freud, Sigmund: 20, 29, 41-2, 279, 294, 304, 305, 323

critique of, in light of this inquiry's formulations, 309-314

Fulton, J. F., 55, 98, 103-4, 157

Functional subcircuits functional-organization pattern: 125-139

as developing in accordance with an hierarchical organizational principle, 139

as providing for CNS influences on the PerNS, 145-150

critique of, as a theoretical model, 137-8

limited vs. complex categories, 126

research in, as requiring the ontogenetic perspective, 139

some behavioral correlates of, 133-6

G

Galambos, R., 123, 149

Gestaut, H., 128

Gerard, R. W., 140, 142, 144

Gesell, A., 173, 265, 359

Glossolalia, 236-7

H

Hamilton, W. J., Table IB; 77, 146

Harlow, H. F.:

"learning sets" period, 269

"skin-comfort" studies, 19-20

Hart, Johnny, 7, Figure 1

Hebb, D. O.:

cell-assembly thesis, 30, 136, 144, 199

critique of s-r theories' limitations by, 14-15

phase-sequence thesis, 136, 213, 257

primary-learning period concept, 269

sensory-deprivation studies, 19-20

Heller's disease, compared with early infantile autism, 204

Herrick, C. Judson, 12, 30, 45-9, 49-54, 54, 105-6, 108, 110, 114, 129, 140-2, 152, 154-5, 156, 161-2, 248

Hierarchical-reduplicative functional-organization pattern, 98-108

as adapted by modern investigators, 101-2

as applied by Herrick to his "integrative" system, 48-9, 106

as demonstrated by the effects of insulin-shock, 104-5

as providing the framework for the over-time investigative perspective, 99

as related to the ANS, 103-4

as related to Innate Releasing Mechanisms, 102

as related to the somatic-motor nervous system, 102

as related to the symptomatology of schizophrenia, 106

functional correlates of, 99

role of nerve-tract connections in, 106-8

Also see Jackson, J. H.

Himwich, H. E., 58, 98

Hoffman, Hallock, 307

Horney, Karen, 304

Hull, C. L., 144

Human behavior:

as dependent upon the neural structure indigenous to the human species, 167

three phylogeneticall derived categories of, 10-11

Also see Behavioral theory

"Human" phylogenetic principle: 60

as expressed in neural ontogeny, 228, 271, 273

as present only as potential at birth, 60-1, 88

as related to a cultural rating-scale, 328

as related to Freudian theory, 310-312

as related to a philosophy of child-rearing, 329-330

as related to psychiatry's preventive responsibility, 324

as related to recommended changes in

child-rearing practices, 312
as related to Skinner's concepts, 343-4
communication aspects of human interaction related to it, 281-7
environmental conditions conducive to its emergence, 278-280
Also see "Mammalian" phylogenetic principle
Hunt, J. McV., 20, 30-1, 239, 361
Hypothalamus: see ANS, Limbic system, Emotional/affective reactions

I

Ingram, W. R., 138
Inhelder, B., 201, 360
Inner experience of individual, emergent/epigenetic nature of, 26
Integrative levels, biological concept of, 9, 10, 11
as critique of comparative/experimental psychology's investigative rationale, 9-12
investigative implications of, 12, 14-15, 18, 19-20
Integrative neural system/CI circuits
as comprising six forebrain branches, 159-60
as developmentally influenced by the growing individual's experiences, 162-3
as one of the systems in the postulated Triple-system functional-organization pattern, 158-60
as related to individual differences, 293-4
as related to personality theory, 315-7
as related to Piaget's and George Mead's concepts, 283
as related to sex differences, 293-4
deteriorative changes in, with aging, 277
functioning of, as related to anxiety, 235-6
ontogeny of: at three months, 187
from three to six months, 194
from six to twelve months, 201
from six weeks to nine months, summarized, 202-4
from one to two years, 211-14

from two to six years, 225-6, 228
from six to eleven years, 251-2
from eleven years to the thirties, 257-260
summarized, Table XII, 263-277
phylogenetic roots of, 45-9
possible role in successful psychotherapy, need for research in, 321
role of, in creative thinking, 160
"Interpersonal-resonance" principle of human development: 282-7
as related to successful psychotherapy, 286
Intraorganismic (vegetative and feeling-tone) neural subsystem:
as one of the systems in the postulated Triple-system functional-organization pattern, 154, 157-8
as related to individual differences, 293-4
as related to personality theory, 315-7
as related to Piaget's and George Mead's concepts, 283
as related to sex differences, 297-8, 300
deteriorative changes in, with aging, 277
functioning of, related to anxiety, 235
ontogeny of: during the first month, 180, 182
from one to three months, 186-7
from three to six months, 193
from six to twelve months, 200
from six weeks to nine months, summarized, 202-4
from one to two years, 211
from two to six years, 227-8
from six to eleven years, 250-3
from twelve to the thirties, 257-8
summarized, 261-277; Table XII
phylogenetic roots of, 45-9, 152-4
possible role in successful psychotherapy, need for research in, 321
sensory components of, diagram, Figure 7
"short" and "long" circuits of, 157

J

Jacksonian concepts/Jackson, J. Hughlings, xii, 29, 30, 41-2, 99-101, 106,

108, 130, 131, 147
concept of dissolution of, 42, 100-1
concept of evolution of, 100-1
concept of re-representation of, 100-1
excerpts from writings by, Orientation Supplement 5
modern adaptations of, 101-6
neuraxial developmental and organizational principles of, 42, 83, Orientation Supplement 5
ontogenetic dictum of, 42, 83, 108, 139
use of term "Jacksonian," 106
Jasper, H. H., 128-9, 155
Judaeo-Christian child-rearing tradition, individual and social ramifications of, 312

K

Kaada, B. R., 130
Korzybski, A., 343
Kundsin, Ruth, 345

L

Langworthy, O. R., 28, 78, 80-2, 181
Lashley, Karl, xiv, 21, 56, 110, 144
Law of anticipatory function/development:
as evidenced in first respiratory movements, 66
as part of rationale for study of prenatal phase of human ontogeny, 63
Learning:
as a secondary modification of innate mechanisms, 11, 22
as dependent upon the reverberatory circuit principle, 136
as related to the Triple-system functional-organization pattern, 164
vs. maturation in behavioral development, 169-171, 175
Levy, S., and Kennard, M. A., 237, 248, 250
Lewin's topological and vector psychology, 21, 319
Limbic system/visceral brain:
as a complex functional subcircuit, 129-131
as the long-circuit of the Intraorganismic subsystem, 157-8

role in perception of, 145
role of gyrus cinguli in, 130-1
Lindsley, D. B., 28, 123-4, 223
Livingston, R. B., 107-8, 144, 148-50, 158
Localization vs. equipotentiality as cortical-functioning principles, 109-110

M

MacLean, P. D., 130
Magoun, H. W., 127
Mammalian neocortex, structural phylogenesis of, 56-8
"Mammalian" phylogenetic principle: 60
as dominant at (human) birth, 88
as expressed in neural ontogeny, 228, 271
as related to a cultural rating-scale, 328
as related to Freudian theory, 309-312
as related to a philosophy of child-rearing, 329, 330
as related to psychiatry's preventive responsibility, 324
as related to recommended changes in child-rearing practices, 312
as related to sex differences in behavior, 299
as related to Skinner's concepts, 343-4
communication aspects of human interaction related to it, 279-280
environmental conditions for its initial firm establishment, 278-280
Also see "Human" phylogenetic principle
McGraw, Myrtle: 27, 173
co-twin control studies, 30
Mead, George H., 238, 282-3
Memory, as involving prolonged reverberation in neural nets, 140
Mid-brain, unique neurogenic characteristics of: 71
possible functional correlates of, in the human neuraxis, 155
Milner, P. M., 136
Mind:
as a function of highly evolved systems, 12

as an electrodynamic-field process, 141-2

Mind-body problem, 11

Model-builders, new generation of conceptual and behavioral, 6-7, 15

Moore, O. K., 286

Mother-child as a primary communication system: 61, 282-7, 294, 306
as related to sex differences in behavior, 299, 300-1
emotional disorders related to, 61, 286-7
societal ramifications of, 306-8

"Mothering":
operationally defined, 307
species role of, 307
social implications of its species role, 308, 345-6

Mussen, P. H., 253

N

Neocerebellum:
as major exception to over-all recapitulatory neurogenic trend, 76-7
functional ontogeny of: see *Neural ontogeny and* Relationships between neural and behavioral orders of development

Neonate, human:
behavioral status of, Table IVA, 178-9, 262
neural status of, Table IVB, 88, 179-180, 261

Nerve-tracts (of human nervous system) : Orientation Supplement 1
as related to the hierarchical-reduplicative functional-organization pattern, 106-8
central-peripheral interconnections, 107
Livingston's schema of, 107-8
myelinated-unmyelinated duality of, 107
ontogenetic patterns of, 79-82
prenatal myelination-patterns of, 80-2
specific-diffuse conduction-mode duality of, 43-4, 45-9, 107, 155
Also see Brain-stem reticular formation

Nervous system, human:
as contributive to individual differences in personality, 25-6, 293-4
as governed by three functional-organization patterns, 96
as the end-product incorporation of a series of hierarchic function patterns at maturity, 83
as organized in a series of functional-dominance levels, 42
as the variable intervening between physical traits and individual differences in personality, 293-4
central vs. peripheral divisions, Orientation Supplement 1
gap between status at birth and at neural maturity, 24, 29, 167
legacy of previous evolutionary stages in, 41
major CNS nerve-centers of, Orientation Supplement 1
"mammalian" and "human" phylogenetic principles in, 60
neuraxis as a developmental derivative of the neural tube, Orientation Supplement 2; 64-76
ontogeny of, Table II; also see Neural ontogeny
primary functional unit of, 33
primary structural unit of, 33
role in experience and behavior-stroke learning, 25-6
spinal cord *cum* medulla as a discrete subsystem within, 45
structural duality (somatic-visceral) of, 44, 49-54
subcortical forebrain, anatomy of, Orientation Supplement 4
subcortical neural centers, functions of, Orientation Supplement 3
Also see Central nervous system, Cerebral cortex, and Peripheral N.S.

Neugarten, B. L., 277

Neural ontogeny, human:
from: conception to birth, Table II
birth to one month, Table IVB; 179, 181
one to three months, Table VII; 185-6

three to six months, Table VIII; 192-3

six to twelve months, Table VIII; 198-9

one to two years, Tables VIII, XI; 208-211

two to six years, Table X; 221, 224, 239

six to eleven years, Table XI; 247-8

twelve years to the thirties, Table XI; 255-6

as related to Jackson's dictum of the "continuous reduction of succession to co-existences," 83

as related to need for research in postnatal changes in brain's electrical activity, 320-1

as related to onset of behavior disorder, 322

caudocephalic growth and time gradients in neuraxial differentiation, 77, 174-5

caudocephalic pattern of spontaneous neuraxial functioning, 78

cephalocaudal sub-pattern of spinal cord development. Orientation Supplement 2; 78

nerve-tract growth and myelination patterns, 79-82

of the cerebral cortex. Table II, Figure 3, Table IVB, 172-3, 173-4, Tables V through XI.

peripheral nervous system growth patterns, 82

postnatal, summarized, 261-4

sex differences in, 88, 175, 177, 182, 295-304

Neural research-designs:
as centered in animal experimentation, 136-7

component-parts approach, rationale for and critique of, 137-8

cortical extirpation, as a contaminating factor of, 148

necessity to broaden frames of reference in, 19-20, 139

point-stimulation technique, Gooddy's criticism of, 117

"sacrifice" techniques, rationale for, 137

sense-organ isolation, critique of, 146

use of anesthesia in, as a contaminating factor, 22, 148, 149

Neuraxis: see Central nervous system and Nervous system, human

Nissen, H. W., 59

Novikoff, Alex, 9, 10, 63

O

Observational perspectives, in behavioral-sciences research:
differences in, 17-18, 22

over-time perspective vs. moment-in-time perspective, 18-19, 99, 108, 138-9

"Open-system" developmental principle, 278-80

(The) "organizing hypothesis," 25

Orientation supplements, rationale for insertion of, 31

Oxygen barrier, role of, in onset of functioning in cerebral cortex, 174-5

P

Patten, B. M., 80, 102

Penfield, Wilder, 113, 130, 131-2, 136, 270

Perception/perceptual process:
as an "analytic" neural function, 47, 161-2

as dependent upon electrodynamic polarization of subject and object, 142, 161

as mediated by the Transactional subsystem, 158, 161-2

as related to sex differences in assessments of space, 256

central influences upon, 146, 150

ontogenetic sources of defects in, 203-4

ontogeny of: see Behavioral ontogeny *and* Relationships between neural and behavioral orders of development.

role of BSRF in, 145

role of thalamus in, 145-6

T-O-P association area as essential locus of, 136, 158, 161

vs. sensorimotor coordinations, as related to cortical layering pattern, 118

Peripheral nervous system (PerNS): Orientation Supplement 1

as contributing to the functional subcircuits functional-organization pattern, 125-6, 134-5

as influencing perception, 145-6

as related to the postnatal pattern of voluntary-motor development, 92

functioning of, as influenced by the CNS, 107, 126, 144, 146, 147-150

prenatal ontogeny of, Table II; 82

Also see Nervous system, human

Personality theory:

as requiring more suitable mathematical systems, 317-320

biologically oriented approaches to, in past, 20-1

classification of current approaches to, 314-5

implications of this inquiry's formulations for, 315-7

need for enunciation of a complex gestalt by, 22-3, 316-7, 319

present lack of a mechanistic basis for, 22, 24

use of theoretical constructs in, 13

Also see The Self.

Phylogeny, neural:

Adam and Eve, biblical story of, interpreted phylogenetically, 61

as being recapitulated in nerve-tract and neocortical myelination-pattern, 80-1, 173-4

as origin of structural duality (somatic-visceral) principle, 49-53, 60

as providing the basis of primary narcissism, 146

behavioral trends accompanying, 59-60, 62

carryovers to human nervous system, 45-9

departures from, four, unique to man, 60-2

encephalization, as trend in, 51

functional shifts accompanying, 58-9

increasing degrees of organization, as

trend in, 51

length of infantile dependency period related to, 59

of mammalian neocortex, 56-7

ontogenetic recapitulation theory, 42, 77, 173-4

prevertebrate, 43-6

principle of hierarchical dominance, as trend in, 55, 58

quantum-jump in, of neocortex from lower primates to man, 58, 62

self-awareness as a human species emergent, 61

the sociocultural world as a human species emergent, 62

successive lowest-ceenter reduplication, as trend, 54

trends, twelve, of, 51-60

vertebrate, 52-55

Piaget, Jean, 30, 118, 178, 180-1, 183, 188, 194, 197, 201, 207-8, 219, 220, 243-4, 254, 360

concepts of assimilation and accommodation of, 183, 194, 208, 219, 282-3

critique of conceptual system of, 239

Pratt, K. C., 27, 84-8

Prenatal phases of human ontogeny:

rationale for study of, 63

from: 2½ to seven fetal weeks, Table IIA

7½ to fifteen fetal weeks, Table IIB

sixteen fetal weeks to birth, Table IIC

emergence of flexures in neural tube during, 70-1, Figure 2

electrical activity of brain during, 70

developmental patterns derived from analysis of, 77-83, 87-9

Preventive mental-health suggestions/programs: 285-6, 347-356

rationale behind, 344-5

as related to: the "battered child syndrome," 348

the early childhood period, 350

the international sphere, 356

neighborhood facilities, 347, 348, 350

the problem of the gap between

adolescents' sexual maturity and personal immaturity, 352-3

school curricula, 351-2

school-entering policies, 355-6

slum-culture Negroes, 349-350

unwanted children, 347-8

Pribram, K. H., 130, 137-8, 144, 151, 156

Primary narcissism, phylogenetic basis of, 146

Psychiatry, preventive responsibility of, 323-5

Psychology as an investigative science: invisible intervening variables as core dilemma of, 7, Figure 1

two long-standing debates within, 5

Also see Comparative/Experimental branch of psychology

Psychosomatic, as an unsatisfactory term, 109

R

Relationships between neural and behavioral orders of development:

during the first month of life, 179-180

at one month, 181-2

from one to three months, 186-7

from three to six months, 193-4

from six to twelve months, 199-201, 202-4

from six weeks to nine months, summarized, 201-2

from one to two years, 211-4

from two to six years, 224-6

from six to eleven years, 248-253

from twelve years to the thirties, 256-260

rationale for selection and organization of data related to, 168-9

rationale for respective roles of learning and of neural maturation in developmental change, 169-171, 175

summarized, 261-277

Ribôt, T. A., 101, 130

Robinson, Frances, 25

Romer, A. S., 44, 49, 50, 152-3, 156, 157, 158, 228-9, 295

Roszak, Theodore, 309, 311

Ruch, T. C., 133

Russell, D. H., 208, 359-362

S

Schizophrenia, 160, 221, 235, 236-7, 244, 247-8, 271, 272, 287-8

Schneirla, T. C., 22, 63, 265

The Self:

anxiety related to development of, 228-9, 233-5

as central teleological mechanism, 150

as a function of polarization in cortical electrodynamic fields, 142

as related to the biological concept of integrative levels, 11-13

as related to cognitive development, 250-2

as related to the Intraorganismic subsystem, 157

cingulate gyrus related to, 131

epigenetic nature of growth in self-awareness, 226-8

human nervous system as biological basis for, 26

integrated, as represented in the PF association area, 259

neural basis of first experiences of, 146

neurally mediated phases in development of: 1st, 269

2nd, 270

3rd, 271-2

4th, 274

5th, 275

ontogeny of: at six months, 193

from six to twelve months, 199-200

between nine and twelve months, 198, 201

from one to two years, 208

from two to six years, 219-221, 225-6

initial stages, analyzed, 226-239

from six to eleven years, 244

from twelve years to neural maturity, 258, 259-260

successive environments postulated as enabling of its optimum development, 330-2

Also see Anxiety as a human species characteristic

Sellars, R. W., 9, 11, 12, 13, 17, 169

Selye, Hans, 127

Sex differences, human:

in behavioral ontogeny, 177, 178, 182, 204, 205, 206, 212, 215, 216, 217, 221, 225, 232, 241-2, 244, 249-50, 253-5, 256-7

in neural ontogeny, 88, 175, 177, 182, 248, 295-304

as contributing to male reaction-formation towards women, 304-5

as influencing school-entering practices, 355-6

critique of Freudian theory's explanations of, 304, 313-4

in American middle-class patterns of child-rearing and their psychological impact, 338-342

in behavior at maturity, as related to sex differences in neural (sub)-systems, 296-304

probable physiological bases of psychological sex differences, 314

social ramifications of, 303, 304-7

Sheldon's physique-temperament theory, 294

Sherrington, Sir Charles, 99, 125

Skinner, B. F.:

ideas of, as a variation on classical S-R theory, 144

critique of his "mammalian principle model," 343-4, 358

(The) sociocultural world as a phylogenetic emergent, 61

Spinal cord *cum* medulla:

as a discrete subsystem within the human neuraxis, 45

developmental pattern of, as related to the Coghill-Windle controversy, 90-2

ontogeny of: see Neural ontogeny

Statistical degrees of freedom:

as applied to the biological realm, 318-19

implications of, for "closed" vs. "open" systems, 317-18

implications of, for research and measurement, 318

the sciences grouped according to, 317

Stevens, S. S., 21

Systems, "closed" and "open," differences between, 16, 317-18

T

Thalamus:

as "gatekeeper" of the cortex, 132, 134

as heart of the Triple-system phylogenetic-legacy functional-organization pattern, 37, 156, 163

as involved in the affective aspect of sensation, 135, 145

effects of barbiturates upon, 236

functional ontogeny of: see Neural ontogeny *and* Relationships between neural and behavioral orders of development

re-interpretation of Pribram's schema's emphasis upon, 156

Thalidomide tragedy, implications of, 288

Thinking, as related to Integrative neural system functioning, 160, 162

Thompson, W. R., 19, 20

Thorndike's connectionism, 14, 22

Tilney, F., 56-7, 146

Time-pattern of development of neuraxial centers:

composite analysis of, 72-6, Figure 3

differentiation sequence in, 76

hierarchical organizational and functional principles embodied in, 82-3

Also see Neural ontogeny

Tinbergen, Nicholas, 9, 11, 15, 17, 21, 22, 98, 101-2, 288, 289

Toilet-training, as converging with emergence of external aspects of self, 236

Transactional-perceptual neural subsystem:

as one of the systems in the postulated Triple-system phylogenetic-legacy functional-organization pattern, 154-5, 158

as phylogenetically newer than the Intraorganismic subsystem, 158

as related to: individual differences, 293-4

the Judaeo-Christian child-rearing tradition, 312

Piaget's and George Mead's concepts, 283

personality theory, 315-7
sex differences, 293-4
deteriorative changes in, with aging, 277
functioning of, related to anxiety, 235-6
ontogeny of: during first month, 180, 182
from one to three months, 187
from three to six months, 193-4
from six to twelve months, 200
from six weeks to nine months, summarized, 202-4
from one to two years, 211-4
from two to six years, 224-5, 228
from six to eleven years, 250-3
from twelve years to the thirties, 256-9
summarized, Table XII; 261-277
phylogenetic roots of, 45-9, 152-4
sensory components of, diagrammed, Figure 7
role in successful psychotherapy, need for research in, 321
"short" and "long" circuits of, 158
Triple-system phylogenetic-legacy functional-organization pattern: 152-160, 162-4
as having three discrete developmental time-tables, 163
Herrick's "analytic" and "integrative" systems as phylogenetic background to, 45-9, 154-5
Integrative system/CI circuits of, 155, 158-160
Intraorganismic subsystem of, 154, 157-8
role of thalamus in, 156, 163
Romer's visceral-somatic duality as phylogenetic background to, 152-3
Transactional subsystem in, 154-5, 158
Turner, O. A., 174

U

"Unabling" developmental environment (s) :
concept of, 260, 327
American middle-class way of life as example of, 336-342
American slum-culture as example of, 333-6
early situation of American lower-lower-class Negro as example of, 335-6
Unspecific thalamocortical integrating system (UTCIS) :
as a complex functional subcircuit, 128-9, 155
as a component of the postulated Integrative system/CI circuits, 155, 159
Urbanism, and schizophrenia, 287-8

V

Value/teleology, as represented in central influences on the PerNS, 148, 150
Vocalization vs. verbalization:
as related to neocortical layering pattern, 118
as related to the Transactional and Intraorganismic neural subsystems, 236
ontogenetic influences upon, 194
Voluntary-motor behavior:
as mediated by reverberatory circuits, 133-4
ontogeny of: see Behavioral ontogeny *and* Relationships between neural and behavioral orders of development
role of neocortex in development of, 147-8

W

Walter, W. Grey, 14, 122-3, 237
Weiss, P., 98
Werner, H.: 30, 197, 297, 362
concept of developmentally lower and higher levels of symptom-expression, 297
Western civilization, distinctive characteristics of:
critique of Freudian analysis of, 310-2
Wiener, Norbert, 15, 319-320

Z

Zubek, J. P., and Solberg, P. A., 58, 359-361